Cambridge Tracts in Mathematics and Mathematical Physics

GENERAL EDITORS
J. G. LEATHEM, M.A.
G. H. HARDY, M.A., F.R.S.

No. 19

The Algebraic Theory of Modular Systems

THE
ALGEBRAIC THEORY OF
MODULAR SYSTEMS

by

F. S. MACAULAY, M.A., D.Sc.

STECHERT-HAFNER SERVICE AGENCY
New York and London
1964

Originally published in 1916
by Cambridge University Press

Reprinted by Arrangement

Printed and Published by
Stechert-Hafner Service Agency, Inc.
31 East 10th Street
New York, N.Y. 10003

Library of Congress Catalog Card Number 64-20384

Lithographed in the U.S.A.
by NOBLE OFFSET PRINTERS, INC.
New York, N. Y. 10003

PREFACE

THE present state of our knowledge of the properties of Modular Systems is chiefly due to the fundamental theorems and processes of L. Kronecker, M. Noether, D. Hilbert, and E. Lasker, and above all to J. König's profound exposition and numerous extensions of Kronecker's theory (p. xiii). König's treatise might be regarded as in some measure complete if it were admitted that a problem is finished with when its solution has been reduced to a finite number of feasible operations. If however the operations are too numerous or too involved to be carried out in practice the solution is only a theoretical one; and its importance then lies not in itself, but in the theorems with which it is associated and to which it leads. Such a theoretical solution must be regarded as a preliminary and not the final stage in the consideration of the problem.

In the following presentment of the subject Section I is devoted to the Resultant, the case of n equations being treated in a parallel manner to that of two equations; Section II contains an account of Kronecker's theory of the Resolvent, following mainly the lines of König's exposition; Section III, on general properties, is closely allied to Lasker's memoir and Dedekind's theory of Ideals; and Section IV is an extension of Lasker's results founded on the methods originated by Noether. The additions to the theory consist of one or two isolated theorems (especially §§ 50—53 and § 79 and its consequences) and the introduction of the Inverse System in Section IV.

The subject is full of pitfalls. I have pointed out some mistakes made by others, but have no doubt that I have made new ones. It may be expected that any errors will be discovered and eliminated in due course, since proofs or references are given for all major and most minor statements.

I take this opportunity of thanking the Editors for their acceptance of this tract and the Syndics of the University Press for publishing it.

F. S. MACAULAY.

LONDON,
  June, 1916.

CONTENTS

III. GENERAL PROPERTIES OF MODULES

IV. THE INVERSE SYSTEM

DEFINITIONS

LIST OF REFERENCES

References to the following in the text are given by their initial letters, e.g., (L, p. 51).

(BN) A. Brill and M. Noether, "Ueber die algebraischen Functionen und ihre Anwendung in der Geometrie" (*Math. Ann.* 7 (1874), p. 269).

(D) R. Dedekind, "Sur la Théorie des Nombres entiers algébriques" (*Bull. Sc. Math.* (1) 11 (1876), p. 278/288 ; (2) 1 (1877), p. 17/41, 69/92, 144/164, 207/248). Also in G. Lejeune Dirichlet's *Vorlesungen über Zahlentheorie* (Brunswick, 2nd edition (1871) and 4th edition (1894)).

(DW) R. Dedekind and H. Weber, "Theorie der algebraischen Functionen einer Veränderlichen" (*J. reine angew. Math.* 92 (1882), p. 181).

(E) E. B. Elliott, *Algebra of Quantics* (Clarendon Press, 2nd ed. 1913).

(H) D. Hilbert, "Ueber die Theorie der algebraischen Formen" (*Math. Ann.* 36 (1890), p. 473).

(H_1) D. Hilbert, "Ein allgemeines Theorem über algebraische Formen" (*Math. Ann.* 42 (1893), p. 320), § 3 of "Ueber die vollen Invariantensysteme."

(K) J. König, *Einleitung in die allgemeine Theorie der algebraischen Grössen* (B. G. Teubner, Leipzig, 1903).

(Kr) L. Kronecker, (i) "Grundzüge einer arithmetischen Theorie der algebraischen Grössen" (*J. reine angew. Math.* 92 (1882), p. 1). Also expounded with additions in (K) especially in Chap. ix.

(ii) "Zur Theorie der Formen höherer Stufen" (*Sitz. Akad. d. Wiss. zu Berlin*, 37 (1883), p. 957).

(L) E. Lasker, "Zur Theorie der Moduln und Ideale" (*Math. Ann.* 60 (1905), p. 20).

(M) F. S. Macaulay, "On the Resolution of a given Modular System into Primary Systems" (*Math. Ann.* 74 (1913), p. 66).

(M_1) F. S. Macaulay, "The Theorem of Residuation" (*Proc. Lond. Math. Soc.* (1) 31 (1900), p. 381).

(M_2) F. S. Macaulay, "Some Formulae in Elimination" (*Proc. Lond. Math. Soc.* (1) 35 (1903), p. 3).

(M₃) F. S. Macaulay, "On a Method of dealing with the Intersections of Plane Curves" (*Trans. Am. Math. Soc.* 5 (1904), p. 385).

(Mo) E. H. Moore, "The decomposition of modular systems of rank n in n variables" (*Bull. Am. Math. Soc.* (2) 3 (1897), p. 372).

(N) M. Noether, "Ueber einen Satz aus der Theorie der algebraischen Functionen" (*Math. Ann.* 6 (1873), p. 351).

(Ne) E. Netto, "Zur Theorie der Elimination" (*Acta Math.* 7 (1886), p. 101).

(S) C. A. Scott, "On a Method for dealing with the Intersections of Plane Curves" (*Trans. Am. Math. Soc.* 3 (1902), p. 216).

(Sa) G. Salmon, "On the order of Restricted Systems of Equations' (*Modern Higher Algebra*, Dublin, 4th ed. (1885), Lesson xix).

(W₁) *Encyklopädie der Mathematischen Wissenschaften* (Teubner, Leipzig, Teil I, Bd. I, Heft 3 (1899), p. 283).   G. Landsberg, "Algebraische Gebilde, etc."

(W₂) *Encyclopédie des Sciences Mathématiques* (Gauthier-Villars, Paris, Tome I, Vol. 2, Fasc. 2, 3 (1910, 11), p. 233).   J. Hadamard and J. Kürschak, "Propriétés générales des corps, etc."

This account of the theory is founded upon that of G. Landsberg but is much fuller both in snbject matter and references.

THE ALGEBRAIC THEORY OF
MODULAR SYSTEMS

Introduction

Definition. A modular system is an infinite aggregate of polynomials, or whole functions* of n variables $x_1, x_2, ..., x_n$, defined by the property that if F, F_1, F_2 belong to the system $F_1 + F_2$ and AF also belong to the system, where A is any polynomial in $x_1, x_2, ..., x_n$.

Hence if $F_1, F_2, ..., F_k$ belong to a modular system so also does $A_1 F_1 + A_2 F_2 + ... + A_k F_k$, where $A_1, A_2, ..., A_k$ are arbitrary polynomials.

Besides the algebraic or relative theory of modular systems there is a still more difficult and varied absolute theory. We shall only consider the latter theory in so far as it is necessary for the former.

In the algebraic theory polynomials such as F and aF, where a is a quantity not involving the variables, are not regarded as different polynomials, and any polynomial of degree zero is equivalent to 1. No restriction is placed on the coefficients of $F_1, F_2, ..., F_k$ except in so far as they may involve arbitrary parameters $u_1, u_2, ...$, in which case they are restricted to being rational functions of such parameters. The same restriction applies to the coefficients of the arbitrary polynomials $A_1, A_2, ..., A_k$ above.

In the absolute theory the coefficients of $F_1, F_2, ..., A_1, A_2, ...$ are restricted to a domain of integrity, generally ordinary integers or whole functions of parameters $u_1, u_2, ...$ with integral coefficients; and a polynomial of degree zero other than 1 or a unit is not equivalent to 1.

---

* We use the term *whole function* throughout the text (but not in the Note at the end) as equivalent to *polynomial* and as meaning a *whole rational function*.

Definitions. A modular system will be called a *module* (of polynomials).

Any polynomial F belonging to a module M is called a *member* (or element) of M.

According as we wish to denote that F is a member of M in the relative or absolute sense we shall write $F = 0 \bmod M$, or $F \equiv 0 \bmod M$. The notation $F \equiv 0 \bmod M$ only comes into use in the sequel in connection with the Resultant.

A *basis* of a module M is any set of members $F_1, F_2, ..., F_k$ such that every member of M is of the form $X_1 F_1 + X_2 F_2 + ... + X_k F_k$, where $X_1, X_2, ..., X_k$ are polynomials.

Every module of polynomials has a basis consisting of a finite number of members (Hilbert's theorem, § 37).

The proof of this theorem is from first principles, and its truth will be assumed throughout.

The theory of modular systems is very incomplete and offers a wide field for research. The object of the algebraic theory is to discover those general properties of a module which will afford a means of answering the question whether a given polynomial is a member of a given module or not. Such a question in its simpler aspect is of importance in Geometry and in its general aspect is of importance in Algebra. The theory resembles Geometry in including a great variety of detached and disconnected theorems. As a branch of Algebra it may be regarded as a generalized theory of the solution of equations in several unknowns, and assumes that any given algebraic equation in one unknown can be completely solved. In order that a polynomial F may be a member of a module M whose basis $(F_1, F_2, ..., F_k)$ is given it is evident that F must vanish for all finite solutions (whether finite or infinite in number) of the equations $F_1 = F_2 = ... = F_k = 0$. These conditions are *sufficient* if M resolves into what are called *prime modules*[*]; otherwise they are not sufficient, and F must satisfy further conditions, also connected with the solutions, which may be difficult to express concretely. The first step is to find all the solutions of the equations $F_1 = F_2 = ... = F_k = 0$; and this is completely accomplished in the theories of the resultant and resolvent.

---

[*] Cayley and Salmon constantly assume this. Salmon also discusses particular cases of a number of important and suggestive problems connected with modular systems (Sa).

I. THE RESULTANT

1. The Resultant is defined in the first instance with respect to n *homogeneous* polynomials F_1, F_2, ..., F_n in n variables, of degrees l_1, l_2, ..., l_n, each polynomial being complete in all its terms with literal coefficients, all different. The resultant of any n given homogeneous polynomials in n variables is the value which the resultant in the general case assumes for the given case. The resultant of n given non-homogeneous polynomials in $n-1$ variables is the resultant of the corresponding homogeneous polynomials of the same degrees obtained by introducing a variable x_0 of homogeneity.

Definitions. An *elementary member* of the module $(F_1, F_2, ..., F_n)$ is any member of the type ωF_i $(i = 1, 2, ..., n)$, where ω is any power product of x_1, x_2, ..., x_n. What is and what is not an elementary member depends on the basis chosen for the module.

The total number of elementary members of an assigned degree is evidently finite.

The diagram below represents the array of the coefficients of all elementary members of $(F_1, F_2, ..., F_n)$ of degree t, arranged under the power products $\omega_1^{(t)}$, $\omega_2^{(t)}$, ..., $\omega_\mu^{(t)}$ of degree t $\left(\mu = \dfrac{\lfloor t+n-1}{\lfloor t \ \lfloor n-1} \right)$:

$$
\begin{array}{c|cccc}
 & \omega_1^{(t)} & \omega_2^{(t)} & \ldots\ldots & \omega_\mu^{(t)} \\
\hline
\lambda_1 & a_1 & b_1 & \ldots\ldots & k_1 \\
\lambda_2 & a_2 & b_2 & \ldots\ldots & k_2 \\
 & \ldots & \ldots & \ldots & \ldots \\
\lambda_\rho & a_\rho & b_\rho & \ldots\ldots & k_\rho
\end{array}
$$

Each row of the array, in association with $\omega_1^{(t)}$, $\omega_2^{(t)}$, ..., $\omega_\mu^{(t)}$, represents an elementary member of degree t; and the rows of the array corresponding to F_i all consist of the same elements (the coefficients of F_i and zeros) but in different columns.

Any member $F = X_1 F_1 + X_2 F_2 + ... + X_n F_n$ of degree t is evidently a linear combination $\lambda_1 \omega_1 F_1 + \lambda_2 \omega_2 F_1 + ... + \lambda_p \omega_p F_i + ... + \lambda_\rho \omega_\rho F_n$ of elementary members of degree t, and is represented by the above array when bordered by λ_1, λ_2, ..., λ_ρ on the left, where λ_1, λ_2, ..., λ_ρ are the coefficients of X_1, X_2, ..., X_n, some of which may be zeros.

This bordered array also shows in a convenient way the whole coefficients of the terms of F, viz. $\Sigma \lambda a$, $\Sigma \lambda b$, ..., $\Sigma \lambda k$.

These remarks and definitions are equally applicable to any module $(F_1, F_2, ..., F_k)$ of homogeneous or non-homogeneous polynomials; but the following definition applies only to the particular module $(F_1, F_2, ..., F_n)$.

The *resultant* R of $F_1, F_2, ..., F_n$ is the H.C.F. of the determinants of the above array for degree $t = l + 1$, where $l = l_1 + l_2 + ... + l_n - n$. It will be shown (§ 7) that R is homogeneous and of degree $l_1 l_2 ... l_n / l_i$ in the coefficients of F_i $(i = 1, 2, ..., n)$.

2. Resultant of two homogeneous polynomials in two variables.

Let
$$F_1 = a_1 x_1^{l_1} + b_1 x_1^{l_1-1} x_2 + ... + k_1 x_2^{l_1},$$
$$F_2 = k_2 x_1^{l_2} + ... + a_2 x_2^{l_2},$$
$$l = l_1 + l_2 - 2.$$

The array of the coefficients of all elementary members of (F_1, F_2) of degree $l + 1$, viz. $x_1^{l_2-1} F_1, x_1^{l_2-2} x_2 F_1, ... x_2^{l_2-1} F_1, x_1^{l_1-1} F_2, ..., x_2^{l_1-1} F_2$, has l_2 rows corresponding to F_1 and l_1 rows corresponding to F_2, and the same number $l_1 + l_2$ of rows in all as columns. The resultant R is therefore the determinant of this array. The array is

$$
\begin{array}{c|ccccccc}
 & \omega_1^{(l+1)} & \omega_2^{(l+1)} & \cdots\cdots & \omega_{l_1+1}^{(l+1)} & \cdots\cdots\cdots & \omega_{l+2}^{(l+1)} & \\
\hline
\lambda_1 & a_1 & b_1 \cdots\cdots\cdots k_1 & & \cdot & \cdot & \cdot & = x_1^{l_2-1} F_1 \\
\lambda_2 & \cdot & a_1 & b_1 \cdots\cdots\cdots k_1 & & \cdot & \cdot & = x_1^{l_2-2} x_2 F_1 \\
\\
\lambda_{l_2} & \cdot & \cdot & a_1 & b_1 \cdots\cdots\cdots k_1 & & & = x_2^{l_2-1} F_1 \\
\lambda_{l_2+1} & k_2 \cdots\cdots\cdots\cdots a_2 & & \cdot & \cdot & & \cdot & = x_1^{l_1-1} F_2 \\
 & \cdot & k_2 \cdots\cdots\cdots\cdots a_2 & & \cdot & & \cdot & = x_1^{l_1-2} x_2 F_2 \\
\\
\lambda_{l+2} & \cdot & \cdot & k_2 \cdots\cdots\cdots\cdots a_2 & & & & = x_2^{l_1-1} F_2
\end{array}
$$

On the right are written the elementary members which the rows represent. Thus, neglecting the left hand border, we may regard the diagram as a set of $l + 2$ identical equations for
$$\omega_1^{(l+1)}, \quad \omega_2^{(l+1)}, ..., \omega_{l+2}^{(l+1)}.$$
Solving them we have
$$R\omega_i^{(l+1)} = A_{i1} F_1 + A_{i2} F_2 \quad (i = 1, 2, ..., l+2),$$
where A_{i1}, A_{i2} are polynomials whose coefficients are whole functions of the coefficients of F_1, F_2. Hence
$$R\omega^{(l+1)} \equiv 0 \bmod (F_1, F_2),$$

where $\omega^{(l+1)}$ is any power product of x_1, x_2 of degree $l + 1$. This expresses the first important property of R.

3. Irreducibility of R. The general expression for the resultant R is irreducible in the sense that it cannot be resolved into two factors each of which is a whole function of the coefficients of F_1, F_2. When this has been proved it follows that any whole function of the coefficients of F_1, F_2 which vanishes as a consequence of R vanishing must be divisible by R.

R has a term $a_1^{l_2} a_2^{l_1}$ obtained from the diagonal of the determinant, and this is the only term of R containing $a_2^{l_1}$. Also, when $a_1 = 0$, R has a term $(-1)^{l_2} k_2 b_1^{l_2} a_2^{l_1-1}$, and this is the only term of R containing $a_2^{l_1-1}$ when $a_1 = 0$. Hence, when R is expanded in powers of a_2 to two terms, we have

$$R = a_1^{l_2} a_2^{l_1} + b a_2^{l_1-1} + \dots,$$

where $$b \equiv (-1)^{l_2} k_2 b_1^{l_2} \bmod a_1.$$

Hence if R can be written as a product of two factors, we have

$$R = (a_1^{p_1} a_2^{p_2} + \dots)(a_1^{q_1} a_2^{q_2} + \dots),$$

where $p_1 + q_1 = l_2$ and $p_2 + q_2 = l_1$, and either p_1 or q_1 is zero; for otherwise the coefficient b of $a_2^{l_1-1}$ would be zero or divisible by a_1, which is not the case. Hence one of the factors of R is independent of the coefficients of F_1, since both factors must be homogeneous in the coefficients of F_1. Similarly one of the factors must be independent of the coefficients of F_2, i.e.

$$R = (a_1^{l_2} + \dots)(a_2^{l_1} + \dots) = a_1^{l_2} a_2^{l_1},$$

since the whole coefficient of $a_1^{l_2}$ in R is $a_2^{l_1}$, and of $a_2^{l_1}$ is $a_1^{l_2}$. This is not true; hence R is irreducible.

4. *The necessary and sufficient condition that the equations* $F_1 = F_2 = 0$ *may have a proper solution (i.e. a solution other than* $x_1 = x_2 = 0$) *is the vanishing of* R.

This is the fundamental property of the resultant. If the equations $F_1 = F_2 = 0$ have a solution other than $x_1 = x_2 = 0$ it follows from

$$R x_1^{l+1} \equiv 0 \bmod (F_1, F_2), \quad R x_2^{l+1} \equiv 0 \bmod (F_1, F_2),$$

that $R = 0$, by giving to x_1, x_2 the values (not both zero) which satisfy the equations $F_1 = F_2 = 0$.

Conversely if $R = 0$ we can choose $\lambda_1, \lambda_2, \dots, \lambda_{l+2}$ so that the sum of their products with the elements in each column of the determinant R vanishes. Multiplying each sum by the power product corresponding to its column, and adding by rows, we have

$$(\lambda_1 x_1^{l_2-1} + \lambda_2 x_1^{l_2-2} x_2 + \ldots + \lambda_{l_2} x_2^{l_2-1})\, F_1$$
$$+ (\lambda_{l_2+1} x_1^{l_1-1} + \ldots + \lambda_{l+2}\, x_2^{l_1-1})\, F_2 = 0,$$

where $\lambda_1, \lambda_2, \ldots \lambda_{l+2}$ do not all vanish. Hence, since $\lambda_1 x_1^{l_2-1} + \ldots$ is of less degree than F_2, F_1 must have a factor in common with F_2, and the equations $F_1 = F_2 = 0$ have a proper solution.

In the following article another proof is given which can be extended more easily to any number of variables.

5. When $R \neq 0$ there are $l+2$ linearly independent members of (F_1, F_2) of degree $l+1$, and l of degree l. When $R = 0$ there are only $l+1$ linearly independent members of degree $l+1$ and still l of degree l, i.e. in each case 1 less than the number of terms in a polynomial of degree $l+1$ and l respectively. Hence there will be one and only one identical linear relation between the coefficients of the general member of (F_1, F_2) whether of degree $l+1$ or l. Let this identical relation for degree $l+1$ be

$$c_{l+1,0}\, z_{l+1,0} + c_{l,1}\, z_{l,1} + \ldots + c_{0,l+1}\, z_{0,l+1} = 0,$$

where $z_{i,j}$ denotes the coefficient of $x_1^i x_2^j$ in the general member of (F_1, F_2) of degree $i+j$, and the $c_{i,j}$ are constants. Then, if F is the general member

$$z_{l,0}\, x_1^l + z_{l-1,1}\, x_1^{l-1} x_2 + \ldots + z_{0,l}\, x_2^l$$

of (F_1, F_2) of degree l, $x_1 F$ is a member of degree $l+1$ whose coefficients must satisfy the relation above. Hence

$$c_{l+1,0}\, z_{l,0} + c_{l,1}\, z_{l-1,1} + \ldots + c_{1,l}\, z_{0,l} = 0.$$

Similarly $\qquad c_{l,1}\, z_{l,0} + c_{l-1,2}\, z_{l-1,1} + \ldots + c_{0,l+1}\, z_{0,l} = 0,$

since $x_2 F$ is a member of (F_1, F_2) of degree $l+1$. These two relations must be equivalent to one only, since only one identical relation exists for degree l. Hence we have

$$\frac{c_{l+1,0}}{c_{l,1}} = \frac{c_{l,1}}{c_{l-1,2}} = \ldots = \frac{c_{1,l}}{c_{0,l+1}} = \frac{a_1}{a_2}\ \text{(say)},$$

i.e. $c_{l+1,0},\, c_{l,1}, \ldots,\, c_{0,l+1}$ are proportional to $a_1^{l+1},\, a_1^l a_2, \ldots,\, a_2^{l+1}$. Hence the original identical relation may be written

$$z_{l+1,0}\, a_1^{l+1} + z_{l,1}\, a_1^l a_2 + \ldots + z_{0,l+1}\, a_2^{l+1} = 0,$$

showing that the general member $z_{l+1,0}\, x_1^{l+1} + \ldots$ of (F_1, F_2) of degree $l+1$ vanishes when $x_1 = a_1$, $x_2 = a_2$, and that the equations $F_1 = F_2 = 0$ have the proper solution (a_1, a_2). The theorem being thus proved true in general is assumed to be true in particular.

6. Resultant of n homogeneous polynomials in n variables.

The general theory of the resultant to be now given is exactly parallel to that already given for two variables, although it involves points of much greater difficulty as might be expected. Another method of exposition depending on a different definition of the resultant is given in (K, p. 260 ff.).

Let $F_1, F_2, \ldots, F_n$ be n homogeneous polynomials of degrees $l_1, l_2, \ldots, l_n$ of which all the coefficients are different letters. In particular, let $a_1, a_2, \ldots, a_n$ be the coefficients of $x_1^{l_1}, x_2^{l_2}, \ldots, x_n^{l_n}$ in $F_1, F_2, \ldots, F_n$ respectively, and $c_1, c_2, \ldots, c_n$ the constant terms of $F_1, F_2, \ldots, F_n$ when x_n is put equal to 1, so that $c_n = a_n$. Let

$$l = l_1 + l_2 + \ldots + l_n - n, \quad L = l_1 l_2 \ldots l_n, \quad L_1 = L/l_1, \quad L_2 = L/l_2, \ldots L_n = L/l_n.$$

The resultant R of $F_1, F_2, \ldots, F_n$ has already been defined (§ 1) as the H.C.F. of the determinants of the array of the coefficients of all elementary members of $(F_1, F_2, \ldots, F_n)$ of degree $l+1$.

We shall first consider a particular determinant D of the array, viz. that representing (§ 1) the polynomial

$$X^{(0)} F_1 + X^{(1)} F_2 + \ldots + X^{(n-1)} F_n \text{ of degree } l+1,$$

where $X^{(i)}$ denotes a polynomial in which all terms divisible by $x_1^{l_1}$ or $x_2^{l_2} \ldots$ or $x_i^{l_i}$ are absent, which may be expressed by saying that $X^{(i)}$ is *reduced* in $x_1, x_2, \ldots, x_i$. The polynomial

$$X^{(0)} F_1 + X^{(1)} F_2 + \ldots + X^{(n-1)} F_n$$

is represented by the bordered array

$$
\begin{array}{c|cccc}
 & \omega_1^{(l+1)} & \omega_2^{(l+1)} \ldots\ldots\ldots\ldots \omega_\mu^{(l+1)} & \\
\hline
\lambda_1 & a_1 & b_1 \ldots\ldots\ldots\ldots k_1 & = \omega_1 F_1 \\
\lambda_2 & a_2 & b_2 \ldots\ldots\ldots\ldots k_2 & = \omega_2 F_1 \\
 & \multicolumn{2}{c}{\ldots\ldots\ldots\ldots\ldots\ldots\ldots} & \\
\lambda_\mu & a_\mu & b_\mu \ldots\ldots\ldots\ldots k_\mu & = \omega_\mu F_n \\
\end{array}
$$

where $\omega_1^{(l+1)}, \omega_2^{(l+1)}, \ldots, \omega_\mu^{(l+1)}$ are all the power products of $x_1, x_2, \ldots, x_n$ of degree $l+1$, and $\lambda_1, \lambda_2, \ldots, \lambda_\mu$ are the coefficients of $X^{(0)}, X^{(1)}, \ldots, X^{(n-1)}$. That this array has the same number μ of rows as columns is seen from the fact that *one and only one of the elements* $a_1, a_2, \ldots, a_n$[*] (*the coefficients of* $x_1^{l_1}, x_2^{l_2}, \ldots, x_n^{l_n}$ *in* $F_1, F_2, \ldots, F_n$) *occurs in each row and each column.* This is evident as regards the rows. To prove

---

[*] These are not the same as the $a_1, a_2, \ldots, a_n$ in the first column of the array. The latter should be represented by some other symbols.

that the same is true of the columns, we notice firstly that there is no power product $\omega^{(l+1)}$ of degree $l + 1$ reduced in all the variables, for the highest power product of this kind is $x_1^{l_1 - 1} x_2^{l_2 - 1} \dots x_n^{l_n - 1}$ which is of degree $l < l + 1$; and secondly, if we put every coefficient of $F_1, F_2, \dots, F_n$, except only $a_1, a_2, \dots, a_n$, equal to zero, the diagram will represent the polynomial

$$X^{(0)} a_1 x_1^{l_1} + X^{(1)} a_2 x_2^{l_2} + \dots + X^{(n-1)} a_n x_n^{l_n},$$

in which each power product $\omega^{(l+1)}$ occurs once and once only, so that one and only one element $a_1, a_2, \dots, a_n$ occurs in each column of D.

Thus D when expanded has a term $\pm a_1^{\mu_1} a_2^{\mu_2} \dots a_n^{\mu_n}$, where μ_i is the number of terms in $X^{(i-1)}$, and by saying that the coefficient of this term in D is to be $+ 1$ we remove any ambiguity as to the sign of D. Also it is to be noted that D *vanishes when* $c_1, c_2, \dots, c_n$ *all vanish*, for the column of D corresponding to x_n^{l+1} contains no elements other than $c_1, c_2, \dots, c_n$ and zeros.

Regarding the diagram as giving μ identical equations for

$$\omega_1^{(l+1)}, \omega_2^{(l+1)}, \dots, \omega_\mu^{(l+1)},$$

and solving, we have

$$D\omega^{(l+1)} \equiv 0 \mod (F_1, F_2, \dots, F_n),$$

where $\omega^{(l+1)}$ is any power product of $x_1, x_2, \dots, x_n$ of degree $l + 1$. It can be proved that the factors of D other than R can be divided out of this congruence equation, so that

$$R\omega^{(l+1)} \equiv 0 \mod (F_1, F_2, \dots, F_n) ;$$

but this will not be assumed in what follows*.

7. The number of rows in D corresponding to F_n is the number of terms in $X^{(n-1)}$. But $X^{(n-1)}$ is of degree $l + 1 - l_n$ or

$$(l_1 - 1) + (l_2 - 1) + \dots + (l_{n-1} - 1),$$

and its terms consist of all the power products in

$$(1 + x_1 + \dots + x_1^{l_1 - 1}) \dots (1 + x_{n-1} + \dots + x_{n-1}^{l_{n-1} - 1})$$

each multiplied by a power of x_n ; hence the number of the terms is $l_1 l_2 \dots l_{n-1} = L_n$. Thus D is homogeneous and of degree L_n in the

---

* No proof of this has been published so far as I know. It can be proved that if A is any whole function of the coefficients of $F_1, F_2, \dots, F_n$ not divisible by R, and $AF \equiv 0 \mod (F_1, F_2, \dots, F_n)$, then $F \equiv 0 \mod (F_1, F_2, \dots, F_n)$. Hence from $D\omega^{(l+1)} \equiv 0 \mod (F_1, F_2, \dots, F_n)$ we have $R\omega^{(l+1)} \equiv 0 \mod (F_1, F_2, \dots, F_n)$. The condition that A is not divisible by R is not needed if F is of degree $\leqslant l$.

coefficients of F_n, and homogeneous and of degree $> L_i$ in the coefficients of F_i $(i = 1, 2, ..., n-1)$. It follows that R, which is a factor of D, is at most of degree L_n in the coefficients of F_n. We shall prove that R is of this degree, and consequently of degree L_i in the coefficients of F_i.

Let D' be any other non-vanishing determinant of the array, viz.

$$
\begin{array}{c}
\omega_1^{(l+1)} \quad \omega_2^{(l+1)} \ldots\ldots\ldots\ldots \omega_\mu^{(l+1)} \\
\begin{array}{c|cccc}
a_1 & a_1' & b_1' & \ldots\ldots\ldots\ldots k_1' \\
a_2 & a_2' & b_2' & \ldots\ldots\ldots\ldots k_2' \\
 & \ldots\ldots\ldots\ldots\ldots\ldots\ldots \\
a_\mu & a_\mu' & b_\mu' & \ldots\ldots\ldots\ldots k_\mu'
\end{array}
\end{array}
$$

This represents the polynomial $A_1 F_1 + A_2 F_2 + ... + A_n F_n$, in which $a_1, a_2, ..., a_n$ are the (arbitrarily chosen) coefficients of $A_1, A_2, ..., A_n$ which are not zeros. Choose $\lambda_1, \lambda_2, ..., \lambda_\mu$ in the previous diagram so that we have identically

$$X^{(0)} F_1 + X^{(1)} F_2 + ... + X^{(n-1)} F_n = A_1 F_1 + A_2 F_2 + ... + A_n F_n.$$

This gives, by equating coefficients of power products on both sides,

$$\Sigma\lambda a = \Sigma a a', \quad \Sigma\lambda b = \Sigma a b', ..., \quad \Sigma\lambda k = \Sigma a k'$$

as equations for $\lambda_1, \lambda_2, ..., \lambda_\mu$; and they have a unique solution, since D does not vanish.

Let $\binom{\lambda}{a}$ denote the determinant of the substitution corresponding to the solution of the above equations for $\lambda_1, \lambda_2, ..., \lambda_\mu$ as linear functions of $a_1, a_2, ..., a_\mu$. Then if we put

$$\Sigma\lambda a = \Sigma a a' = \lambda_1', \quad \Sigma\lambda b = \Sigma a b' = \lambda_2', \quad ..., \quad \Sigma\lambda k = \Sigma a k' = \lambda_\mu'$$

we have

$$\binom{\lambda'}{\lambda} = D, \quad \binom{\lambda'}{a} = D', \quad \text{and} \quad \binom{\lambda'}{\lambda}\binom{\lambda}{a} = \binom{\lambda'}{a}, \quad \text{i.e.} \quad D\binom{\lambda}{a} = D',$$

by the rule of successive substitutions, or the rule for multiplying determinants. Hence

$$\frac{D'}{D} = \binom{\lambda}{a}.$$

Now we can find the solution for $\lambda_1, \lambda_2, ..., \lambda_\mu$, or the solution of

$$X^{(0)} F_1 + X^{(1)} F_2 + ... + X^{(n-1)} F_n = A_1 F_1 + A_2 F_2 + ... + A_n F_n,$$

in the following way. First solve the equation

$$Y^{(0)} F_1 + Y^{(1)} F_2 + ... + Y^{(n-2)} F_{n-1} + X^{(n-1)} = A_n$$

for the unknowns $Y^{(0)}, Y^{(1)}, \ldots, Y^{(n-2)}, X^{(n-1)}$. This equation has a unique solution, since the more particular equation

$$Y^{(0)} x_1^{l_1} + Y^{(1)} x_2^{l_2} + \ldots + Y^{(n-2)} x_{n-1}^{l_{n-1}} + X^{(n-1)} = A_n$$

has a unique solution (for any given polynomial A_n can be expressed in one and only one way in the form on the left) and shows that the number of the coefficients of $Y^{(0)}, Y^{(1)}, \ldots, Y^{(n-2)}, X^{(n-1)}$ is equal to the number of equations they have to satisfy.

Substituting the value thus found for $X^{(n-1)}$ in the equation

$$X^{(0)} F_1 + X^{(1)} F_2 + \ldots + X^{(n-1)} F_n = A_1 F_1 + A_2 F_2 + \ldots + A_n F_n,$$

it becomes

$$X^{(0)} F_1 + X^{(1)} F_2 + \ldots + X^{(n-2)} F_{n-1}$$
$$= (A_1 + Y^{(0)} F_n) F_1 + \ldots + (A_{n-1} + Y^{(n-2)} F_n) F_{n-1},$$

where $Y^{(0)}, Y^{(1)}, \ldots, Y^{(n-2)}$ have been found. Next solve the equation

$$Z^{(0)} F_1 + Z^{(1)} F_2 + \ldots + Z^{(n-3)} F_{n-2} + X^{(n-2)} = A_{n-1} + Y^{(n-2)} F_n,$$

which has a unique solution for $Z^{(0)}, Z^{(1)}, \ldots, Z^{(n-3)}, X^{(n-2)}$. We can proceed in this way till $X^{(0)}, X^{(1)}, \ldots, X^{(n-1)}$, i.e. $\lambda_1, \lambda_2, \ldots, \lambda_\mu$, have all been found.

In this method of solving the unknowns on the left are associated with $F_1, F_2, \ldots, F_{n-1}$ only and not with F_n. Hence $\binom{\lambda}{a}$ is a rational function of the coefficients of $F_1, F_2, \ldots, F_n$ whose denominator is independent of the coefficients of F_n, and the same is therefore true of $\dfrac{D'}{D} = \binom{\lambda}{a}$. Hence every determinant D' of the array has a factor in common with D which is of degree L_n in the coefficients of F_n. The resultant R, which is the H.C.F. of all the determinants D', is therefore of degree L_i in the coefficients of $F_i (i = 1, 2, \ldots, n)$.

If we put $D = AR$, A is called the *extraneous factor* of D. We have proved that A is independent of the coefficients of F_n; and it is proved at the end of § 8 that A depends only on the coefficients of $(F_1, F_2, \ldots, F_{n-1})_{x_n=0}$.

8. Properties of the Resultant.

Since D has a term $a_1^{\mu_1} \ldots a_n^{\mu_n}$ (§ 6) R *has a term* $a_1^{L_1} a_2^{L_2} \ldots a_n^{L_n}$. This is called the *leading term* of R.

Since D *vanishes when* $c_1, c_2, \ldots, c_n$ *all vanish* (§ 6) *the same is true of* R; for $D = AR$ and A is independent of $c_1, c_2, \ldots, c_n$.

The extraneous factor A of D is a minor of D, viz. the minor obtained by omitting all the columns of D corresponding to power *products reduced in* $n-1$ *of the variables and the rows which contain the elements* $a_1, a_2, \ldots, a_n$ *in the omitted columns* (M_2, *p.* 14). *Thus* D/A, *where* A *is this minor of* D, *is an explicit expression for* R.

Each coefficient a of $F_1, F_2, \ldots, F_n$ is said to have a certain numerical *weight*, equal to the index of the power of one particular variable (say x_n) in the term of which a is the coefficient. In the case of non-homogeneous polynomials the variable chosen is generally the variable x_0 of homogeneity. Also the weight of a^p is defined as p times the weight of a, and the weight of $a^p b^q c^r \ldots$ as the sum of the weights of $a^p, b^q, c^r, \ldots$. A whole function of the coefficients is said to be *isobaric* when all its terms are of the same weight.

The resultant is isobaric and of weight L. Assign to $x_1, x_2, \ldots, x_n$ the weights $0, 0, \ldots, 0, 1$. Then the coefficients of $F_1, F_2, \ldots, F_n$ have the same weights as the power products of which they are the coefficients. The ith row of the determinant D represents the polynomial $\omega_i F_j = a_i \omega_1^{(l+1)} + b_i \omega_2^{(l+1)} + \ldots + k_i \omega_\mu^{(l+1)}$. Thus the weights of $a_i, b_i, \ldots, k_i$ are less than the weights of $\omega_1^{(l+1)}, \omega_2^{(l+1)}, \ldots, \omega_\mu^{(l+1)}$ respectively by the same amount, viz. the weight of ω_i. Hence, on expanding D, the weight of any term is less than the sum of the weights of $\omega_1^{(l+1)}, \omega_2^{(l+1)}, \ldots, \omega_\mu^{(l+1)}$ by the sum of the weights of $\omega_1, \omega_2, \ldots, \omega_\mu$; i.e. D is isobaric. Again, if in D each letter a is changed to au^q, where q is the weight of a, D becomes Du^w, where w is the weight of D; and consequently if D be expressed as a product of whole factors each factor must be isobaric. Thus R is isobaric and its weight is that of its leading term $a_1^{L_1} a_2^{L_2} \ldots a_n^{L_n}$, which is $l_n L_n = L$. The weight of D is the weight of $a_1^{\mu_1} a_2^{\mu_2} \ldots a_n^{\mu_n}$, which is also L, since $\mu_n = L_n$.

The whole coefficient of $a_1^{L_1} a_2^{L_2} \ldots a_{n-1}^{L_{n-1}}$ *in* R *is* $a_n^{L_n}$. For the coefficient must be a whole function of the coefficients of F_n only of degree L_n and weight $l_n L_n$, and a_n is the only coefficient of F_n of weight l_n.

A more general result (§ 9) is that *the whole coefficient of* $a_n^{L_n}$ *in* R *is* $R_n^{l_n}$ *where* R_n *is the resultant of* $(F_1, F_2, \ldots, F_{n-1})_{x_n=0}$. Hence also *the whole coefficient of* $a_r^{L_r} a_{r+1}^{L_{r+1}} \ldots a_n^{L_n}$ *is* $R_r^{l_r l_{r+1} \ldots l_n}$ *where* R_r *is the resultant of* $(F_1, F_2, \ldots, F_{r-1})_{x_r = \ldots = x_n = 0}$.

Since the weights of D and R are the same *the weight of the extraneous factor* A *of* D *is zero*. This, taken in conjunction with the fact that A is independent of the coefficients of F_n, shows that A *is a whole function of the coefficients of* $(F_1, F_2, \ldots, F_{n-1})_{x_n=0}$ *only.*

9. *The resultant of $F_1, F_2, \ldots, F_n$ is irreducible and invariant.* It has been proved that the resultant is irreducible when $n = 2$ (§ 3); and the proof can be extended to the general case by induction.

Let $R_n =$ the resultant of $(F_1, F_2, \ldots, F_{n-1})_{x_n=0}$;

$\quad F_0 =$ the resultant of the homogeneous polynomials $F_1^{(0)}$, $F_2^{(0)}, \ldots, F_{n-1}^{(0)}$ in $x_1, x_2, \ldots, x_{n-2}, x_0$ obtained from F_1, $F_2, \ldots, F_{n-1}$ by changing x_{n-1}, x_n to $x_{n-1}x_0, x_n x_0$;

$\quad F_n' = (F_n)_{x_1 = \ldots = x_{n-2} = 0} = k_n x_{n-1}^{l_n} + \ldots + a_n x_n^{l_n}$;

$\quad R' =$ the resultant of $F_1, F_2, \ldots, F_{n-1}, F_n'$;

$\quad R_0 =$ the resultant of F_0, F_n', two polynomials in x_{n-1}, x_n;

$\quad L_1' l_1 = L_2' l_2 = \ldots = L_{n-1}' l_{n-1} = l_1 l_2 \ldots l_{n-1} = L_n$.

Finally let $a_1, a_2, \ldots, a_n, c_1, c_2, \ldots, c_{n-1}$ denote the same coefficients of $F_1, F_2, \ldots, F_n$ as in § 6. We assume R_n irreducible and have to prove that R is irreducible.

F_0 is of weight L_n in the coefficients of $F_1^{(0)}, F_2^{(0)}, \ldots, F_{n-1}^{(0)}$ and each coefficient is a homogeneous polynomial in x_{n-1}, x_n of degree equal to its weight in reference to x_0. Hence

$$F_0 = A x_{n-1}^{L_n} + B x_{n-1}^{L_n - 1} x_n + \ldots,$$

where $A, B, \ldots$ are whole functions of the coefficients of $F_1, F_2, \ldots, F_{n-1}$ of the same dimensions as R_n. When $x_n = 0$, F_0 becomes the resultant of $(F_1^{(0)}, F_2^{(0)}, \ldots, F_{n-1}^{(0)})_{x_n=0}$, viz. $R_n x_{n-1}^{L_n}$; hence $A = R_n$. Also the whole coefficient of $a_1^{L_1'} a_2^{L_2'} \ldots a_{n-2}^{L'_{n-2}}$ in F_0 is $a'^{L'_{n-1}}_{n-1}$, where a'_{n-1} is the coefficient of $x_0^{l_{n-1}}$ in $F_{n-1}^{(0)}$ (§ 8), viz.

$$a'_{n-1} = a_{n-1} x_{n-1}^{l_{n-1}} + b x_{n-1}^{l_{n-1}-1} x_n + \ldots + c_{n-1} x_n^{l_{n-1}}.$$

Hence B has a term $L'_{n-1} a_1^{L_1'} \ldots a_{n-2}^{L'_{n-2}} a_{n-1}^{L'_{n-1}-1} b$, and cannot be divisible by R_n, since R_n does not involve b. Hence we find that

$$F_0 = R_n x_{n-1}^{L_n} + B x_{n-1}^{L_n-1} x_n + \ldots$$

where B is neither zero nor divisible by R_n.

Now if R' vanishes one of the solutions of $F_n' = 0$ for $x_{n-1} : x_n$ will be the same as in one of the solutions of $F_1 = \ldots = F_{n-1} = 0$ (§ 10), and will therefore be a solution of $F_0 = 0$; i.e. $R' = 0$ requires $R_0 = 0$, and R_0 is divisible by each irreducible factor of R'. But (§ 3)

$$R_0 = R_n^{l_n} a_n^{L_n} + B' a_n^{L_n - 1} + \ldots, \text{ where } B' \equiv (-1)^{l_n} k_n B^{l_n} \bmod R_n,$$

so that B' is neither zero nor divisible by R_n. Hence, as in § 3, R_0 has an irreducible factor of the form $R_n^{l_n} a_n^p + \ldots$, and has no other factor involving the coefficients of F_1, F_2, ..., F_{n-1}. This must therefore be a factor of R'.

Again R' is what R becomes when all the coefficients of F_n other than those of F_n' are put equal to zero. Hence R has an irreducible factor of the form $R_n{}^{ln}a_n{}^q + ...$, where $q \geqslant p$. The remaining factor of R is independent of the coefficients of $F_1, F_2, ..., F_{n-1}$, and therefore also of the coefficients of F_n when $n > 2$. Hence R is irreducible.

It easily follows that R is invariant for a homogeneous linear substitution whose determinant $\begin{pmatrix} x \\ x' \end{pmatrix}$ does not vanish. Suppose that $R = 0$ and that this is the only relation existing between the coefficients of $F_1, F_2, ..., F_n$. Then not more than one relation can exist between the coefficients of $F_1', F_2', ..., F_n'$, the polynomials into which $F_1, F_2, ..., F_n$ transform. Since $R = 0$ there are less than μ linearly independent members of $(F_1, F_2, ..., F_n)$ of degree $l + 1$ and therefore less than μ linearly independent members of $(F_1', F_2', ..., F_n')$ of degree $l + 1$, and the only single relation between the coefficients of $F_1', F_2', ..., F_n'$ which will admit this is $R' = 0$. Hence $R = 0$ requires $R' = 0$, and R' is divisible by R. The remaining factor of R' is independent of the coefficients of

$F_1, F_2, ..., F_n$, and can be shown to be $\begin{pmatrix} x \\ x' \end{pmatrix}^L$. A proof that R is

invariant without assuming it irreducible is given in (E, p. 17).

10. *The necessary and sufficient condition that the equations $F_1 = F_2 = ... = F_n = 0$ may have a proper solution is the vanishing of R.*

In the general case, when the coefficients are letters,

$$ARx_n{}^{l+1} \equiv 0 \mod (F_1, F_2, ..., F_n).$$

Put $x_n = 1$ and change* c_i to $c_i - F_i$ $(i = 1, 2, ..., n)$; then A does not change, being independent of $c_1, c_2, ..., c_n$ (§ 8); but R changes to $R - A_1 F_1 - A_2 F_2 - ... - A_n F_n$, and this must vanish; hence

$$R \equiv 0 \mod (F_1, F_2, ..., F_n)_{x_n=1}.$$

Hence R vanishes if the equations $F_1 = F_2 = ... = F_n = 0$ have a solution in which $x_n = 1$, i.e. if they have a proper solution.

To prove that $R = 0$ is a sufficient condition, we shall assume that $R = 0$ is the only relation existing between the coefficients of $F_1, F_2, ..., F_n$. There are then less than μ linearly independent members of $(F_1, F_2, ..., F_n)$ of degree $l + 1$. Hence the coefficients $z_{p_1, p_2, ..., p_n}$ of

* Called the Kronecker substitution.

the general member of degree $l + 1$ must satisfy an identical linear relation

$$\Sigma c_{p_1, p_2, \ldots, p_n} z_{p_1, p_2, \ldots, p_n} = 0, \quad p_1 + p_2 + \ldots + p_n = l + 1.$$

The coefficients of the general member of degree l also satisfy one *and only one* identical linear relation, whether R vanishes or not. To prove this it has to be shown that the number N of linearly independent members of $(F_1, F_2, \ldots, F_n)$ of degree l is 1 less than the number ρ of power products of degree l. If no relation exists between the coefficients of $F_1, F_2, \ldots, F_n$ the equation

$$X^{(0)} F_1 + X^{(1)} F_2 + \ldots + X^{(n-1)} F_n = A_1 F_1 + A_2 F_2 + \ldots + A_n F_n$$

can always be solved by the method of § 7, where $A_1, A_2, \ldots, A_n$ are arbitrary given polynomials. Hence N is not greater than the number of coefficients in $X^{(0)}, X^{(1)}, \ldots, X^{(n-1)}$, or in

$$X^{(0)} x_1^{l_1} + X^{(1)} x_2^{l_2} + \ldots + X^{(n-1)} x_n^{l_n},$$

viz. $\rho - 1$, since, when this expression is of degree l, every power product except $x_1^{l_1-1} x_2^{l_2-1} \ldots x_n^{l_n-1}$ occurs once and only once in it. Hence $N \leqslant \rho - 1$.

Any particularity in $F_1, F_2, \ldots, F_n$ can only affect the value of N by diminishing it. Hence for the remainder of the proof it will be sufficient to show that $N = \rho - 1$ in a particular example in which $R = 0$. Let

$$F_1 = (x_1 - x_2)\, x_1^{l_1-1}, \quad F_2 = (x_2 - x_3)\, x_2^{l_2-1}, \ldots, \quad F_n = (x_n - x_1)\, x_n^{l_n-1}.$$

Then $R = 0$ since the equations $F_1 = F_2 = \ldots = F_n = 0$ have the proper solution $x_1 = x_2 = \ldots = x_n = 1$. Let $x_1^{p_1} x_2^{p_2} \ldots x_n^{p_n}$ be any power product of degree l. If $p_1 \geqslant l_1$ change $x_1^{p_1} x_2^{p_2}$ to $x_1^{l_1-1} x_2^{q_2}$ where $p_1 + p_2 = l_1 - 1 + q_2$; this is equivalent to changing $x_1^{p_1} x_2^{p_2} \ldots x_n^{p_n}$ to $x_1^{p_1} x_2^{p_2} \ldots x_n^{p_n} + A_1 F_1$. Again if $q_2 \geqslant l_2$ change $x_2^{q_2} x_3^{p_3}$ to $x_2^{l_2-1} x_3^{q_3}$; and if $q_2 < l_2$ proceed to the first $p_r \geqslant l_r$ and change $x_r^{p_r} x_{r+1}^{p_{r+1}}$ to $x_r^{l_r-1} x_{r+1}^{q_{r+1}}$. If we continue this process, going round the cycle $x_1, x_2, \ldots, x_n$ as many times as is necessary, the power product $x_1^{p_1} x_2^{p_2} \ldots x_n^{p_n}$ will eventually become changed to $x_1^{l_1-1} x_2^{l_2-1} \ldots x_n^{l_n-1}$. Hence these two power products are congruent mod $(F_1, F_2, \ldots, F_n)$, while neither of them is a member of $(F_1, F_2, \ldots, F_n)$, since they do not vanish when $x_1 = \ldots = x_n = 1$. Hence $N = \rho - 1$.

Let $F = \Sigma z_{q_1, q_2, \ldots, q_n} x_1^{q_1} x_2^{q_2} \ldots x_n^{q_n}$ be the general member of $(F_1, F_2, \ldots, F_n)$ of degree l; then $x_i F$ is a member of degree $l + 1$ in which the coefficient of $x_1^{p_1} x_2^{p_2} \ldots x_n^{p_n}$ is $z_{p_1, p_2, \ldots, p_i-1, \ldots, p_n}$. Hence

$$\Sigma c_{p_1, p_2, \ldots, p_n} z_{p_1, p_2, \ldots, p_i-1, \ldots, p_n} = 0 \quad (i = 1, 2, \ldots, n),$$

or

$$\Sigma c_{q_1, q_2, \ldots, q_i+1, \ldots, q_n} z_{q_1, q_2, \ldots, q_n} = 0 \quad (i = 1, 2, \ldots, n).$$

These n equations in $z_{q_1, q_2, \dots, q_n}$ are therefore equivalent to one only; and the continued ratio $c_{q_1+1, q_2, \dots, q_n} : c_{q_1, q_2+1, \dots, q_n} : \dots : c_{q_1, q_2, \dots, q_n+1}$ is the same for all sets of values of $q_1, q_2, \dots, q_n$ whose sum is l. Equating to $a_1 : a_2 : \dots : a_n$, it follows that $c_{p_1, p_2, \dots, p_n}$ is proportional to $a_1{}^{p_1} a_2{}^{p_2} \dots a_n{}^{p_n}$ $(p_1 + p_2 + \dots + p_n = l + 1)$. Hence it follows that $(a_1, a_2, \dots, a_n)$ is a solution of the equations $F_1 = F_2 = \dots = F_n = 0$.

11. The Product Theorem. *If F_n is the product of two polynomials $F_n{}'$, $F_n{}''$, the resultant R of $F_1, F_2, \dots, F_n$ is the product of the resultants R', R'' of $F_1, F_2, \dots, F_n{}'$ and $F_1, F_2, \dots, F_n{}''$.*

For in the general case R' and R'' are irreducible, and if either vanishes R vanishes. Hence R is divisible by $R'R''$. Also it can be easily verified that the leading terms of R and $R'R''$ are identical. Hence $R = R'R''$.

This result can easily be extended to the case in which any or all of $F_1, F_2, \dots, F_n$ resolve into two or more factors.

If $F_1, F_2, \dots, F_n$ are all members of the module $(F_1{}', F_2{}', \dots, F_n{}')$ the resultant R of $F_1, F_2, \dots, F_n$ is divisible by the resultant R' of $F_1{}', F_2{}', \dots, F_n{}'$. For if $R' = 0$ then $R = 0$.

12. Solution of Equations by means of the Resultant. The method of the resultant for solving equations can only be applied in what is called the principal case, that is, the case in which the number r of the equations is not greater than the number n of the unknowns, and the resultant F_0 of the equations with respect to $x_1, x_2, \dots, x_{r-1}$ (after a linear substitution of the unknowns) does not vanish identically. When F_0 vanishes identically the method of the resultant fails, but the equations can be solved by the method of the resolvent, due to Kronecker, as explained later. The method of the resolvent is also applicable to any number of equations whether greater or less than the number of unknowns.

Homogeneous Equations. Let the equations be $F_1 = F_2 = \dots = F_r = 0$ of degrees $l_1, l_2, \dots, l_r$, where $r \leqslant n$. We assume that their resultant F_0 with respect to $x_1, x_2, \dots, x_{r-1}$ does not vanish. We regard $x_1, x_2, \dots, x_r$ as the unknowns, the solutions being functions of $x_{r+1}, \dots, x_n$. But instead of solving for one of the unknowns $x_1, x_2, \dots, x_r$ we solve for a linear combination of them, viz. for $x = u_1 x_1 + u_2 x_2 + \dots + u_r x_r$,[*] where $u_1, u_2, \dots, u_r$ are undetermined quantities. Let F_u stand for $x - u_1 x_1 - u_2 x_2 - \dots - u_r x_r$. Then we regard $F_1 = F_2 = \dots = F_r = F_u = 0$

---

[*] Called the Liouville substitution.

as the given system of equations with $x_1, \ldots, x_r, x$ as unknowns, and their resultant $F_0^{(u)}$ with respect to $x_1, x_2, \ldots, x_r$ gives the equation $F_0^{(u)} = 0$ for x.

Definition. $F_0^{(u)}$ is called the *u-resultant* of $(F_1, F_2, \ldots, F_r)$.

Applying the reasoning of § 9 it is seen that F_0 is the resultant (with respect to $x_1, \ldots, x_{r-1}, x_0$) of $F_1, F_2, \ldots, F_r$ when $x_r, x_{r+1}, \ldots, x_n$ are changed to $x_r x_0, x_{r+1} x_0, \ldots, x_n x_0$, and is a homogeneous polynomial in $x_r, x_{r+1}, \ldots, x_n$ of degree $L = l_1 l_2 \ldots l_r$, viz.

$$F_0 = R_{r+1} \, x_r^L + \ldots,$$

where R_{r+1} is the resultant of $(F_1, F_2, \ldots, F_r)_{x_{r+1} = \ldots = x_n = 0}$, and does not vanish; for a homogeneous substitution beforehand between $x_r, x_{r+1}, \ldots, x_n$ only would be carried through to F_0.

Similarly $F_0^{(u)}$ is the resultant (with respect to $x_1, \ldots, x_r, x_0$) of $F_1, F_2, \ldots, F_r, F_u$ when $x, x_{r+1}, \ldots, x_n$ are changed to $x x_0, x_{r+1} x_0, \ldots, x_n x_0$, and is a homogeneous polynomial $R'_{r+1} x^L + \ldots$ in $x, x_{r+1}, \ldots, x_n$ where R'_{r+1} is the resultant of $(F_1, F_2, \ldots, F_r, F_u)_{x_{r+1} = \ldots = x_n = 0}$. It is easily seen* that $R'_{r+1} = R_{r+1}$. Hence

$$F_0^{(u)} = R_{r+1} \, x^L + \ldots, \text{ where } R_{r+1} \neq 0.$$

To each solution $x_r = x_{ri}$ of $F_0 = 0$ corresponds a solution $(x_{1i}, x_{2i}, \ldots, x_{ri})$ of the equations $F_1 = F_2 = \ldots = F_r = 0$ for $x_1, x_2, \ldots, x_r$ (§ 10). There are therefore L solutions altogether, and they are all finite, since $R_{r+1} \neq 0$.

Similarly to each of the L solutions $x = x_i$ of $F_0^{(u)} = 0$ there corresponds a solution $(x_{1i}, x_{2i}, \ldots, x_{ri}, x_i)$ of $F_1 = \ldots = F_r = F_u = 0$; and as regards $(x_{1i}, x_{2i}, \ldots, x_{ri})$ the L solutions must be the same as those obtained by solving $F_0 = 0$. Hence it follows that

$$x_i = u_1 x_{1i} + u_2 x_{2i} + \ldots + u_r x_{ri},$$

where $x_{1i}, x_{2i}, \ldots, x_{ri}$ are independent of $u_1, u_2, \ldots, u_r$. Hence

$$F_0^{(u)} = R_{r+1} \, \Pi \, (x - u_1 x_{1i} - \ldots - u_r x_{ri}) \quad (i = 1, 2, \ldots, L).$$

Thus $F_0^{(u)}$ is a product of L factors which are linear in x, u_1, u_2, ..., u_r, and the coefficients of u_1, u_2, ..., u_r in each factor supply a solution of the equations $F_1 = F_2 = \ldots = F_r = 0$.

Also the number of solutions is either $L = l_1 l_2 \ldots l_r$ or infinite, the latter being the case when F_0 vanishes identically.

---

* By introducing a as coefficient of x in F_u it is seen that R'_{r+1} is divisible by a^L by considering weight with respect to x. Also the whole coefficient of a^L in R'_{r+1} is R_{r+1} (§ 8). Hence $R'_{r+1} = a^L R_{r+1} = R_{r+1}$.

If D_u is the determinant for $(F_1, F_2, ..., F_r, F_u)$, regarding $x_1, x_2, ...,$ x_r, x_0 as the variables, like the D of § 6, we have $D_u = AF_0^{(u)}$. The extraneous factor A depends only on the coefficients of $(F_1, F_2, ..., F_r)_{x_0=0}$, that is, of $(F_1, F_2, ..., F_r)_{x_{r+1}=...=x_n=0}$. *Hence A is a pure constant, independent of $x_{r+1}, ..., x_n$ and of $u_1, u_2, ..., u_r$, and we may take $D_u = 0$ as the equation for x.*

Definition. The number of times a linear factor $x - u_1 x_{1i} - ... - u_r x_{ri}$ is repeated in $F_0^{(u)}$ or D_u is called the *multiplicity* of the solution $(x_{1i}, x_{2i}, ..., x_{ri})$. This term has a definite geometrical interpretation; it is the number of solutions or points, in the general case distinct, which come into coincidence with a particular solution or point in the particular example considered.

In the case of n homogeneous equations in n unknowns such that $R \neq 0$, the complete solution consists of the non-proper solution $(0, 0, ..., 0)$ with multiplicity $L = l_1 l_2 ... l_n$.

Non-homogeneous Equations. In the case of non-homogeneous equations a linear substitution beforehand affects only $x_1, x_2, ..., x_n$ and not the variable x_0 of homogeneity. Hence it is possible for R_{r+1} to vanish identically, while F_0 and $F_0^{(u)}$ do not, no matter what the original substitution may be. In this case there is a diminution in the number of finite solutions for x, but not in the number of linear factors of $F_0^{(u)}$. To a factor $u_1 x_{1i} + u_2 x_{2i} + ... + u_r x_{ri}$ of $F_0^{(u)}$ not involving x corresponds what is called an infinite solution of $F_1 = F_2 = ... = F_r = 0$ in the ratio $x_{1i} : x_{2i} : ... : x_{ri}$. Infinite solutions are however non-existent in the theory of modular systems (§ 42). An extreme case is that in which $F_0^{(u)}$ does not vanish identically, but is independent of x, when all the L solutions are at infinity.

It may happen that a system of non-homogeneous equations has only a finite number of finite solutions while the resultant F_0 vanishes identically. In such a case the method of the resultant fails to give the solutions.

Example. The equations $x_1^2 = x_2 + x_1 x_3 = x_3 + x_1 x_2 = 0$ have the finite solution $x_1 = x_2 = x_3 = 0$; but the resultant vanishes identically because the corresponding homogeneous equations

$$x_1^2 = x_0 x_2 + x_1 x_3 = x_0 x_3 + x_1 x_2 = 0$$

are satisfied by $x_0 = x_1 = 0$, a system of two independent equations only.

II. THE RESOLVENT

13. We shall follow, with some material deviations, König's exposition of Kronecker's method of solving equations by means of the resolvent. The equations are in general supposed to be non-homogeneous; and homogeneous equations are regarded as a particular case. Thus a homogeneous equation in n variables represents a cone of $n-1$ dimensions with its vertex at the origin. *Homogeneous co-ordinates are excluded.*

The problem is to find all the solutions of any given system of equations $F_1 = F_2 = \ldots = F_k = 0$ in n unknowns $x_1, x_2, \ldots, x_n$. The unknowns are supposed if necessary to have been subjected to a homo-geneous linear substitution beforehand, the object being to make the equations and their solutions of a general character, and to prevent any inconvenient result happening (such as an equation or polynomial being irregular* in any of the variables) which could have been avoided by a linear substitution at the beginning. In theoretical reasoning *this preliminary homogeneous substitution is always to be understood* ; but is seldom necessary in dealing with a particular example.

The solutions we shall seek are (i) those, if any, which exist for x_1 when $x_2, x_3, \ldots, x_n$ have arbitrary values; (ii) those which exist for x_1, x_2, not included in (i), when $x_3, \ldots, x_n$ have arbitrary values; (iii) those which exist for x_1, x_2, x_3, not included in (i) or (ii), when $x_4, \ldots, x_n$ have arbitrary values ; and so on. A set of solutions for $x_1, x_2, \ldots, x_r$ when $x_{r+1}, \ldots, x_n$ have arbitrary values is said to be of *rank r*, and the *spread* of the points whose coordinates are the solutions is of *rank r* and *dimensions $n-r$*. If there are solutions of rank r and no solutions of rank $< r$ the system of equations $F_1 = F_2 = \ldots = F_k = 0$ and the module $(F_1, F_2, \ldots, F_k)$ are both said to be of rank r.

14. The polynomials $F_1, F_2, \ldots, F_k$, and also all their factors are regular in x_1. Hence their common factor D can be found by the ordinary process of finding the H.C.F. of $F_1, F_2, \ldots, F_k$ treated as polynomials in a single variable x_1. If D does not involve the variables we take it to be 1. If it does involve the variables the solutions of $D = 0$ treated as an equation for x_1 give the first set of solutions of the equations $F_1 = F_2 = \ldots = F_k = 0$ mentioned above.

---

* A polynomial of degree l is said to be regular or irregular in x_1 according as the term $x_1{}^l$ is present in it or not.

In the algebraic theory of modules we regard any algebraic equation in one unknown, whether the coefficients involve parameters or not, as completely soluble, i.e. we regard any given non-linear polynomial in one variable as *reducible*. A polynomial in two or more variables is called reducible if it is the product of two polynomials both of which involve the variables. A polynomial which is not reducible is called (absolutely) *irreducible*. Any given polynomial is either irreducible or uniquely expressible as a product of irreducible factors, leaving factors of degree zero out of account. It is assumed that the irreducible factors of any given polynomial are known. Thus the polynomial D above may be supposed to be expressed in its irreducible factors in $x_1, x_2, \ldots, x_n$, and to each irreducible factor corresponds an irreducible or non-degenerate spread.

Put $F_i = D\phi_i$ $(i = 1, 2, \ldots, k)$. Then $\phi_1, \phi_2, \ldots, \phi_k$ have no common factor involving the variables, and the same is true of the two polynomials

$$\lambda_1\phi_1 + \lambda_2\phi_2 + \ldots + \lambda_k\phi_k \text{ and } \mu_1\phi_1 + \mu_2\phi_2 + \ldots + \mu_k\phi_k,$$

where the λ's and μ's are arbitrary quantities. Regarding them as two polynomials in a single variable x_1 we calculate their resultant, and arrange it in the form

$$\rho_1 F_1^{(1)} + \rho_2 F_2^{(1)} + \ldots + \rho_{k_1} F_{k_1}^{(1)},$$

where $\rho_1, \rho_2, \ldots, \rho_{k_1}$ are different power products of the λ's and μ's, and $F_1^{(1)}, F_2^{(1)}, \ldots, F_{k_1}^{(1)}$ are polynomials in $x_2, x_3, \ldots, x_n$ not involving the λ's and μ's. Each $F_i^{(1)}$ is regular in x_2; for any homogeneous linear substitution beforehand of $x_2, x_3, \ldots, x_n$ among themselves only would be carried through to the $F_i^{(1)}$.

Find the H.C.F. $D^{(1)}$ of $F_1^{(1)}, F_2^{(1)}, \ldots, F_{k_1}^{(1)}$ treated as polynomials in a single variable x_2, and put $F_i^{(1)} = D^{(1)} \phi_i^{(1)}$ $(i = 1, 2, \ldots, k_1)$. Then find the resultant of

$$\lambda_1 \phi_1^{(1)} + \lambda_2 \phi_2^{(1)} + \ldots + \lambda_{k_1}\phi_{k_1}^{(1)} \text{ and } \mu_1\phi_1^{(1)} + \mu_2\phi_2^{(1)} + \ldots + \mu_{k_1}\phi_{k_1}^{(1)}$$

and arrange it in the form

$$\rho_1 F_1^{(2)} + \rho_2 F_2^{(2)} + \ldots + \rho_{k_2} F_{k_2}^{(2)}$$

as before, where $F_1^{(2)}, F_2^{(2)}, \ldots, F_{k_2}^{(2)}$ are polynomials in $x_3, x_4, \ldots, x_n$, which may be assumed regular in x_3, and whose H.C.F. $D^{(2)}$ can be found. We thus get the following series in succession :

$$F_1, \quad F_2, \quad \ldots, \quad F_k, \quad \text{with H.C.F. } D,$$
$$\phi_1, \quad \phi_2, \quad \ldots, \quad \phi_k,$$
$$F_1^{(1)}, \ F_2^{(1)}, \ldots, \ F_{k_1}^{(1)}, \ \text{with H.C.F. } D^{(1)},$$
$$\phi_1^{(1)}, \ \phi_2^{(1)}, \ \ldots, \ \phi_{k_1}^{(1)},$$
$$F_1^{(2)}, \ F_2^{(2)}, \ldots, \ F_{k_2}^{(2)}, \ \text{with H.C.F. } D^{(2)},$$
$$\phi_1^{(2)}, \ \phi_2^{(2)}, \ \ldots, \ \phi_{k_2}^{(2)}, \ \text{and so on.}$$

Now any solution of $F_1 = F_2 = \ldots = F_k = 0$ is a solution of $D = 0$ or of $\phi_1 = \phi_2 = \ldots = \phi_k = 0$. And any solution of $\phi_1 = \phi_2 = \ldots = \phi_k = 0$ is a solution of $F_1^{(1)} = F_2^{(1)} = \ldots = F_{k_1}^{(1)} = 0$, since $\Sigma \rho_i F_i^{(1)} \equiv 0 \bmod (\Sigma \lambda_i \phi_i, \ \Sigma \mu_i \phi_i)$, and therefore a solution of $D^{(1)} = 0$ or of $\phi_1^{(1)} = \phi_2^{(1)} = \ldots = \phi_{k_1}^{(1)} = 0$. Hence any solution of $F_1 = F_2 = \ldots = F_k = 0$ is a solution of $D = 0$ or of $D^{(1)} = 0$ or of $\phi_1^{(1)} = \phi_2^{(1)} = \ldots = \phi_{k_1}^{(1)} = 0$. Proceeding in a similar way we find that any solution of $F_1 = \ldots = F_k = 0$ is a solution of $D D^{(1)} \ldots D^{(n-1)} = 0$, since $\phi_1^{(n-1)}$, $\phi_2^{(n-1)}$, $\ldots$, $\phi_{k_{n-1}}^{(n-1)}$ are polynomials in a single variable x_n at most and have no common factor.

Conversely if $\xi_3, x_4, \ldots, x_n$ is any solution of $D^{(2)} = 0$ the resultant of $\Sigma \lambda_i \phi_i^{(1)}$ and $\Sigma \mu_i \phi_i^{(1)}$ with respect to x_2 vanishes when $x_3 = \xi_3$, and $\Sigma \lambda_i \phi_i^{(1)} = \Sigma \mu_i \phi_i^{(1)} = 0$ have a solution $x_2 = \xi_2$ when $x_3 = \xi_3$; i.e. the equations $\phi_1^{(1)} = \ldots = \phi_{k_1}^{(1)} = 0$, and therefore also the equations $F_1^{(1)} = \ldots = F_{k_1}^{(1)} = 0$, have a solution $\xi_2, \xi_3, x_4, \ldots, x_n$; and, by the same reasoning, the equations $F_1 = F_2 = \ldots = F_k = 0$ have a solution $\xi_1, \xi_2, \xi_3, x_4, \ldots, x_n$. Similarly to any solution of $D D^{(1)} \ldots D^{(n-1)} = 0$, say a solution $\xi_i, x_{i+1}, \ldots, x_n$ of $D^{(i-1)} = 0$, there corresponds a solution $\xi_1, \xi_2, \ldots, \xi_i, x_{i+1}, \ldots, x_n$ of the equations $F_1 = F_2 = \ldots = F_k = 0$. Hence from the solutions of the single equation $D D^{(1)} \ldots D^{(n-1)} = 0$ we can get all the solutions of the system $F_1 = F_2 = \ldots = F_k = 0$, since all the solutions of the latter satisfy the former.

Definitions. $D D^{(1)} \ldots D^{(n-1)}$ is called the *complete (total) resolvent* of the equations $F_1 = F_2 = \ldots = F_k = 0$ and of the module $(F_1, F_2, \ldots, F_k)$. $D^{(i-1)}$ is called the *complete partial resolvent of rank* i, and any whole factor of $D^{(i-1)}$ is called a partial resolvent of rank i.

15. *The complete resolvent is a member of the module* $(F_1, F_2, \ldots, F_k)$.

For $\qquad \Sigma \rho_i F_i^{(1)} \equiv 0 \bmod (\Sigma \lambda_i \phi_i, \ \Sigma \mu_i \phi_i) = A \Sigma \lambda_i \phi_i + B \Sigma \mu_i \phi_i,$

where A, B are whole functions of $x_1, x_2, \ldots, x_n, \lambda_1, \ldots, \lambda_k, \mu_1, \ldots, \mu_k$. Hence by equating coefficients of the power products ρ_i on both sides, we have
$$F_i^{(1)} \equiv 0 \bmod (\phi_1, \phi_2, \ldots, \phi_k),$$
and $\qquad\qquad D F_i^{(1)} = 0 \bmod (F_1, F_2, \ldots, F_k),$*

or $\qquad\qquad D D^{(1)} \phi_i^{(1)} = 0 \bmod (F_1, F_2, \ldots, F_k).$

Similarly $\quad D D^{(1)} \ldots D^{(n-1)} \phi_i^{(n-1)} = 0 \bmod (F_1, F_2, \ldots, F_k);$

and since the $\phi_i^{(n-1)}$ include one variable only (or none at all) and have

---

* Not $D F_i^{(1)} \equiv 0 \bmod (F_1, F_2, \ldots, F_k)$ because any common factor of $F_1, F_2, \ldots, F_k$ not involving the variables is not included in D and is left out of account.

no common factor, we can choose polynomials a_i in the single variable so that $\Sigma a_i \phi_i^{(n-1)} = 1$. Hence

$$D D^{(1)} \dots D^{(n-1)} = 0 \bmod (F_1, F_2, \dots, F_k).$$

If the equations $F_1 = F_2 = \dots = F_k = 0$ have no finite solution the complete resolvent is equal to 1; consequently 1 is a member of $(F_1, F_2, \dots, F_k)$, and every polynomial is a member.

16. We have seen that to every solution $x_i = \xi_i$ of $D^{(i-1)} = 0$ there corresponds a solution $\xi_1, \xi_2, \dots, \xi_i, x_{i+1}, \dots, x_n$ of the equations $F_1 = F_2 = \dots = F_k = 0$. It may happen that there is an earlier complete partial resolvent $D^{(j-1)}$ which vanishes when $x_j = \xi_j, \dots, x_i = \xi_i$. In such a case the solution $\xi_1, \dots, \xi_i, x_{i+1}, \dots, x_n$ of $F_1 = \dots = F_k = 0$ corresponding to a solution of $D^{(i-1)} = 0$ is included in the solutions corresponding to $D^{(j-1)} = 0$, and may be neglected if we are seeking merely the complete solution of $F_1 = F_2 = \dots = F_k = 0$. Such a solution is called an *imbedded* solution. All solutions corresponding to an irreducible factor of $D^{(i-1)}$ will be imbedded if one of them is imbedded.

17. Examples on the Resolvent. Geometrically the resolvent enables us to resolve the whole spread represented by any given set of algebraic equations into definite irreducible spreads (§ 21). It has been supposed that the complete resolvent also supplies a definite answer to certain other questions. The following examples disprove this to some extent.

Example i. Find the resolvent of n homogeneous equations $F_1 = F_2 = \dots = F_n = 0$ of the same degree l and having no proper solution.

Since there are no solutions of rank $< n$ the complete resolvent is $D^{(n-1)}$. The first derived set of polynomials $F_1^{(1)}, F_2^{(1)}, \dots, F_{k_1}^{(1)}$ are homogeneous and of degree l^2, the 2nd set $F_1^{(2)}, F_2^{(2)}, \dots$ are homogeneous and of degree l^4, and the $(n-1)$th set $F_1^{(n-1)}, F_2^{(n-1)}, \dots$ are homogeneous and of degree $l^{2^{n-1}}$. This last set involve only one variable x_n, and therefore have the common factor $x_n^{l^{2^{n-1}}}$, which is therefore the required complete resolvent.

We should arrive at a similar result if we changed x_i to $x_i + a_i$ $(i = 1, 2, \dots, n)$ beforehand, thus making the polynomials non-homogeneous. The complete resolvent would then be $(x_n + a_n)^{l^{2^{n-1}}}$. The resultant would be $(x_n + a_n)^{l^n}$. The difference in the two results is explained by the fact that the resultant is obtained by a process applying uniformly to all the variables, and the resolvent by a process applied to the variables in succession.

Example ii. König (K, p. 219) defines a module or system of equations as being *simple* or *mixed* according as only one or more than one of the complete partial resolvents D, $D^{(1)}$, ... , $D^{(n-1)}$ differs from unity. Kronecker (Kr, p. 31) says that the system of equations $F_1 = F_2 = ... = F_k = 0$ is irreducible in this case; and the *Ency. des Sc. Math.* (W₂, p. 352) repeats König's definition. We give two examples to show that this definition is a valueless one.

If u, v, w are three linear functions of three or more variables, any polynomial which contains the spread of $u = v = 0$ is of the form $Au + Bv$; if it also contains the spread of $u = w = 0$, B must vanish when $u = w = 0$, hence B must be of the form $Cu + Dw$, and $Au + Bv$ of the form $A'u + B'vw$; if it also contains the spread of $v = w = 0$, A' must be of the form $C'v + D'w$, and $A'u + B'vw$ of the form $C''uv + D'uw + B'vw$. Hence a polynomial which contains all three spreads is a member of the module (vw, wu, uv), and also any member of the module contains the three spreads. This module, although composite, is not mixed in any proper sense of the word.

Besides having partial resolvents of rank 2 corresponding to the three spreads the module has a partial resolvent of rank 3 corresponding to its singular spread $u = v = w = 0$. This last partial resolvent does not correspond to any property of the module which is not included in the properties corresponding to its partial resolvents of rank 2 ; in other words the partial resolvent of rank 3 is purely redundant.

The resolvent $D^{(1)} D^{(2)}$ can be found as follows : Suppose

$$u = a_0 + a_1 x_1 + a_2 x_2 + ..., \quad v = b_0 + b_1 x_1 + b_2 x_2 + ..., \quad w = c_0 + c_1 x_1 + c_2 x_2 + ...$$

Then the resultant of $\lambda_1 vw + \lambda_2 wu + \lambda_3 uv$ and $\mu_1 vw + \mu_2 wu + \mu_3 uv$ with respect to x_1, apart from a constant factor, is

$$(c_1 v - b_1 w)(a_1 w - c_1 u)(b_1 u - a_1 v)$$
$$\times \left\{ \frac{c_1 v - b_1 w}{\lambda_2 \mu_3 - \lambda_3 \mu_2} + \frac{a_1 w - c_1 u}{\lambda_3 \mu_1 - \lambda_1 \mu_3} + \frac{b_1 u - a_1 v}{\lambda_1 \mu_2 - \lambda_2 \mu_1} \right\},$$

its four irreducible factors corresponding to the spreads

$$v = w = 0, \quad w = u = 0, \quad u = v = 0,$$

$$(\lambda_2 \mu_3 - \lambda_3 \mu_2) u = (\lambda_3 \mu_1 - \lambda_1 \mu_3) v = (\lambda_1 \mu_2 - \lambda_2 \mu_1) w.$$

Hence $D^{(1)} = (c_1 v - b_1 w)(a_1 w - c_1 u)(b_1 u - a_1 v)$;

and $\phi_1^{(1)} = (c_1 v - b_1 w)$, $\phi_2^{(1)} = (a_1 w - c_1 u)$, $\phi_3^{(1)} = (b_1 u - a_1 v)$, from which we obtain

$$D^{(2)} = (b_1 c_2 - b_2 c_1)\, u + (c_1 a_2 - c_2 a_1)\, v + (a_1 b_2 - a_2 b_1)\, w.$$

Example iii.　Compare and find the resolvents of the two modules

$$M = (x_1^3,\ x_2^3,\ x_1^2 + x_2^2 + x_1 x_2 x_3),$$

$$M' = (x_1^3,\ x_1^2 x_2,\ x_1 x_2^2,\ x_2^3,\ x_1^2 + x_2^2 + x_1 x_2 x_3).$$

The resolvent of M' will be found by obtaining the resultant with respect to x_1 of the two equations

$$\lambda_1 x_1^3 + \lambda_2 x_1^2 x_2 + \lambda_3 x_1 x_2^2 + \lambda_4 x_2^3 + \lambda_5 (x_1^2 + x_2^2 + x_1 x_2 x_3) = 0,$$

and　　$$\mu_1 x_1^3 + \mu_2 x_1^2 x_2 + \mu_3 x_1 x_2^2 + \mu_4 x_2^3 + \mu_5 (x_1^2 + x_2^2 + x_1 x_2 x_3) = 0.$$

This resultant is the same as that of the first equation and

$$(\lambda_1 \mu_5)\, x_1^3 + (\lambda_2 \mu_5)\, x_1^2 x_2 + (\lambda_3 \mu_5)\, x_1 x_2^2 + (\lambda_4 \mu_5)\, x_2^3 = 0$$

except for a factor λ_5^3. The roots of the last equation are $a_1 x_2$, $a_2 x_2$, $a_3 x_2$. Hence the resultant, apart from a constant factor, is

$$\Pi \left\{ (\lambda_1 a^3 + \lambda_2 a^2 + \lambda_3 a + \lambda_4)\, x_2^3 + \lambda_5 (a^2 + 1 + a x_3)\, x_2^2 \right\}, \quad (a = a_1,\ a_2,\ a_3)$$

or　　$$x_2^6 \,\Pi \left\{ (\lambda_1 a^3 + \lambda_2 a^2 + \lambda_3 a + \lambda_4)\, x_2 + \lambda_5 (a^2 + 1 + a x_3) \right\}.$$

Hence the complete resolvent is x_2^6, since no values of x_2, x_3 independent of the λ's and μ's will make the remaining product of factors of the above resultant vanish.

The complete resolvent of M, worked in the same way, is also x_2^6; i.e. M and M' have the same complete resolvent, although they are not the same module. M, but not M', contains the two modules

$$M'' = (x_3 - 1,\ x_1^2 + x_1 x_2 + x_2^2,\ x_1^2 x_2 + x_1 x_2^2),$$

$$M''' = (x_3 + 1,\ x_1^2 - x_1 x_2 + x_2^2,\ x_1^2 x_2 - x_1 x_2^2),$$

i.e. every member of M is a member of M'' and of M'''.　Thus

$$x_1^3 = x_1 (x_1^2 + x_1 x_2 + x_2^2) - (x_1^2 x_2 + x_1 x_2^2),$$

$$x_2^3 = x_2 (x_1^2 + x_1 x_2 + x_2^2) - (x_1^2 x_2 + x_1 x_2^2),$$

$$x_1^2 + x_2^2 + x_1 x_2 x_3 = (x_1^2 + x_1 x_2 + x_2^2) + x_1 x_2 (x_3 - 1).$$

The module M is what is called the l.c.m. of M', M'', M'''.　The two modules M'', M''' have $x_1 = x_2 = x_3 - 1 = 0$ and $x_1 = x_2 = x_3 + 1 = 0$ for their spreads, which are imbedded in the spread $x_1 = x_2 = 0$ of the first component of M, viz. M'.

M is then properly speaking a mixed module although this is not indicated by its complete resolvent x_2^6. It has two imbedded spreads, the points $(0,\ 0,\ \pm 1)$. The complete resolvent should have the factors

$x_3 \pm 1$ to indicate these, but it has no such factors. The complete resolvent may indicate imbedded modules which do not exist as in Ex. ii, or it may give no indication of them when they do exist as in Ex. iii.

Example iv. It is stated in the *Encyk. der Math. Wiss.* (W$_1$, p. 305) and repeated in (W$_2$, p. 354) that if only one complete partial resolvent $D^{(r)}$ differs from 1, and $D^{(r)}$ has no repeated factor, the module is the product of the prime modules corresponding to the irreducible factors of $D^{(r)}$. The absurdity of this statement is shown by applying it to the module (u, vw), where u, v, w are the same as in Ex. ii. The complete resolvent is $D^{(1)} = (b_1 u - a_1 v)(c_1 u - a_1 w)$, and the product of the prime modules (u, v), (u, w) corresponding to its two factors is $(u^2, uv, uw, vw) \neq (u, vw)$.

18.   The u-resolvent.   The solutions of $F_1 = F_2 = ... = F_k = 0$ are obtained in the most useful way by introducing a general unknown x standing for $u_1 x_1 + u_2 x_2 + ... + u_n x_n$, where $u_1, u_2, ..., u_n$ are undetermined coefficients. This is done by putting

$$x_1 = \frac{x - u_2 x_2 - ... - u_n x_n}{u_1}$$

in the system of equations $F_1 = F_2 = ... = F_k = 0$. We thus get a new system $f_1 = f_2 = ... = f_k = 0$ in $x, x_2, x_3, ..., x_n$, where

$$f_i = u_1{}^{l_i} F_i \left(\frac{x - u_2 x_2 - ... - u_n x_n}{u_1}, x_2, ..., x_n \right) \quad (i = 1, 2, ..., k),$$

the multiplier $u_1{}^{l_i}$ being introduced to make f_i integral in u_1. There is evidently a one-one correspondence between the solutions of the two systems, viz. to the solution $\xi_1, \xi_2, ..., \xi_n$ of $F_1 = F_2 = ... = F_k = 0$ there corresponds the solution $\xi, \xi_2, ..., \xi_n$ of $f_1 = f_2 = ... = f_k = 0$, and *vice versa*, where $\xi = u_1 \xi_1 + u_2 \xi_2 + ... + u_n \xi_n$.

Definition.   The complete resolvent $D_u D_u{}^{(1)} ... D_u{}^{(n-1)} (= F_u)$ of $(f_1, f_2, ..., f_k)$ obtained by eliminating $x_2, x_3, ..., x_n$ in succession is called the *complete u-resolvent* of $(F_1, F_2, ..., F_k)$.

Since $F_u = 0 \bmod (f_1, f_2, ..., f_k)$, by § 15, we have

$$(F_u)_{x = u_1 x_1 + ... + u_n x_n} = 0 \bmod (F_1, F_2, ..., F_k).$$

F_u is a whole function of $x, x_2, ..., x_n, u_1, u_2, ..., u_n$ which resolves into linear factors when regarded as a function of x only. The linear factors of rank r, that is, the linear factors of $D_u{}^{(r-1)}$, are of the type

$$x - u_1 \xi_1 - ... - u_r \xi_r - u_{r+1} x_{r+1} - ... - u_n x_n$$

where ξ_1, ..., ξ_r, x_{r+1}, ..., x_n is a solution of $F_1 = F_2 = ... = F_k = 0$. For if $x - \xi$ is any linear factor of $D_u^{(r-1)}$ then ξ is a root of $D_u^{(r-1)} = 0$ to which corresponds a solution ξ, ξ_2, ..., ξ_r, x_{r+1}, ..., x_n of $f_1 = f_2 = ... = f_k = 0$ (§ 14) and a solution ξ_1, ξ_2, ..., ξ_r, x_{r+1}, .., x_n of $F_1 = F_2 = ... = F_k = 0$, where $\xi = u_1\xi_1 + ... + u_r\xi_r + u_{r+1}x_{r+1} + ... + u_nx_n$.

The linear factors of F_u expressed in the above form supply all the solutions of $f_1 = f_2 = ... = f_k = 0$, viz. ξ, ξ_2, ..., ξ_r, x_{r+1}, ..., x_n, and all the solutions of $F_1 = F_2 = ... = F_k = 0$, viz. ξ_1, ξ_2, ..., ξ_r, x_{r+1}, ..., x_n, of the several ranks $r = 1, 2, ..., n$; but it is only when ξ_1, ξ_2, ..., ξ_r are independent of $u_1, u_2, ..., u_n$ that we know the solution from merely knowing the factor.

19. A linear factor of F_u of rank r such as the above will be called a *true* linear factor if ξ_1, ξ_2, ..., ξ_r are independent of $u_1, u_2, ..., u_n$, that is, if it is linear in $x, u_1, u_2, ..., u_n$.

If a linear factor of F_u is not a true linear factor the solution supplied by it is an imbedded one.

Let $x - \xi$ or $x - u_1\xi_1 - ... - u_s\xi_s - u_{s+1}x_{s+1} - ... - u_nx_n$ be a non-true linear factor of F_u, so that ξ_1, ξ_2, ..., ξ_s depend on $u_1, u_2, ..., u_n$. Then ξ_1, ξ_2, ..., ξ_s, x_{s+1}, ..., x_n is a solution of $F_1 = F_2 = ... = F_k = 0$, and so also is η_1, η_2, ..., η_s, x_{s+1}, ..., x_n where η_1, η_2, ..., η_s are obtained from ξ_1, ξ_2, ..., ξ_s by changing $u_1, u_2, ..., u_n$ to $v_1, v_2, ..., v_n$. Hence η, η_2, ..., η_s, x_{s+1}, ..., x_n (where $\eta = u_1\eta_1 + ... + u_s\eta_s + u_{s+1}x_{s+1} + ... + u_nx_n$) is a solution of $f_1 = f_2 = ... = f_k = 0$, and therefore makes F_u vanish. But it does not make $D_u^{(s-1)}...D_u^{(n-1)}$ vanish since this does not involve $x_2, ..., x_s$, and cannot have a factor $x - \eta$, where η involves $v_1, v_2, ..., v_n$. Hence it makes some factor $D_u^{(r-1)}$ of F_u of rank $r < s$ vanish. Then $D_u^{(r-1)}$ vanishes when $x, x_{r+1}, ..., x_s$ are put equal to η, $\eta_{r+1}, ..., \eta_s$; and by putting $v_1, v_2, ..., v_n$ (of which $D_u^{(r-1)}$ is independent) equal to $u_1, u_2, ..., u_n$ it follows that $D_u^{(r-1)}$ vanishes when $x, x_{r+1}, ..., x_s$ are put equal to ξ, $\xi_{r+1}, ..., \xi_s$. Hence the solution ξ, ξ_2, ..., ξ_s, x_{s+1}, ..., x_n is an imbedded one (§ 16).

It follows that all the solutions of $F_1 = F_2 = ... = F_k = 0$ are obtainable from true linear factors of F_u; and that all the linear factors of the first complete partial u-resolvent (different from 1) are true linear factors.

It also follows that if there is a spread of rank s which is not imbedded there must be true linear factors of F_u of rank s corresponding to the spread.

We have not proved that all linear factors of F_u are true linear factors*, and whether this is so or not must be considered doubtful.

20. *If an irreducible factor R_u of F_u considered as a whole function of all the quantities x, x_2, ..., x_n, u_1, u_2, ..., u_n has a true linear factor all its linear factors are true linear factors.*

Let R_u be of rank r. Then R_u is independent of x_1, x_2, ..., x_r and there is a one-one correspondence between its true linear factors and the sets of values ξ_1, ξ_2, ..., ξ_r of $x_1, x_2, ..., x_r$ (not involving $u_1, u_2, ..., u_n$) for which $(R_u)_{x = u_1 x_1 + ... + u_n x_n}$ vanishes. Let

$$(R_u)_{x = u_1 x_1 + ... + u_n x_n} = \rho_1 R_1 + \rho_2 R_2 + ... + \rho_\mu R_\mu,$$

where $\rho_1, \rho_2, ..., \rho_\mu$ are different power products of $u_1, u_2, ..., u_n$ and $R_1, R_2, ..., R_\mu$ are whole functions of $x_1, x_2, ..., x_n$ independent of $u_1, u_2, ..., u_n$. Then the sets of values $\xi_1, \xi_2, ..., \xi_r$ required are the solutions of $R_1 = R_2 = ... = R_\mu = 0$ regarded as equations for $x_1, x_2, ..., x_r$. These come from the solutions $\xi_1, \xi_2, ..., \xi_r, x_{r+1}, ..., x_n$ of rank r of the same equations in $x_1, x_2, ..., x_n$. Now there is at least one solution of rank r, since R_u has a true linear factor; and only a finite number of such solutions altogether, since R_u has only a finite number of such factors. Hence the first complete partial u-resolvent (different from 1) of the equations $R_1 = R_2 = ... = R_\mu = 0$ is of rank r, and resolves completely into true linear factors (§ 19)

$$x - u_1 \xi_1 - ... - u_r \xi_r - u_{r+1} x_{r+1} - ... - u_n x_n.$$

This complete partial u-resolvent of rank r is therefore R_u itself (or else a power of R_u), which proves the theorem.

If F_u is resolved into factors of the R_u type (irreducible with respect to x, x_2, ..., x_n, u_1, u_2, ..., u_n), and these into irreducible factors as regards x, x_2, ..., x_n only, F_u will be resolved into all its irreducible factors. Hence *every irreducible factor of F_u is a factor of a factor of the R_u type, and has all or none of its linear factors true linear factors.*

It follows that any factor of F_u irreducible with respect to x, x_2, ..., x_n, and having a true linear factor, has all its linear factors true linear factors, and is a whole function of u_1, u_2, ..., u_n.

---

* Kronecker states this as a fact without proving it. König's proof contains an error (K, p. 210). It is not correct to say as he does that $\overline{E}_t^{(h)} \overline{X}_t^{(h)}$ vanishes when $x = \xi_t$, but only when x, ξ_1, ξ_2, ..., ξ_h are put equal to ξ_t, ξ_1', ξ_2', ..., ξ_h'.

21. The irreducible spreads of a module. Let R_u be any irreducible factor of F_u of rank r having a true linear factor. We know that

$$R_u = A \prod_{i=1}^{i=d} (x - u_1 x_{1i} - \dots - u_r x_{ri} - u_{r+1}\, x_{r+1} - \dots - u_n x_n).$$

Hence $(R_u)_{x=u_1 x_1 + \dots + u_n x_n} = A \prod_{i=1}^{i=d} \{u_1 (x_1 - x_{1i}) + \dots + u_r (x_r - x_{ri})\}.$

To R_u corresponds what is called an *irreducible spread*, viz. the spread of all points x_{1i}, ..., x_{ri}, x_{r+1}, ..., x_n in which x_{r+1}, ..., x_n take all finite values, and x_{1i}, ..., x_{ri} the d sets of values supplied by the linear factors of R_u, which vary as x_{r+1}, ..., x_n vary.

The degree d of R_u is called the *order* of the irreducible spread.

From the two identities above several useful results can be deduced. It must be remembered that R_u is a known polynomial in x, x_{r+1}, ..., x_n, u_1, u_2, ..., u_n. No linear factor of R_u can be repeated, unless x_{r+1}, ..., x_n are given special values; for otherwise R_u and $\dfrac{\partial R_u}{\partial x}$ would have an H.C.F. involving x, and R_u would be the product of two factors. Whatever set of values x_{r+1}, ..., x_n have, whether general or special, the d sets of corresponding values of x_1, x_2, ..., x_r, viz. x_{1i}, x_{2i}, ..., x_{ri} are definite and finite, because R_u is regular in x.

From the second identity it is seen that $(R_u)_{x=u_1 x_1 + \dots + u_n x_n}$ is independent of u_{r+1}, ..., u_n, and vanishes identically (i.e. irrespective of u_1, u_2, ..., u_n) at every point of the spread and no other point. *Hence the whole coefficients** of the power products of u_1, u_2, ..., u_r in $(R_u)_{x=u_1 x_1 + \dots + u_n x_n}$ all vanish at every point of the spread and do not all vanish at any other point.* These coefficients equated to zero give a system of equations for the spread; but it is not necessary to take them all, and some are simpler than others. The coefficient of $u_r{}^d$ gives an equation $\phi(x_r, x_{r+1}, ..., x_n) = A \prod (x_r - x_{ri}) = 0$ for x_r, whose roots are the d values of x_r corresponding to given arbitrary values of x_{r+1}, ..., x_n. The coefficient of $u_1 u_r{}^{d-1}$ gives an equation

$$x_1 \phi' - \phi_1 = \phi \Sigma \frac{x_1 - x_{1i}}{x_r - x_{rt}} = 0,$$

where ϕ' is $\dfrac{\partial \phi}{\partial x_r}$ and ϕ_1, or $\phi \Sigma \dfrac{x_{1i}}{x_r - x_{ri}}$, is a polynomial in x_r, x_{r+1}, ..., x_n.

---

* Also these coefficients are members of $(F_1, F_2, ..., F_k)$ if $(R_u)_{x=u_1 x_1 + \dots + u_n x_n}$ is a member of $(F_1, F_2, ..., F_k)$, as it will be proved to be when $(F_1, F_2, ..., F_k)$ is a prime module (§ 31).

Similarly we have $x_2\phi' - \phi_2 = 0, \ldots, x_{r-1}\phi' - \phi_{r-1} = 0$.   The equations

$$\phi = 0, \quad x_1 = \frac{\phi_1}{\phi'}, \quad x_2 = \frac{\phi_2}{\phi'}, \quad \ldots, \quad x_{r-1} = \frac{\phi_{r-1}}{\phi'}$$

are called more particularly the equations of the spread, the first giving the different values of x_r as functions of $x_{r+1}, \ldots, x_n$, and the others giving $x_1, x_2, \ldots, x_{r-1}$ as rational functions of $x_r, x_{r+1}, \ldots, x_n$.   If $x_r, x_{r+1}, \ldots, x_n$ have such values that $\phi = \phi' = 0$ then $\phi_1, \phi_2, \ldots, \phi_{r-1}$ all vanish and the expressions above for $x_1, x_2, \ldots, x_{r-1}$ become indeterminate.   In such a case the values of $x_1, x_2, \ldots, x_{r-1}$ may be found by taking other equations from $(R_u)_{x = u_1 x_1 + \ldots + u_n x_n}$ for them.

22. Geometrical property of an irreducible spread.
An algebraic spread in general is one which is determined by any finite system of algebraic equations, and consists of all points whose coordinates satisfy the equations and no other points.   Such a spread has already been shown to consist of a finite number of irreducible spreads each of which is determined by a finite system of equations. The characteristic property of an irreducible spread is that any algebraic spread which contains a part of it, of the same dimensions as the irreducible spread, contains the whole of it.

Let $F_1 = F_2 = \ldots = F_k = 0$ be the equations determining any algebraic spread, and $F_1' = F_2' = \ldots = F'_{k'} = 0$ the equations determining an irreducible spread.   The spread they have in common is determined by the combined system of equations $F_1 = F_2 = \ldots = F_k = F_1' = \ldots = F'_{k'} = 0$, and is contained in the irreducible spread and has the same or less dimensions.   If it is of the same dimensions as the irreducible spread the complete u-resolvent of $F_1 = \ldots = F_k = F_1' = \ldots = F'_{k'} = 0$ will have an irreducible factor R_u'' of the same rank as the irreducible factor R_u' of the complete u-resolvent of $F_1' = F_2' = \ldots = F'_{k'} = 0$ corresponding to the spread of the same.   Also all the roots of $R_u'' = 0$ regarded as an equation for x are roots of $R_u' = 0$.   Hence R_u' is divisible by R_u'', and since they are both irreducible they must be identical.   Hence the spread of $F_1 = \ldots = F_k = F_1' = \ldots = F'_{k'} = 0$ contains the whole of the spread of $F_1' = F_2' = \ldots = F'_{k'} = 0$, and the spread of $F_1 = F_2 = \ldots = F_k = 0$ contains the same.   This proves the property stated above.

III.　GENERAL PROPERTIES OF MODULES

23.　Several arithmetical terms are used in connection with modules suggesting an analogy between the properties of polynomials and the properties of natural numbers.　Two modules have a G.C.M., an L.C.M., a product, and a residual (integral quotient); but no sum or difference.　Also a prime module answers to a prime number and a primary module to a power of a prime number.　Such terms must not be used for making deductions by analogy.

Definitions.　Any member F of a module M is said to *contain* M. Also the module (F) contains M.　It is immaterial in this statement as in many others whether we regard F as a polynomial or a module. The term *contains* is used as an extension and generalisation of the phrase *is divisible by.*

More generally a module M is said to *contain* another M' if every member of M contains M'; and this will be the case if every member of the basis of M contains M'.　Thus $(F_1, F_2, ..., F_k)$ contains $(F_1, F_2, ..., F_{k+1})$, and a module becomes less by adding new members to it.

If M contains M' and M' contains M we say that M, M' are the same module, or $M = M'$.

If M contains M' the spread of M contains the spread of M', but the converse is not true in general.

If in a given finite or infinite set of modules there is one which is contained in every other one, that one is called the *least* module of the set; or if there is one which contains every other one, that one is called the *greatest* module of the set.　Two modules cannot be compared as to greater or less unless one contains the other.

There is a module which is contained in all modules, the *unit module* (1).　Also (0) may be conceived of as a module which contains all modules; but it seldom comes into consideration and will not be mentioned again.　These two modules are called non-proper modules, and all others are *proper* modules.　In general by a module a proper module is to be understood.

The G.C.M. of k given modules $M_1, M_2, ..., M_k$ is the greatest of all modules M contained in M_1 and $M_2 ...$ and M_k, and is denoted by $(M_1, M_2, ..., M_k)$.　In order that M may be contained in each of $M_1, M_2, ..., M_k$, or that each of $M_1, M_2, ..., M_k$ may contain M, it is necessary and sufficient that all the members of the bases of M_1, M_2, ..., M_k should contain M; hence the module whose basis consists of all these members contains all the modules M, and is at the same time one of the modules M. It is therefore the greatest of all the modules M and the G.C.M. of M_1, M_2, ..., M_k. The notation $(M_1, M_2, ..., M_k)$ agrees with the notation $(F_1, F_2, ..., F_k)$, since the latter is the G.C.M. of F_1, F_2, ..., F_k regarded as modules.

The L.C.M. of M_1, M_2, ..., M_k is the least of all modules M containing M_1 and M_2 ... and M_k, and is denoted by $[M_1, M_2, ..., M_k]$. Its members consist of all polynomials which contain M_1 and M_2 ... and M_k; for the basis of any module M containing M_1 and M_2 ... and M_k must consist of a certain number of such polynomials, and the whole aggregate of such polynomials constitutes a module M which is the least of all the modules M.

The *product* of M_1, M_2, ..., M_k is the module whose basis consists of all products $F_1 F_2 ... F_k$, where F_i is any member of the basis of M_i $(i = 1, 2, ..., k)$. The product is denoted by $M_1 M_2 ... M_k$, and is evidently a definite module independent of what bases may be chosen for M_1, M_2, ..., M_k. The product $M_1 M_2 ... M_k$ contains the L.C.M. $[M_1, M_2, ..., M_k]$.

The product of γ modules each of which is the same module M is denoted by M^γ and is called a power of M. If P is the point $(a_1, a_2, ..., a_n)$ the module $(x_1 - a_1, x_2 - a_2, ..., x_n - a_n)$ is denoted by P. If O is the origin the module O is $(x_1, x_2, ..., x_n)$, and O^γ is a module having for basis all power products of $x_1, x_2, ..., x_n$ of degree γ. A polynomial F, or module M, which contains P^γ is said to have a γ-point at P.

The *residual* (L, p. 49) of a given module M' with respect to another M is the least module whose product with M' contains M and is denoted by M/M'. Its members consist of every polynomial whose product with each member separately of the basis of M' is a member of M; for the basis of any module whose product with M' contains M must consist of a certain number of such polynomials, and the whole aggregate of such polynomials constitutes the least such module.

In the case of the natural numbers the residual of m' with respect to m is the least number whose product with m' contains m, and is the quotient of m by the G.C.M. of m and m'. It is the same to some extent with modules, viz. $M/M' = M/(M, M')$; for if $M/M' = M''$ then M'' is the least module such that $M'M''$ contains M, and is therefore the least module such that $(M, M')M''$ contains M, i.e. $M'' = M/(M, M')$.

Nevertheless $M/(M, M')$ is not called the quotient of M by (M, M') because it is not true in general that the product of (M, M') and $M/(M, M')$ is M.

If M, M', M'' are three modules such that $M'M''$ contains M it is clear that M' contains M/M'' and M'' contains M/M'. Since MM' contains M, M contains M/M'. The module M/M' is a module contained in M having a special relation to M independently of what M' may be (§ 26 (i)).

There is a least module which can be substituted for M' without changing M/M', viz. $M/(M/M')$, § 26 (ii).   This module is contained in (M, M'), for (M, M') can be substituted for M' without changing M/M', but is in general different from (M, M').

24. Comment on the definitions.   The non-proper unit module (1) has no spread. Conversely a module which has no spread is the module (1), since the complete resolvent is 1 and is a member of the module. The unit module is of importance from the fact that it often comes at the end of a series of modules derived by some process from a given module.

$(M_1, M_2, ..., M_k)$ and $[M_1, M_2, ..., M_k]$ obey the associative law $[M_1, M_2, M_3] = [[M_1, M_2], M_3] = [M_1, [M_2, M_3]]$, and the commutative law $(M_1, M_2) = (M_2, M_1)$. Also $(M_1, M_2, ..., M_k)$ obeys the distributive law $M (M_1, M_2) = (MM_1, MM_2)$; but $[M_1, M_2, ..., M_k]$ does not.

Example.   As an example of the last statement we have

$$(x_1, x_2) [(x_1^2, x_2^2), (x_1 x_2)] = (x_1, x_2) (x_1^2 x_2, x_1 x_2^2) = (x_1 x_2) (x_1, x_2)^2,$$
while $$[(x_1, x_2) (x_1^2, x_2^2), (x_1, x_2) (x_1 x_2)] = (x_1 x_2) (x_1, x_2).$$

Given the bases of $M_1, M_2, ..., M_k, M, M'$ we know at once a basis for $(M_1, M_2, ..., M_k)$ and for $M_1 M_2 ... M_k$; but it may be extremely difficult to find a basis for $[M_1, M_2, ..., M_k]$ or for M/M'. Hilbert (H, pp. 492–4, 517) has given a process for finding a basis of $[M_1, M_2, ..., M_k]$; and the same process can be applied for finding a basis for M/M'. This process is chiefly of theoretical value in so far as it has any value.

We can have (i) $MM' = MM''$, or $M/M' = M/M''$, without $M' = M''$; (ii) $M/M' = M''$ without $M/M'' = M'$; (iii) $M/M' = M''$ and $M/M'' = M'$ without $M = M' M''$; and (iv) $M = M' M''$ without $M/M' = M''$ or $M/M'' = M'$.

Examples.   (i) $(x_1, x_2) (x_1, x_2)^2 = (x_1, x_2) (x_1^2, x_2^2),$

$$(x_1, x_2)^3/(x_1, x_2)^2 = (x_1, x_2)^3/(x_1^2, x_2^2) ;$$

(ii) $(x_1, x_2)^3/(x_1^2, x_2^2) = (x_1, x_2)$,   while $(x_1, x_2)^3/(x_1, x_2) = (x_1, x_2)^2$;

(iii) $(x_1^2, x_2^2)/(x_1, x_2) = (x_1, x_2)^2$ and $(x_1^2, x_2^2)/(x_1, x_2)^2 = (x_1, x_2)$,

while $(x_1^2, x_2^2) \neq (x_1, x_2)(x_1, x_2)^2$;

(iv) $(x_1, x_2)^6 = (x_1^3, x_1^2 x_2, x_2^3)(x_1^3, x_1 x_2^2, x_2^3)$,

while $(x_1, x_2)^6/(x_1^3, x_1^2 x_2, x_2^3)$ and $(x_1, x_2)^6/(x_1^3, x_1 x_2^2, x_2^3)$ are   both
equal to $(x_1, x_2)^3$.

25.   *The product of the* G.C.M. *and* L.C.M. *of two modules contains
the product of the modules.*

Let $M = (F_1, F_2, ..., F_k)$ and $M' = (F_1', F_2', ..., F'_{k'})$ be the two
modules and let F_L be any member of the basis of their L.C.M.   Then,
since $F_L = 0 \bmod M$, $F_i' F_L = 0 \bmod MM'$; and since $F_L = 0 \bmod M'$,
$F_i F_L = 0 \bmod MM'$; i.e. the product of any member of the basis of
(M, M') with any member of the basis of $[M, M']$ contains MM', or
$(M, M')[M, M']$ contains MM'.

When M, M' have no point in common $(M, M') = (1)$ and consequently $[M, M']$ contains MM', i.e. $[M, M'] = MM'$.   This case is
proved by König (K, p. 356); although it is to be noticed that
(M, M') cannot be (1) in the case of modules of homogeneous polynomials.   Thus the L.C.M. of any finite number of simple modules
(§ 33) is the same as their product (Mo).

26.   *The modules M/M' and $M/(M/M')$ are mutually residual
with respect to M, i.e. each is the residual of the other with respect to M.*

Let $M/M' = M''$ and $M/(M/M') = M'''$; then we have $M''' = M/M''$,
and we have to prove that $M'' = M/M'''$. Let $M/M''' = M^{iv}$.   Now
$M'M''$ contains M ; therefore M' contains M/M'' or M'''.   Also
$M''M'''$ contains M ; therefore M'' contains M/M''' or M^{iv}.   Again,
since M' contains M''' (proved) and $M'''M^{iv}$ contains M, $M'M^{iv}$
contains M, i.e. M^{iv} contains M/M' or M''.   But M'' contains M^{iv}
(proved).   Hence $M'' = M^{iv} = M/M'''$.

Two results follow from this :

(i) M/M' *is a module contained in M of a particular type;* for
M/M' and its residual with respect to M are mutually residual with
respect to M, and this is not true in general of any module contained
in M and the residual module (Ex. ii, § 24).

(ii)   *The least module which can be substituted for M' without
changing M/M' is $M/(M/M')$.* Let M^{iv} be any module such that
$M/M^{iv} = M/M'$; then the product of M^{iv} and M/M' contains M, and
M^{iv} contains $M/(M/M')$.   Also $M/(M/M')$ is one of the modules M^{iv} ;

for if $M/(M/M') = M'''$ then $M/M''' = M/M'$, by the theorem. Hence $M/(M/M')$ is the least of the modules M^{iv} which can be substituted for M' without changing M/M'.

27. *If M', M'' are mutually residual with respect to any module they are mutually residual with respect to $M'M''$.*

Suppose M', M'' are mutually residual with respect to M. Then $M'M''$ contains M; and if $M'M''/M' = M'''$, $M'M'''$ contains $M'M''$ which contains M; hence M''' contains M/M' or M''. Also M''' contains $M'M''/M'$ or M'''. Hence $M'' = M''' = M'M''/M'$. Similarly $M' = M'M''/M''$ (cf. statement iv, § 24).

Any module M with respect to which M', M'' are mutually residual contains $[M', M'']$ and is contained in $M'M''$.

28. *If $M, M_1, M_2, ..., M_k$ are any modules, then*
$$M/(M_1, M_2, ..., M_k) = [M/M_1, M/M_2, ..., M/M_k],$$
and $$[M_1, M_2, ..., M_k]/M = [M_1/M, M_2/M, ..., M_k/M].$$

For $M/(M_1, M_2, ..., M_k)$ contains M/M_i and therefore contains $[M/M_1, M/M_2, ..., M/M_k]$. Also $M_i[M/M_1, ..., M/M_k]$ contains $M_i \times M/M_i$ which contains M; hence $(M_1, ..., M_k)[M/M_1, ..., M/M_k]$ contains M, and $[M/M_1, ..., M/M_k]$ contains $M/(M_1, ..., M_k)$. This proves the first part.

Again $[M_1, ..., M_k]/M$ contains M_i/M and therefore contains $[M_1/M, ..., M_k/M]$. Also $M[M_1/M, ..., M_k/M]$ contains M_i and therefore contains $[M_1, ..., M_k]$; hence $[M_1/M, ..., M_k/M]$ contains $[M_1, ..., M_k]/M$. This proves the second part.

29. Prime and Primary Modules. *Definitions.* A *prime module* is defined by the property that no product of two modules contains it without one of them containing it.

A *primary module* is defined by the property that no product of two modules contains it without one of them containing it or both containing its spread. Hence if one does not contain the spread the other contains the module.

Primary modules will be understood to include prime modules.

Lasker introduced and defined the term primary (L, p. 51), though not in the same words as given here. The conception of a primary module is a fundamental one in the theory of modular systems.

Any irreducible spread determines a prime module, viz. the module whose members consist of all polynomials containing the spread. That this module is prime follows from the fact that no product of two polynomials can contain the spread without one of them containing it (§ 22) and the module; and the same is true if for polynomials we write modules.

If $M = (F_1, F_2, \ldots, F_k)$ is the prime module of rank r determined by an irreducible spread of dimensions $n - r$, and if the origin be moved to a general point of the spread, the constant terms of $F_1, F_2, \ldots, F_k$ will vanish, and the linear terms will be equivalent to r independent linear polynomials, i.e. the sub-determinants of order $> r$ of the matrix

$$\begin{vmatrix} \dfrac{\partial F_1}{\partial x_1}, & \dfrac{\partial F_1}{\partial x_2}, & \cdots & \dfrac{\partial F_1}{\partial x_n} \\ \cdots\cdots\cdots\cdots\cdots\cdots \\ \dfrac{\partial F_k}{\partial x_1}, & \dfrac{\partial F_k}{\partial x_2}, & \cdots & \dfrac{\partial F_k}{\partial x_n} \end{vmatrix}$$

will vanish, while those of order r will not vanish, at the origin. This will be equally true for any general point of the spread without moving the origin to it. Any point of the spread for which the sub-determinants of order r of this matrix vanish is called a *singular point* of the spread, and the aggregate of such points the *singular spread* contained in the given spread. The singular spread (if any exists) is therefore the spread determined by $F_1, F_2, \ldots, F_k$ and the sub-determinants of order r of the above matrix.

If $M = (F_1, F_2, \ldots, F_k)$ is the L.C.M. of the prime modules determined by any finite number of irreducible spreads of the same dimensions $n - r$, the same definition holds concerning singularities of the whole spread. In this case the singular spread consists of the intersections of all pairs of the irreducible spreads, together with all the singular spreads contained in the irreducible spreads considered individually.

30. *The spread of any prime or primary module is irreducible.* For if not the complete u-resolvent has at least two factors corresponding to two different irreducible spreads of the module neither of which contains the other, and is the product of two polynomials neither of which contains the whole spread of the module, i.e. the module is neither prime nor primary.

31. *There is only one prime module with a given (irreducible) spread, viz. the module whose members consist of all polynomials containing the spread.*

Let $M = (F_1, F_2, ..., F_k)$ be any prime module of rank r. It will be sufficient to prove that every polynomial which contains the spread of M contains the module M. The first complete partial u-resolvent of M other than 1 will be a power $R_u{}^m$ of an irreducible polynomial R_u in x, x_{r+1}, ..., x_n. Also the complete u-resolvent is a member of $(f_1, f_2, ..., f_k)$, § 18, which is prime ; and every factor except $R_u{}^m$ is of too high rank to contain the spread of $(f_1, f_2, ..., f_k)$. Hence $R_u{}^m$, and therefore R_u itself, is a member of $(f_1, f_2, ..., f_k)$. Hence $(R_u)_{x=u_1 x_1 + ... + u_n x_n}$ is a member of M, and also the whole coefficient of any power product of u_1, u_2, ..., u_n in $(R_u)_{x=u_1 x_1 + ... + u_n x_n}$. We have proved (§ 21) that

$$(R_u)_{x=u_1 x_1 + ... + u_n x_n} = \cdots + u_r{}^{d-1}(u_1 \psi_1 + ... + u_{r-1} \psi_{r-1}) + u_r{}^d \phi,$$

where $\psi_1 = x_1 \phi' - \phi_1$, ..., $\psi_{r-1} = x_{r-1} \phi' - \phi_{r-1}$. Hence $\psi_1, ..., \psi_{r-1}, \phi$ are all members of M.

Let F be any polynomial which contains the spread of M. In F put $x_1 = \phi_1/\phi'$, $x_2 = \phi_2/\phi'$, ..., $x_{r-1} = \phi_{r-1}/\phi'$; then F becomes a rational function of x_r, x_{r+1}, ..., x_n of which the denominator is ϕ'^l, where l is the degree of F. This rational function vanishes for all points of the spread at which ϕ' does not vanish, and its numerator is therefore divisible by ϕ. We have then

$$F\left(\frac{\phi_1}{\phi'}, \frac{\phi_2}{\phi'}, ..., \frac{\phi_{r-1}}{\phi'}, x_{r+1}, ..., x_n\right) = \frac{X\phi}{\phi'^l},$$

where X is a whole function of x_r, x_{r+1}, ..., x_n ; i.e.

$$F\left(x_1 - \frac{\psi_1}{\phi'}, x_2 - \frac{\psi_2}{\phi'}, ..., x_{r-1} - \frac{\psi_{r-1}}{\phi'}, x_{r+1}, ..., x_n\right) = \frac{X\phi}{\phi'^l},$$

or $\phi'^l F(x_1, x_2, ..., x_n) = 0 \bmod (\psi_1, ..., \psi_{r-1}, \phi) = 0 \bmod M$.
Hence $F = 0 \bmod M$, which proves the theorem.

It follows that a module which is the L.C.M. of a finite number of prime modules, whether of the same rank or not, is uniquely determined by its spread, and any polynomial containing the spread contains the module.

32. *If M is a primary module and M_1 the prime module determined by its spread some finite power of M_1 contains M.*

This theorem, in conjunction with Lasker's theorem (§ 39), is equivalent to the Hilbert-Netto theorem (§ 46). The proofs of the theorem by Lasker and König are both wrong. Lasker first assumes the theorem (L, p. 51) and then proves it (L, p. 56) ; and König makes an absurdly false assumption concerning divisibility (K, p. 399).

By the same reasoning as in the last theorem it follows that $R_u{}^m$ (but not R_u) is a member of $(f_1, f_2, \ldots, f_k)$, and

$$(R_u{}^m)_{x=u_1 x_1 + \ldots + u_n x_n} = \{\ldots + u_r{}^{d-1}(u_1 \psi_1 + \ldots + u_{r-1} \psi_{r-1}) + u_r{}^d \phi\}^m = 0 \bmod M.$$

Picking out the coefficients of $u_r{}^{dm}$ and $u_r{}^{dm-m} u_1{}^m$, we have

$$\phi^m = 0 \bmod M, \quad \text{and} \quad \psi_1{}^m = X\phi \bmod M; \quad \therefore \quad \psi_1{}^{m^2} = 0 \bmod M;$$

and similarly $\psi_2{}^{m^2} = \ldots = \psi_{r-1}^{m^2} = 0 \bmod M$. Also if F is any member of M_1, then, by the last theorem,

$$\phi'^l F = 0 \bmod (\psi_1, \ldots, \psi_{r-1}, \phi).$$

Hence the product of any rm^2 polynomials F and ϕ'^{lrm^2} is a member of $(\psi_1{}^{m^2}, \psi_2, \ldots \psi_{r-1}^{m^2}, \phi^{m^2})$ and of M, i.e. $M_1{}^{rm^2}$ contains M.

33. *Definitions.* If M is a primary module and M_1 the corresponding prime module the least number γ such that $M_1{}^\gamma$ contains M is called the *characteristic number* of M.

A *simple* module is a module containing one point only (Mo). For example, $O^\gamma = (x_1, x_2, \ldots, x_n)^\gamma$ is a simple module with characteristic number γ.

A module of homogeneous polynomials will be called an *H-module*. A simple *H*-module has the origin for its spread; but a simple module having the origin for spread is not in general an *H*-module.

A simple module is primary. For if M is a simple module, and M', M'' any two modules whose product contains M, of which M' does not contain the spread of M, then (M, M') contains no point and is the module (1); but $(M, M') M''$ contains M, i.e. M'' contains M; hence M is primary.

34. *There is no higher limit to the number of members that may be required to constitute a basis of a prime module.* This is not in conflict with Kronecker's statement, proved by König (K, p. 234), that there always exist $n + 1$ polynomials containing a given algebraic spread which have no point in common outside the spread.

Example. Consider $\frac{1}{2} l(l-1)$ straight lines through the origin O in 3-dimensional space, not lying on any cone of order $l-2$. Draw a cone of order l and a surface (not a cone) of order l through the $\frac{1}{2} l(l-1)$ lines so as to intersect again in an irreducible curve of order $\frac{1}{2} l(l+1)$ with $\frac{1}{2} l(l-1)$ tangents at O. Then no basis of the prime module determined by this curve can have less than l members, where l is a number which can be chosen as high as we please.

This can be proved by considering residuation on the cone. The original $\frac{1}{2} l(l-1)$ generators have a residual on the cone of $\frac{1}{2} l(l-1)$ generators, which again have a residual of $\frac{1}{2} l(l-1)$ generators, of which $l-1$ can be chosen at will. This last set of generators is residual to the irreducible curve and together they make the whole intersection of the cone with a surface of order l having an $(l-1)$-point at O. Hence there are l surfaces of order l containing the irreducible curve which have an $(l-1)$-point at O and in which the terms of degree $l-1$ are linearly independent, while there is no surface containing the curve with less than an $(l-1)$-point at O. The prime module determined by the curve must therefore have at least l members in its basis. The module has in fact a basis of $l+1$ members, the $l+1$ linearly independent surfaces of order l containing it (including the cone); and these can be reduced to l members.

In the case $n = 2$ the curve is an ordinary space cubic determining a prime module

$$(f_1, f_2, f_3) = (vw' - v'w, \ wu' - w'u, \ uv' - u'v),$$

where u, v, w, u', v', w' are linear. The basis of three members can be reduced to two $f_1 - a f_2, f_1 - b f_3$ provided constants a, b, λ, λ' and linear functions α, β can be chosen so that

$$f_1 = \alpha \ (f_1 - a f_2) + \beta \ (f_1 - b f_3),$$

or $\qquad (1 - \alpha - \beta) f_1 + a \alpha f_2 + b \beta f_3 = 0,$

or $\qquad 1 - \alpha - \beta = \lambda u + \lambda' u', \quad a \alpha = \lambda v + \lambda' v', \quad b \beta = \lambda w + \lambda' w' \ ;$

and this can be done.

35. *The* L.C.M. *of any number of primary modules with the same spread is a primary module with the same spread.*

Let $M_1, M_2, \ldots, M_k$ be primary modules with the same spread, and let M be their L.C.M. Then M has the same irreducible spread, since the product, which contains the L.C.M., has the same spread. Also if the product $M'M''$ contains M, and M' does not contain the spread, then M'' contains M_1 and $M_2 \ldots$ and M_k, i.e. M'' contains M. Hence M is primary. The G.C.M. is not primary in general.

36. *If M is primary and M' is any module not containing M then M/M' is primary and has the same spread as M.*

Let $M/M' = M''$. Then since $M'M''$ contains M, and M' does not contain M, M'' contains the spread of M. Also M contains M''; hence M'' has the same spread as M. Also if $M_1 M_2$ contains M'' then

$M'M_1M_2$ contains $M'M''$ which contains M; and if M_1 does not contain the spread of M (that is of M'') $M'M_2$ contains M, and M_2 contains M/M' or M''; i.e. M'' is primary.

37. Hilbert's Theorem (H, p. 474). *If F_1, F_2, F_3, ... is an infinite series of homogeneous polynomials there exists a finite number k such that $F_h = 0 \bmod (F_1, F_2, ..., F_k)$ when $h > k$.*

The following proof is substantially König's (K, p. 362). It must be clearly understood that $F_1, F_2, F_3, ...$ *are given in a definite order*. In the case of a single variable the series F_1, F_2, F_3, ... consists of powers of the variable, and if F_k is the least power then $F_h = 0 \bmod F_k$ when $h > k$. Hence the theorem is true in this case. We shall assume it for $n-1$ variables and prove it for n variables.

The series F_1', F_2', F_3', ... is called a modified form of the series F_1, F_2, F_3, ... if $F_1' = F_1$ and $F_i' = F_i \bmod (F_1, F_2, ..., F_{i-1})$ for $i > 1$. Thus the modules $(F_1, F_2, ..., F_i)$ and $(F_1', F_2', ..., F_i')$ are the same. The theorem will be proved if we show that the series F_1', F_2', ... can be so chosen that all its terms after a certain finite number become zero. We assume that F_1 is regular in x_n, and we choose the modified series so that each of its terms F_i' after the first is of as low degree as possible in x_n, and therefore of lower degree in x_n than F_1'. The terms of the series F_1', F_2', ... of degree zero in x_n will be polynomials in $x_1, x_2, .., x_{n-1}$ and these can be modified so that all after a certain finite number become zero, since the theorem is assumed true for $n-1$ variables. Let F'_{l_1}, F'_{l_2}, F'_{l_3}, ... be all the terms of $F_1', F_2', F_3', ...,$ taken in order, which are of one and the same degree $l > 0$ in x_n; and let $f'_{l_1}, f'_{l_2}, ...$ be the whole coefficients of x_n^l in them. Then $f'_{l_1}, f'_{l_2}, f'_{l_3}, ...$ are polynomials in $n-1$ variables; and we cannot have $f'_{l_i} = 0 \bmod (f'_{l_1}, f'_{l_2}, .., f'_{l_{i-1}})$ for any value of i; for if $f'_{l_i} = A_1 f'_{l_1} + A_2 f'_{l_2} + ... + A_{i-1} f'_{l_{i-1}}$, then $F'_{l_i} - A_1 F'_{l_1} - ... - A_{i-1} F'_{l_{i-1}}$ is of less degree than l in x_n, which cannot be. Hence the number of the polynomials $f'_{l_1}, f'_{l_2}, ...,$ or the number of terms $F'_{l_1}, F'_{l_2}, ...$ in the series $F_1', F_2', ...,$ is finite. And the number of values of l is also finite, the greatest value of l being the value it has in F_1'. Hence the theorem is proved.

The theorem can be extended at once to an infinite series $F_1, F_2, ...$ of non-homogeneous polynomials since they can all be made homogeneous by introducing a variable x_0 of homogeneity.

The following is an immediate consequence of the theorem :

Any module of polynomials has a basis consisting of a finite number of members.

To prove this it is only necessary to show that a complete linearly independent set of members of any module can be arranged in a definite order in an infinite series. If l is the lowest degree of any member we can first take any complete linearly independent set of members of degree l, then any complete set of members of degree $l + 1$ whose terms of degree $l + 1$ are linearly independent, then a similar set of members of degree $l + 2$, and so on. In this way a complete linearly independent set of members is obtained in a definite order. It does not matter in what order the members of a set are taken, nor is it necessary to know how to find the members of a set. It is sufficient to know that there is a definite finite number of members belonging to each set.

38. The H-module equivalent to a given module.

Consider a complete linearly independent set of members of a given module M, not an H-module, arranged in a series in the order described above; and make all the members homogeneous by introducing a new variable x_0. We then have a series of homogeneous polynomials belonging to an H-module M_0, whose basis consists of a finite number of members of the series. The module M_0 is called *the H-module equivalent to* M, and a basis of M obtained from any basis of M_0 by putting $x_0 = 1$ is called an *H-basis* of M. The distinctive property of an H-basis $(F_1, F_2, ..., F_k)$ of M is that any member F of M can be put in the form $A_1F_1 + A_2F_2 + ... + A_kF_k$ where A_iF_i $(i = 1, 2, ..., k)$ *is not of greater degree than F.* *Every module has an H-basis*, which may necessarily consist of more members than would suffice for a basis in general.

The following relations exist between M and its equivalent H-module M_0: (i) to any member F of M corresponds a member F_0 of M_0 of the same degree as F, and an infinity of members $x_0{}^p F_0$ of higher degree; (ii) to any member F_0 of M_0 corresponds one and only one member of M, viz. $(F_0)_{x_0=1}$; (iii) there is a one-one correspondence between the members of M_0 of degree l and the members of M of degree $\leqslant l$.

If $x_0 F_0 = 0 \bmod M_0$, then $(F_0)_{x_0=1} = 0 \bmod M$, and $F_0 = 0 \bmod M_0$ by (i), i.e. there is no member $x_0 F_0$ of M_0 such that F_0 is not a member of M_0, and $M_0/(x_0) = M_0$. Conversely *an H-module M in n variables $x_1, x_2, ..., x_n$ is equivalent to the module $M_{x_n=1}$ if $M/(x_n) = M$, and not otherwise.*

In any basis $(F_1, F_2, \ldots, F_k)$ of an H-module in which no member is irrelevant, i.e. no $F_i = 0 \bmod (F_1, \ldots, F_{i-1}, F_{i+1}, \ldots, F_k)$, the number of members of each degree is fixed; as can be easily seen by arranging $F_1, F_2, \ldots, F_k$ in order of degree. *Hence in any H-basis of a module in which no member is irrelevant the number of members of each degree is fixed.* On account of this and the other properties of an H-basis mentioned above an H-basis gives a simpler and clearer representation of a module than a basis which is not an H-basis.

Example. Find an H-basis of the module $(x_1^2, x_2 + x_1 x_3)$.

Take the H-module $(x_1^2, x_2 x_0 + x_1 x_3)$ and solve the equation

$$x_0 X_0 = 0 \bmod (x_1^2, x_2 x_0 + x_1 x_3),$$

or $\qquad x_0 X_0 = x_1^2 X_1 + (x_2 x_0 + x_1 x_3) X_2.$

Putting $x_0 = 0$ we have

$$(x_1^2 X_1 + x_1 x_3 X_2)_{x_0 = 0} = 0,$$

i.e. $\qquad X_1 = x_3 X, \quad X_2 = - x_1 X, \quad$ when $x_0 = 0,$

i.e. $\qquad X_1 = x_3 X + x_0 Y_1, \quad X_2 = - x_1 X + x_0 Y_2.$

Hence

$$x_0 X_0 = x_1^2 (x_3 X + x_0 Y_1) + (x_2 x_0 + x_1 x_3)(-x_1 X + x_0 Y_2)$$
$$= x_0 (x_1^2 Y_1 - x_1 x_2 X + \overline{x_2 x_0 + x_1 x_3}\, Y_2),$$

i.e. $\qquad X_0 = 0 \bmod (x_1^2, x_1 x_2, x_2 x_0 + x_1 x_3).$

Again, if we solve the equation

$$x_0 Y_0 = 0 \bmod (x_1^2, x_1 x_2, x_2 x_0 + x_1 x_3),$$

we find $\qquad Y_0 = 0 \bmod (x_1^2, x_1 x_2, x_2^2, x_2 x_0 + x_1 x_3);$

and if we solve

$$x_0 Z_0 = 0 \bmod (x_1^2, x_1 x_2, x_2^2, x_2 x_0 + x_1 x_3),$$

we find $\qquad Z_0 = 0 \bmod (x_1^2, x_1 x_2, x_2^2, x_2 x_0 + x_1 x_3).$

Hence $(x_1^2, x_1 x_2, x_2^2, x_2 x_0 + x_1 x_3)$ is the H-module equivalent to $(x_1^2, x_2 + x_1 x_3)$, and $(x_1^2, x_1 x_2, x_2^2, x_2 + x_1 x_3)$ is an H-basis of $(x_1^2, x_2 + x_1 x_3)$.

The extra members $x_1 x_2$, x_2^2 might of course have been found more quickly by multiplying $x_2 + x_1 x_3$ first by x_1 and then by x_2. The method given is a general one.

39. Lasker's Theorem (L, p. 51). *Any given module M is the* L.C.M. *of a finite number of primary modules.*

Let M be of rank r. Express its first complete partial u-resolvent $D_u^{(r-1)}$ in irreducible factors, viz.

$$D_u^{(r-1)} = R_1^{m_1} R_2^{m_2} \ldots R_j^{m_j};$$

and let C_1, C_2, ..., C_j denote the irreducible spreads, of dimensions $n - r$, corresponding to R_1, R_2, ..., R_j respectively.

Consider the whole aggregate M_i of polynomials F for each of which there exists a polynomial F', not containing C_i, such that $FF' = 0$ mod M. We shall prove first that M_i is a primary module whose spread is C_i ($i = 1, 2, ..., j$).

Let F_1, F_2 be any two members of M_i. Then since $F_1F_1' = 0$ mod M, and $F_2F_2' = 0$ mod M, where neither F_1' nor F_2' contains C_i, we have $(A_1F_1 + A_2F_2) F_1'F_2' = 0$ mod M, where $F_1'F_2'$ does not contain C_i. Hence $A_1F_1 + A_2F_2$ belongs to the aggregate M_i, i.e. M_i is a module.

Again, since $FF' = 0$ mod M, F contains C_i, and M_i contains C_i. Now, if F_u is the complete u-resolvent of M,

$$(F_u)_{x=u_1x_1+...+u_nx_n} = 0 \text{ mod } M,$$

while $(R_i{}^{m_i})_{x=u_1x_1+...+u_nx_n}$ is the only factor of $(F_u)_{x=u_1x_1+...+u_nx_n}$ which contains C_i. Hence $(R_i{}^{m_i})_{x=u_1x_1+...+u_nx_n} = 0$ mod M_i. But the polynomial $(R_i)_{x=u_1x_1+...+u_nx_n}$ does not vanish identically (i.e. irrespective of u_1, u_2, ..., u_n) for any point outside C_i (§ 21); hence M_i contains no point outside C_i, i.e. C_i is the spread of M_i.

Lastly M_i is primary; for if $F''F''' = 0$ mod M_i, then

$$F'F''F''' = 0 \text{ mod } M,$$

where F' does not contain C_i; hence, if F'' does not contain C_i, $F'F''$ does not, and $F''' = 0$ mod M_i. Hence also if $M''M'''$ contains M_i, and M'' does not contain C_i, M''' contains M_i. Thus M_i is a primary module whose spread is C_i. Also M contains M_i, for every member of M is a member of M_i.

The module M/M_i does not contain C_i; for if $M_i = (F_1, F_2, ..., F_k)$ and F_1', F_2', ..., F_k' are polynomials not containing C_i such that

$$F_lF_l' = 0 \text{ mod } M \quad (l = 1, 2, ..., k),$$

then $\qquad F_lF_1'F_2'...F_k' = 0$ mod $M \quad (l = 1, 2, ..., k)$.

Hence $F_1'F_2'...F_k'$ is a member of M/M_i not containing C_i; and therefore M/M_i cannot contain C_i.

Since M/M_i does not contain C_i, $(M/M_1, M/M_2, ..., M/M_j)$ does not contain any of the spreads C_1, C_2, ..., C_j. We can now prove that if ϕ is any single member of $(M/M_1, M/M_2, ..., M/M_j)$ which does not contain any of the spreads C_1, C_2, ..., C_j, then

$$M = [M_1, M_2, ..., M_j, (M, \phi)].$$

Since M contains $[M_1, M_2, ..., M_j, (M, \phi)]$ it has only to be proved that the latter contains M, or that

$F = 0$ mod $[M_1, M_2, ..., M_j, (M, \phi)]$ requires $F = 0$ mod M.

We have $F = 0 \bmod (M, \phi) = f\phi \bmod M = f\phi \bmod M_i$;

but $F = 0 \bmod M_i$; therefore $f\phi = 0 \bmod M_i$, and, since ϕ does not contain C_i,

$$f = 0 \bmod M_i = 0 \bmod [M_1, M_2, \dots, M_j].$$

Hence $f\phi = 0 \bmod [M_1, M_2, \dots, M_j]$ $(M/M_1, \dots, M/M_j) = 0 \bmod M$ (§ 28), and $F = f\phi \bmod M = 0 \bmod M$.   Hence $M = [M_1, M_2, \dots, M_j, (M, \phi)]$.

Now the spread of (M, ϕ) is of dimensions $< n - r$, since ϕ does not contain any spread of M of dimensions $n - r$.   Hence the same process can be applied to (M, ϕ) as to M; and we finally arrive at a module $(M, \phi, \phi', \dots)$ with no spread, which is the module (1).   Hence $M = [Q_1, Q_2, \dots, Q_k]$ where $Q_1, Q_2, \dots, Q_k$ are all primary modules of ranks $\leqslant r$.

40.   Comment on Lasker's Theorem.   The above is in all essentials the remarkable proof given by Lasker of this fundamental theorem.   He considers H-modules only and makes use of homogeneous coordinates, in consequence of which his enunciation of the theorem is not quite as simple as the one above.

Any module among $Q_1, Q_2, \dots, Q_k$ which is contained in the L.C.M. of all the rest is *irrelevant* and may be omitted.   It will be understood in writing $M = [Q_1, Q_2, \dots, Q_k]$ that all irrelevant modules have been omitted.   Those that remain will be called the *relevant primary modules* into which M resolves, and their spreads will be called the *relevant spreads* of M.   A relevant spread which is not contained in another of higher dimensions is called an *isolated spread* and the corresponding module an *isolated primary module* of M.   The other relevant spreads and modules are called *imbedded* spreads and modules of M.   All the relevant spreads of M whether isolated or imbedded are unique.   Also the isolated primary modules are unique, but the imbedded primary modules are to some extent indeterminate.

A process by which $Q_1, Q_2, \dots, Q_k$ can be theoretically obtained, without bringing in any irrelevant modules, is described in (M).   The isolated spreads are found from the irreducible factors of the complete u-resolvent after rejecting all factors which give imbedded spreads.   To these correspond unique primary modules of M which can be found. Let $M^{(0)}$ be their L.C.M.   The isolated spreads of $M/M^{(0)}$ are the relevant spreads of M imbedded to the first degree.   To these correspond indeterminate imbedded primary modules of M which are chosen as simply as possible.   Although not uniquely determinate the L.C.M. of each one and $M^{(0)}$ is unique, and the L.C.M. of them all and $M^{(0)}$ is a unique module $M^{(1)}$. The isolated spreads of $M/M^{(1)}$ are the relevant spreads of M imbedded to the second degree ; and the L.C.M. of the corresponding (indeterminate) primary modules and $M^{(1)}$ is a unique module $M^{(2)}$. The process is continued until a module $M^{(l)}$ is obtained such that $M/M^{(l)} = (1)$, when there will be no more relevant primary modules to find.

41. An *unmixed module* is usually understood to be one whose *isolated* irreducible spreads are all of the same dimensions ; but it is clear from the above that this cannot be regarded as a satisfactory view. It should be defined as follows :

Definition. An *unmixed module* is one whose relevant spreads, both isolated and imbedded, are all of the same dimensions ; and a *mixed module* is one having at least two relevant spreads of different dimensions.

An unmixed module cannot have any relevant imbedded spreads.

A primary module is an unmixed module whose spread is irreducible. This cannot be taken as a definition because the meaning of *unmixed* depends on the meaning of *primary*.

Condition that a module may be unmixed. In order that a module M of rank r may be unmixed it is necessary and sufficient that it should have no relevant spread of rank $> r$. This condition may be expressed by saying that $\phi F = 0 \bmod M$ requires $F = 0 \bmod M$ where ϕ is any polynomial involving $x_{r+1}, \ldots, x_n$ only. For if M contains a relevant primary module of rank $> r$ a ϕ can be chosen which contains it, and an F which does not contain it but contains all the other relevant primary modules of M, so that $\phi F = 0 \bmod M$ does not require $F = 0 \bmod M$; while if M contains no relevant primary module of rank $> r$ there is no ϕ containing a relevant spread of M and $\phi F = 0 \bmod M$ requires $F = 0 \bmod M/(\phi) = 0 \bmod M$ (§ 42).

A primary module Q has a certain *multiplicity* (§ 68). To a given primary module $Q^{(\mu)}$ of multiplicity μ corresponds a series of primary modules $Q^{(1)}, Q^{(2)}, \ldots, Q^{(\mu)}$ of multiplicities $1, 2, \ldots, \mu$ all having the same spread as $Q^{(\mu)}$ and such that $Q^{(p)}$ contains $Q^{(p-1)}$ and is contained in $Q^{(p+1)}$. $Q^{(1)}$ is the prime module determined by the spread of $Q^{(\mu)}$ and is unique ; but the intermediate modules $Q^{(2)}, Q^{(3)}, \ldots, Q^{(\mu-1)}$ are to a great extent indeterminate (M, p. 89). Thus $Q^{(1)}, Q^{(2)}, \ldots, Q^{(\mu)}$ may be regarded as successive stages in constructing $Q^{(\mu)}$. *Two primary modules with the same spread and the same multiplicity such that one contains the other must be the same module.*

42. Deductions from Lasker's Theorem. *A module of rank n resolves into simple (primary) modules of which it is the product* (§ 25).

If M' does not contain any relevant spread of M then $M/M' = M$. Let $M/M' = M''$. Then since $M'M''$ contains M, and M' does not contain any relevant spread of M, M'' contains all the relevant primary modules into which M resolves, i.e. $M'' = M$.

It follows that if $M/M' \neq M$, M' must contain a relevant spread of M. *Thus if a polynomial F exists such that $(x_1 - a_1) F, (x_2 - a_2) F, \ldots, (x_n - a_n) F$ are all members of M, while F is not, M contains a relevant simple module whose spread is the point $P(a_1, a_2, \ldots, a_n)$; for $M/P \neq M$.*

Example. The module $M = (x_1^3, x_2^3, \overline{x_1^2 + x_2^2} \, x_4 + x_1 x_2 x_3)$ has a relevant simple module at the origin; for $x_i x_1^2 x_2^2$ is a member of M ($i = 1, 2, 3, 4$), but $x_1^2 x_2^2$ is not. The simplest corresponding imbedded primary module, not contained in the L.C.M. of all the other relevant primary modules of M, is (x_1^3, x_2^3, x_3, x_4); cf. Ex. iii, § 17. This example shows that *it is possible for a mixed module M to contain a relevant primary module of higher rank than the number of members in a basis of M.* For the rank of (x_1^3, x_2^3, x_3, x_4) is 4.

If M is an H-module not having a relevant simple module at the origin the variables can be subjected to such a linear homogeneous substitution that x_n will not contain any relevant spread of M, and we shall then have $M/(x_n) = M$, and M will be equivalent to $M_{x_n=1}$ (§ 38). *Thus the only condition (remaining permanent under a linear substitution) that an H-module M may be equivalent to the module $M_{x_n=1}$ is that M should not contain a relevant simple module.*

A simple H-module M is not equivalent to $M_{x_n=1}$; in fact $M_{x_n=1}$ is in this case the module (1).

If M' contains any relevant spread of M then $M/M' \neq M$. Let $M = [Q_1, Q_2, \ldots, Q_k]$, and let M' contain the spread of Q_i. Then some power M'^γ of M' contains Q_i (§ 32), and $Q_i/M'^\gamma = (1)$. Hence the spread of Q_i is not a relevant spread of

$$M/M'^\gamma = [Q_1/M'^\gamma, Q_2/M'^\gamma, \ldots, Q_k/M'^\gamma], \S 28 \, ;$$

and consequently $M/M'^\gamma \neq M$. Hence also $M/M' \neq M$; for if $M/M' = M$ then $M/M'^\gamma = M$.

It follows that if $M/M' = M$ then M' does not contain any relevant spread of M. If M_0 is the H-module equivalent to M we know that $M_0/(x_0) = M_0$ (§ 38); hence x_0 does not contain any relevant spread of M_0, i.e. *no module has a relevant spread at infinity.*

If M, M' are any two modules such that M resolves into isolated primary modules only, viz. Q_1, Q_2, ..., Q_k, and (M, M') into primary modules Q_1', Q_2', ..., Q_l', of which Q_1', Q_2', ..., Q_k have the same spreads as Q_1, Q_2, ..., Q_k respectively, then

$$M/M' = [Q_1/Q_1', \ Q_2/Q_2', \ ..., \ Q_k/Q_k'].$$

The spread of (M, M') is contained in the spread of M; and it is to be understood that if (M, M') does not contain the spread of Q_i, then $Q_i' = (1)$. The spreads of $Q'_{k+1}, ..., Q_l'$ are contained in those of Q_1, Q_2, ..., Q_k, but do not contain any of the latter. Now we have

$$M/M' = M/(M, M') = [Q_1, \ Q_2, \ ..., \ Q_k]/[Q_1', \ Q_2', \ ..., \ Q_l'].$$

Hence the theorem follows, by the second part of § 28, provided

$$Q_i/[Q_1', \ Q_2', \ ..., \ Q_l'] = Q_i/Q_i'.$$

This is true; for Q_i/Q_i' contains $Q_i/[Q_1', Q_2', ..., Q_l']$, since $[Q_1', Q_2', ..., Q_l']$ contains Q_i', and, for a similar reason, $Q_i/[Q_1', Q_2', ..., Q_l']$ contains $Q_i/Q_1'Q_2'...Q_l'$ or Q_i/Q_i'.

43. *If a module M of rank r is regarded as a module $M^{(s)}$ in s variables x_1, x_2, ..., x_s, while x_{s+1}, ..., x_n are regarded as parameters; and if $F^{(s)}$ is a whole member of $M^{(s)}$, that is, a whole function of the parameters as well as of the variables, then $F^{(s)}$, regarded as a polynomial in x_1, x_2, ..., x_n, contains all the relevant primary modules of M of rank $\leqslant s$; and conversely, any polynomial which contains all these primary modules is a member of $M^{(s)}$. The most important case is that in which s = r.*

In other words, to treat a module M as a module in s variables has the sole effect of eliminating all the primary modules of M of rank $> s$; and when $s < r$ it reduces M to the module (1).

Let $M = (F_1, F_2, ..., F_k)$; then $F^{(s)} = A_1F_1 + A_2F_2 + ... + A_kF_k$, where A_1, A_2, ..., A_k are whole functions of x_1, x_2, ..., x_s and rational functions of x_{s+1}, ..., x_n, with a common denominator $D^{(s)}$. Hence $D^{(s)}F^{(s)} = 0 \bmod M$, and $F^{(s)}$ contains all the primary modules of M of rank $\leqslant s$, since $D^{(s)}$ does not contain any of their spreads.

Conversely, if $F^{(s)}$ contains all the primary modules of M of rank $\leqslant s$, and $D^{(s)}$, a whole function of x_{s+1}, ..., x_n only, contains all the primary modules of M of rank $> s$, then $D^{(s)}F^{(s)} = 0 \bmod M$, and $F^{(s)} = 0 \bmod M^{(s)}$, since $D^{(s)}$ in respect to $M^{(s)}$ does not involve the variables.

The module $M^{(r)}$ resolves into simple modules, any primary module of M of rank r and order d contributing d simple modules to $M^{(r)}$. By finding these simple modules we are able to find the primary modules of M of rank r; and this completely resolves M if M is unmixed.

44.   *If M is a module of rank $r < n$ and no-one of the modules M, $(M, x_n - a_n)$, $(M, x_{n-1} - a_{n-1}, x_n - a_n)$, ... $(M, x_{r+2} - a_{r+2}, ..., x_n - a_n)$ contains a relevant simple module $(a_{r+2}, ..., a_n$ having non-special values) then M is unmixed.   In the contrary case M is mixed.*

This theorem will be used later for proving that certain modules are unmixed.   We shall prove first that if M is mixed and does not contain a relevant simple module then $(M, x_n - a_n)$ is mixed.   Let M' be the prime module determined by a relevant spread of M of rank $> r$ and $< n$, since M is mixed and has no relevant spread of rank n. To prove that $(M, x_n - a_n)$ is mixed it is sufficient to show that $(M', x_n - a_n)$ contains a relevant spread of $(M, x_n - a_n)$.

Suppose this is not the case; then (§ 42)

$$(M, x_n - a_n)/(M', x_n - a_n) = (M, x_n - a_n),$$

i.e. $$(M, x_n - a_n)/M' = (M, x_n - a_n),$$

and therefore M/M' contains $(M, x_n - a_n)$.   Let F be any member of M/M' and $(F_1, F_2, ..., F_k)$ a basis of M; then

$$F = A_1 F_1 + ... + A_k F_k \bmod (x_n - a_n),$$

i.e. $$F_{x_n = a_n} = (A_1 F_1 + ... + A_k F_k)_{x_n = a_n}.$$

Here we may regard a_n as a parameter replacing x_n.   Hence F is a member of M regarded as a module in $n - 1$ variables, and therefore contains all the primary modules of M of rank $\leqslant n - 1$ (§ 43); i.e. $F = 0 \bmod M$.   Hence M/M' contains M, which is not true.   It follows that $(M, x_n - a_n)$ is mixed in general, i.e. if a_n has a non-special value. By the same reasoning, if $(M, x_n - a_n)$ does not contain a relevant simple module, $(M, x_{n-1} - a_{n-1}, x_n - a_n)$ is mixed, and so on.   Finally if $(M, x_{r+2} - a_{r+2}, ..., x_n - a_n)$ is mixed it must contain a relevant simple module since it is of rank $n - 1$.   Hence if M is mixed one of the above modules contains a relevant simple module.   It follows that if no-one of the modules contains a relevant simple module, then M is unmixed.

Conversely if one of the above modules contains a relevant simple module (or more generally if one is mixed) then M is mixed.   Suppose for instance that $(M, x_n - a_n)$ is mixed.   Then since $(M, x_n - a_n)$ is of rank $r + 1$ it has a relevant spread of rank $\geqslant r + 2$.   Hence there is a whole function ϕ of $x_{r+1}, ..., x_{n-1}$ only containing this spread, and a polynomial F in $x_1, x_2, ..., x_n$ such that

$$\phi F = 0 \bmod (M, x_n - a_n), \text{ while } F \neq 0 \bmod (M, x_n - a_n).$$

Let $(F_1, F_2, ..., F_k)$ be a basis of M.   Then

$$\phi F = A_1 F_1 + ... + A_k F_k \bmod (x_n - a_n),$$

where we may assume that F, ϕ, $A_1, ..., A_k$ are whole functions of a_n as well as of $x_1, x_2, ... x_n$.   Putting $x_n = a_n$,

$$(\phi F)_{x_n = a_n} = (A_1 F_1 + ... + A_k F_k)_{x_n = a_n}.$$

In this we can replace a_n by x_n, and we then have

$$(\phi F)_{a_n = x_n} = 0 \bmod M.$$

But $\phi_{a_n = x_n}$ is a whole function of $x_{r+1}, ..., x_n$ only, and $F_{a_n = x_n} \neq 0 \bmod M$, since $F \neq 0 \bmod (M, x_n - a_n)$.   Hence M is mixed.   This completes the proof of the theorem.

If M is unmixed all the modules are unmixed; nevertheless *if $a_{r+2}, ..., a_n$ have special values, some of the modules may be mixed notwithstanding that M is unmixed.*

Example.   The module

$$M = (u_0 u_4 - u_1 u_3,\ u_1{}^3 - u_0{}^2 u_3,\ u_3{}^3 - u_1 u_4{}^2,\ u_1{}^2 u_4 - u_0 u_3{}^2)$$

is prime and of rank 2 $\left(\text{its spread being given by } \dfrac{u_0}{\lambda^0} = \dfrac{u_1}{\lambda^1} = \dfrac{u_3}{\lambda^3} = \dfrac{u_4}{\lambda^4}\right)$ while the module $(M, c_4 u_0 + c_3 u_1 + c_1 u_3 + c_0 u_4)$ is of rank 3 and mixed. For the latter has $u_0 F$, $u_1 F$, $u_3 F$, $u_4 F$ as members, where

$$F = c_4 u_1{}^2 + c_3 u_0 u_3 + c_1 u_1 u_4 + c_0 u_3{}^2 \neq 0 \bmod (M, c_4 u_0 + c_3 u_1 + c_1 u_3 + c_0 u_4).$$

Hence if u_0, u_1, u_3, u_4 are linear functions of x_1, x_2, x_3, x_4 and (a_1, a_2, a_3, a_4) their common point, the module $(M, x_4 - a_4)$ is mixed notwithstanding that M is unmixed (cf. § 89, end).

45.   *If M contains a relevant simple module at the point $(a_1, a_2, ..., a_n)$ then $(M, x_n - a_n)$ contains a relevant simple module at the same point.*

Let u, u', $u'', ...$ be linear functions of $x_1, x_2, ..., x_n$ containing the point $(a_1, a_2, ..., a_n)$ and no other relevant spread of M.   Suppose that $(M, x_n - a_n)$ does not contain a relevant simple module at $(a_1, a_2, ..., a_n)$; then it may be assumed that (M, u), (M, u'), $(M, u''), ...$ do not either. Let F be a polynomial such that $u F = 0 \bmod M$ and $F \neq 0 \bmod M$.

Then $\qquad\qquad u F = 0 \bmod (M, u')$,

therefore $\qquad F = 0 \bmod (M, u') = u' F'' \bmod M$,

therefore $\qquad u u' F'' = 0 \bmod M = 0 \bmod (M, u'')$,

therefore $\qquad F'' = 0 \bmod (M, u'') = u'' F''' \bmod M$,

and $\qquad\qquad F = u' u'' F''' \bmod M$.

Similarly $\qquad F = u' u'' ... u^{(l)} F'^{(l)} \bmod M$.

Now l can be chosen so great that $u'u''...u^{(l)}$ contains the relevant simple module of M at $(a_1, a_2, ..., d_n)$; and since F contains all the other relevant primary modules of M we have $F = 0 \bmod M$, which is not true.   Hence $(M, x_n - a_n)$ does contain a relevant simple module at the point $(a_1, a_2, ..., a_n)$.

46.   The Hilbert-Netto Theorem (H_1, Ne).   *If M' is any module containing the spread of a given module M some finite power of M' contains M.*

For M' contains all the relevant spreads of M and some finite power of M' contains all the relevant primary modules of M (§ 32) and therefore contains M.

The theorem is proved in (Ne) for the case of two variables and in (H_1) for the general case.

47.   *Definition.*   A module of rank r having a basis consisting of r members only is called a *module of the principal class* (Kr, p. 80). Hence a module $(F_1, F_2, ..., F_r)$ of rank r is of the principal class.

It is possible for the resultant of a module of the principal class to vanish identically.   An example is given at the end of § 12.

The H-module equivalent to a given module of the principal class is not necessarily of the principal class, e.g. the H-module equivalent to $(x_1^2, x_2 + x_1 x_3)$ has four members in its basis $(x_1^2, x_1 x_2, x_2^2, x_2 x_0 + x_1 x_3)$, § 38.

A proper module is of rank $\leqslant n$ and $\geqslant 1$.

A proper module with a basis consisting of r members is of rank $\leqslant r$ (cf. ex. § 42); for the module contains some point P in the finite region and a spread of dimensions $n - r$ at least through any such point. Nevertheless a module with a basis of two or more members may be the non-proper module (1); e.g. $(F, 1 + F) = (1)$.

The unit module is sometimes said to be of rank $n + 1$; but it is better to say that it is without rank, and that no module is of rank $> n$.   In the absolute theory a module can be of rank $n + 1$.

If $(F_1, F_2, ..., F_r)$ is of rank r it does not necessarily follow that $(F_2, F_3, ..., F_r)$ is of rank $r - 1$.   Thus $(f, f_1 + ff_1, f_2 + ff_2)$ is the same as (f, f_1, f_2), and can be of rank 3, while $(f_1 + ff_1, f_2 + ff_2)$ contains $(1 + f)$ and is of rank 1.   If however the series $F_1, F_2, ..., F_r$ is suitably modified beforehand (§ 37) then $(F_{s+1}, ..., F_r)$ will be of rank $r - s$ if $(F_1, F_2, ..., F_r)$ is of rank r.   It will be sufficient to prove that $(F_2 + a_2 F_1, F_3 + a_3 F_1, ..., F_r + a_r F_1)$ is of rank $r - 1$ when $a_2, a_3, ..., a_r$

are (at first) undetermined constants. If it is of rank $s < r - 1$ then
the module $(\phi_1, \phi_2, ..., \phi_s)$ is of rank s, where

$$\phi_i = \lambda_{i2}(F_2 + a_2 F_1) + \lambda_{i3}(F_3 + a_3 F_1) + ... + \lambda_{ir}(F_r + a_r F_1)$$
$$= \lambda_{i1} F_1 + \lambda_{i2} F_2 + ... + \lambda_{ir} F_r$$
$$(\lambda_{i1} = \lambda_{i2} a_2 + \lambda_{i3} a_3 + ... + \lambda_{ir} a_r, \quad i = 1, 2, ..., s),$$

and the λ_{ij} are all arbitrary constants. We may regard the s relations
$\lambda_{i1} = \lambda_{i2} a_2 + ... + \lambda_{ir} a_r$ as determining the s constants $a_2, a_3, ..., a_{s+1}$,
leaving at least $a_r (s + 1 \leqslant r - 1)$ quite arbitrary, whatever the values of
the λ_{ij} are. Now some spread of $(\phi_1, \phi_2, ..., \phi_s)$ of rank s is a spread
of $(F_2 + a_2 F_1, ..., F_r + a_r F_1)$ and is contained in $F_r + a_r F_1$, and therefore
in F_1 (since a_r is independent of the λ_{ij}), and in each of $F_2, F_3, ..., F_r$.
This would make $(F_1, F_2, ..., F_r)$ of rank s, which is not the case.

Unmixed Modules

48. A useful test as to whether a given module is mixed or
unmixed is proved in § 44.

Theorem. *A module of the principal class is unmixed.* Lasker
proves this for H-modules (L, p. 58). The following is a general proof.

It is clear that any module of rank n is unmixed, since it resolves
into primary modules which are all of rank n. Also a module of the
principal class of rank 1 is unmixed. Hence the theorem is true for
two variables, since in this case the module can only be of rank 1 or 2.
We shall assume the theorem true for $n - 1$ variables and prove it for
n variables. We also assume that the members of the basis have been
modified if necessary so that, when $(F_1, F_2, ..., F_r)$ is of rank r,
$(F_2, F_3, ..., F_r)$ is of rank $r - 1$ (§ 47).

We prove first that a module $M = (F_1, F_2, ..., F_r)$ of rank
$r < n$ cannot contain any relevant simple module by showing that
$(x_n - c_n) F = 0 \bmod M$ requires $F = 0 \bmod M$ no matter what value,
special or otherwise, c_n may have.

Let $(x_n - c_n) F = X_1 F_1 + X_2 F_2 + ... + X_r F_r$;

then $(X_1 F_1 + X_2 F_2 + ... + X_r F_r)_{x_n = c_n} = 0$,

and $(X_1 F_1)_{x_n = c_n} = 0 \bmod (F_2, F_3, ..., F_r)_{x_n = c_n}.$

But $(F_2, F_3, ..., F_r)_{x_n = c_n}$ is a module of rank $r - 1$ in $n - 1$ variables,
so that (by the assumption) all its relevant spreads are of rank $r - 1$,
and $(F_1)_{x_n = c_n}$ does not contain any of them. Hence

$$(X_1)_{x_n = c_n} = 0 \bmod (F_2, F_3, ..., F_r)_{x_n = c_n},$$

i.e. $X_1 = X_{12} F_2 + X_{13} F_3 + ... + X_{1r} F_r + (x_n - c_n) Y_1.$

Substituting this value for X_1 in the equation

$$(X_1 F_1 + X_2 F_2 + \ldots + X_r F_r)_{x_n = c_n} = 0,$$

we have $\{(X_2 + X_{12} F_1) F_2 + \ldots + (X_r + X_{1r} F_1) F_r\}_{x_n = c_n} = 0.$

Hence, by the same reasoning as before,

$$X_2 + X_{12} F_1 = X_{23} F_3 + \ldots + X_{2r} F_r + (x_n - c_n) Y_2,$$
$$X_3 + X_{13} F_1 + X_{23} F_2 = X_{34} F_4 + \ldots + X_{3r} F_r + (x_n - c_n) Y_3,$$
$$\ldots\ldots\ldots\ldots\ldots\ldots\ldots\ldots\ldots\ldots\ldots\ldots\ldots\ldots$$
$$X_r + X_{1r} F_1 + X_{2r} F_2 + \ldots + X_{r-1, r} F_{r-1} = (x_n - c_n) Y_r.$$

Multiplying these equations by $F_1, F_2, \ldots, F_r$ and adding we have

$$X_1 F_1 + X_2 F_2 + \ldots + X_r F_r = (x_n - c_n) (Y_1 F_1 + Y_2 F_2 + \ldots + Y_r F_r),$$

all the terms $\Sigma X_{ij} F_i F_j \, (i < j)$ cancelling from both sides.   It follows that

$$F = Y_1 F_1 + Y_2 F_2 + \ldots + Y_r F_r = 0 \bmod M,$$

and that $(F_1, F_2, \ldots, F_r)$ does not contain any relevant simple module.

Now if $(F_1, F_2, \ldots, F_r)$ were mixed then for some value of $s \geqslant r + 2$ the module $(F_1, \ldots, F_r, x_s - a_s, \ldots, x_n - a_n)$ would contain a relevant simple module (§ 44); but it does not, because it is of the principal class.   Hence $(F_1, F_2, \ldots, F_r)$ is unmixed.

49.   Deductions from the theorem.   *A basis $(F_1, F_2, \ldots, F_r)$ of a module M of the principal class of rank r is an H-basis of M or not, and an H-basis of $M^{(r)}$ or not, according as the H-module determined by the terms of highest degree in $F_1, F_2, \ldots, F_r$ is of rank r or not.*

Let M_0 be the H-module in $x_1, x_2, \ldots, x_n, x_0$ corresponding to the basis $(F_1, F_2, \ldots, F_r)$, so that $(M_0)_{x_0 = 0}$ is the H-module mentioned in the enunciation.   Let $(M_0)_{x_0 = 0}$ be of rank r.   Then it follows by the same reasoning as in the theorem that $x_0 F_0 = 0 \bmod M_0$ requires $F_0 = 0 \bmod M_0$. Hence M_0 is equivalent to M (§ 38), i.e. $(F_1, F_2, \ldots, F_r)$ is an H-basis of M.   It is also an H-basis of $M^{(r)}$.   This follows in the same way by considering the H-module $M_0^{(r)}$ in $x_1, x_2, \ldots, x_r, x_0$ corresponding to $(F_1, F_2, \ldots, F_r)$ regarded as a basis of $M^{(r)}$.   The module $(M_0^{(r)})_{x_0 = 0}$ is a simple H-module not involving $x_{r+1}, \ldots, x_n$.

If on the contrary $(M_0)_{x_0 = 0}$ is not of rank r it is of rank $< r$, and x_0 contains a relevant spread of M_0 of rank $\leqslant r$, so that $M_0/(x_0) \neq M_0$ and M_0 is not equivalent to M (§ 38).   Hence $(F_1, F_2, \ldots, F_r)$ is not an H-basis of M or of $M^{(r)}$.

If $(F_1, F_2, \ldots, F_k)$ is an H-basis of a module of rank r the H-module determined by the terms of highest degree in $F_1, F_2, \ldots, F_k$ is of rank r.

But the converse is not true in general when $k > r$; i.e. if the module determined by the terms of highest degree in $F_1, F_2, ..., F_k$ is of the same rank r as the module $(F_1, F_2, ..., F_k)$ the basis $(F_1, F_2, ..., F_k)$ is not in general an H-basis when $k > r$.

50. *Any power of a module of the principal class is unmixed.*

Let the module be $M = (F_1, F_2, ..., F_r)$ of rank r. The spread of M^γ is the same as the spread of M. Hence it will be sufficient to show that $AF = 0 \bmod M^\gamma$ requires $F = 0 \bmod M^\gamma$ provided A does not contain any relevant spread of M. When $\gamma = 2$ we have

$$AF = 0 \bmod M^2; \text{ hence } F = 0 \bmod M = A_1F_1 + ... + A_rF_r,$$

and $A(A_1F_1 + ... + A_rF_r) = 0 \bmod M^2 = F_1 F^{(1)} \bmod (F_2, ..., F_r)^2,$

where $\qquad\qquad F^{(1)} = 0 \bmod M.$

Hence $\qquad (AA_1 - F^{(1)}) F_1 = 0 \bmod (F_2, ..., F_r),$

$$AA_1 - F^{(1)} = 0 \bmod (F_2, ..., F_r),$$

$$AA_1 = 0 \bmod M, \text{ and } A_1 = 0 \bmod M.$$

Similarly $A_i = 0 \bmod M$, and $F = A_1F_1 + ... + A_rF_r = 0 \bmod M^2$.

Next suppose $\gamma = 3$. Then since

$$AF = 0 \bmod M^3,$$

$$F = 0 \bmod M^2 = F_1 F^{(1)} + \phi^{(2)},$$

where $F^{(1)} = A_1F_1 + ... + A_rF_r$, and $\phi^{(2)} = 0 \bmod (F_2, ..., F_r)^2.$

Now $A(F_1 F^{(1)} + \phi^{(2)}) = 0 \bmod M^3 = F_1 F^{(2)} \bmod (F_2, ..., F_r)^3,$

where $\qquad\qquad F^{(2)} = 0 \bmod M^2;$

hence $\qquad (AF^{(1)} - F^{(2)}) F_1 = 0 \bmod (F_2, ..., F_r)^2,$

$$AF^{(1)} - F^{(2)} = 0 \bmod (F_2, ..., F_r)^2,$$

$$F^{(1)} = 0 \bmod M^2.$$

Thus every coefficient A_i in $F^{(1)} (= A_1F_1 + ... + A_rF_r)$ is a member of M (as proved when $\gamma = 2$), i.e. every coefficient of the terms of $F = F_1 F^{(1)} + \phi^{(2)}$ furnished by $F_1 F^{(1)}$ is a member of M; and the same must therefore be true of the terms of F furnished by $\phi^{(2)}$. Hence

$$F = 0 \bmod M^3.$$

Similarly, if $AF = 0 \bmod M^\gamma$, and the theorem is assumed true for $M^{\gamma-1}$ we have $F = 0 \bmod M^{\gamma-1} = F_1 F^{(\gamma-2)} + \phi^{(\gamma-1)}$, and can prove that every coefficient in $F^{(\gamma-2)}$ and $\phi^{(\gamma-1)}$ is a member of M. Hence

$$F = 0 \bmod M^\gamma.$$

51. *If M is a module of the principal class which resolves into prime modules the module whose members consist of all polynomials having a γ-point at every point of M is the module M^γ.*

The theorem is true when $\gamma = 1$. We shall prove it for M^γ assuming it for $M^{\gamma-1}$. Let $M = (F_1, F_2, \ldots, F_r)$ be of rank r and let $F^{(\gamma)}$ be any polynomial with a γ-point at every point of M.

Then
$$F^{(\gamma)} = 0 \bmod M^{\gamma-1},$$

i.e. $F^{(\gamma)} = \Sigma A_{p_1, p_2, \ldots, p_r} F_1^{p_1} F_2^{p_2} \ldots F_r^{p_r}$, where $p_1 + p_2 + \ldots + p_r = \gamma - 1$. Take $\xi_1, \xi_2, \ldots, \xi_n$ for the variables instead of $x_1, x_2, \ldots, x_n$, and move the origin to any point $(x_1, x_2, \ldots, x_n)$ of M. Then F_1 becomes

$$F_1(\xi_1 + x_1, \ldots, \xi_n + x_n) = \xi_1 \frac{\partial F_1}{\partial x_1} + \ldots + \xi_n \frac{\partial F_1}{\partial x_n} + \tfrac{1}{2}\xi_1^2 \frac{\partial^2 F_1}{\partial x_1^2} + \ldots ,$$

and the terms of lowest degree in $F^{(\gamma)}$ are

$$\Sigma A_{p_1, p_2, \ldots, p_r} \left(\xi_1 \frac{\partial F_1}{\partial x_1} + \ldots + \xi_n \frac{\partial F_1}{\partial x_n} \right)^{p_1} \ldots \left(\xi_1 \frac{\partial F_r}{\partial x_1} + \ldots + \xi_n \frac{\partial F_r}{\partial x_n} \right)^{p_r},$$

where $A_{p_1, p_2, \ldots, p_r}$ have their original values as functions of $x_1, x_2, \ldots, x_n$. This last expression is of degree $\gamma - 1$ in $\xi_1, \xi_2, \ldots, \xi_n$ and must vanish identically, since $F^{(\gamma)}$ has a γ-point at every point of M. Now the r quantities $\xi_1 \frac{\partial F_i}{\partial x_1} + \ldots + \xi_n \frac{\partial F_i}{\partial x_n}$ $(i = 1, 2, \ldots, r)$ are either capable of taking any r values ($\xi_1, \ldots, \xi_n$ being undetermined quantities and $x_1, \ldots, x_n$ fixed quantities) or they are not. If they are, every $A_{p_1, p_2, \ldots, p_r}$ vanishes. If they are not, every determinant of the matrix

$$\begin{vmatrix} \dfrac{\partial F_1}{\partial x_1} & \dfrac{\partial F_1}{\partial x_2} & \ldots & \dfrac{\partial F_1}{\partial x_n} \\ \ldots\ldots\ldots\ldots\ldots \\ \dfrac{\partial F_r}{\partial x_1} & \dfrac{\partial F_r}{\partial x_2} & \ldots & \dfrac{\partial F_r}{\partial x_n} \end{vmatrix}$$

vanishes, i.e. $(x_1, x_2, \ldots, x_n)$ is a singular point of M (§ 29). Hence every $A_{p_1, p_2, \ldots, p_r}$ vanishes for every non-singular point of M and is therefore a member of M (§ 22). Hence $F^{(\gamma)} = 0 \bmod M^\gamma$, which proves the theorem.

52. *Definition.* The module whose basis consists of all the determinants of the matrix

$$\begin{vmatrix} u_1, & u_2, & \ldots, & u_k \\ v_1, & v_2, & \ldots, & v_k \\ \ldots\ldots\ldots\ldots\ldots \end{vmatrix},$$

where the elements u, v, w,... are polynomials, will be denoted by

$$\begin{pmatrix} u_1, & u_2, & ..., & u_k \\ v_1, & v_2, & ..., & v_k \\ & \cdots\cdots\cdots\cdots & & \end{pmatrix}.$$

This is only an extension of the notation $(F_1, F_2, ..., F_k)$ for a module M.

If M_1 is a prime module of rank r, and $F_1, F_2, ..., F_r$ any r members of M_1 such that $M = (F_1, F_2, ..., F_r)$ resolves into M_1 and a second prime module M_1' of rank r, then it may happen that M_1' must have a certain fixed spread in common with M_1 irrespective of the choice of $F_1, F_2, ..., F_r$. Such a spread (if any exists) must be a singular spread of M_1; but it does not necessarily follow from M_1 having a singular spread that M_1' must contain the spread; it depends on the nature of the singularity. *If M_1' does not cut M_1 in a fixed spread then M_1^γ is unmixed, and is the module whose members consist of all polynomials having a γ-point at every point of M_1. In the contrary case some power M_1^γ of M_1 will be mixed and will have the fixed spread in which M_1' cuts it as a relevant imbedded spread, while polynomials $F^{(\gamma)}$ having a γ-point at every point of M_1, but not members of M_1^γ, will exist.*

Example i.   The square of the prime module M_1 determined by an irreducible curve in space of three dimensions having a triple* point, the tangents at which do not lie in one plane, is mixed; and there is consequently a surface having a 2-point at every point of the curve which is not a member of M_1^2.

Thus if

$$M_1 = \begin{pmatrix} x_1, & x_2, & x_3 \\ x_2, & x_3, & x_1^2 \end{pmatrix} = (x_1 x_3 - x_2^2, \; x_2 x_3 - x_1^3, \; x_3^2 - x_1^2 x_2),$$

the surface $(x_2 x_3 - x_1^3)^2 - (x_2^2 - x_1 x_3)(x_3^2 - x_1^2 x_2)$, after removal of the factor x_1, will have a 2-point at every point of M_1, but is not a member of M_1^2; for the surface has only a 3-point at the origin, whereas every member of M_1^2 has a 4-point.

Example ii.   If $M_1 = \begin{pmatrix} u_1, & u_2, & u_3, & u_4 \\ v_1, & v_2, & v_3, & v_4 \\ w_1, & w_2, & w_3. & w_4 \end{pmatrix} = (F_1, F_2, F_3, F_4),$

---

* A triple point is not a 3-point. The general member of M_1 has only a 2-point at the triple point of the curve.

It is evident that the module whose members consist of all polynomials having a γ-point at every point of a given irreducible spread is primary and unmixed.

where each u, v, w is a homogeneous linear function of x_1, x_2, x_3, x_4, M_1 being a prime module of rank 2, we have

$$u_1 F_1 + u_2 F_2 + u_3 F_3 + u_4 F_4 = 0,$$

and two other similar identities. From these we can find the continued ratio $x_1 : x_2 : x_3 : x_4$ as the ratio of four members of $M_1{}^3$ by expressing each u, v, w in full. The common factor of these four members is a polynomial of degree 8 having a 3-point at every point of M_1, but not a member of $M_1{}^3$. In this example $M_1{}^3$ is mixed while $M_1{}^2$ is unmixed.

53. Theorem. *The module with a basis of r rows and k columns*

$$M = \begin{pmatrix} u_1, & u_2, & \dots, & u_k \\ v_1, & v_2, & \dots, & v_k \\ w_1, & w_2, & \dots, & w_k \\ \dots\dots\dots\dots \end{pmatrix}$$

is of rank $\leqslant k - r + 1$ $(0 < k - r + 1 \leqslant n)$, and if of rank $k - r + 1$ is unmixed.
  Also if $D_{p_1, p_2, \dots, p_r}$ denotes the determinant formed by the $p_1{}^{th}$, $p_2{}^{th}$, $\dots$, $p_r{}^{th}$ columns of the basis, the general solution of the equation

$$\Sigma D_{p_1, p_2, \dots, p_r} X_{p_1, p_2, \dots, p_r} = 0 \quad (p_1, p_2, \dots, p_r = 1, 2, \dots, k)$$

is
$$X_{p_1, p_2, \dots, p_r} = \sum_{p=1}^{p=k} U_{p_1, \dots, p_r, p} u_p + \sum_{p=1}^{p=k} V_{p_1, p_2, \dots, p_r, p} v_p + \dots,$$

where $U_{p_1, \dots, p_r, p}, V_{p_1, \dots, p_r, p}, \dots$ are arbitrary polynomials subject with the unknowns $X_{p_1, p_2, \dots, p_r}$ to the same law of signs as the determinants $D_{p_1, p_2, \dots, p_r}$, viz. each $X_{p_1, p_2, \dots, p_r}, U_{p_1, p_2, \dots, p_r, p}, \dots$ changes in sign (but not in magnitude) for each interchange of any pair of suffixes $p_1, \dots, p_r, p$.

These two theorems will be proved together by a double process of induction. Assuming both theorems for $r - 1$ rows and $k - 1$ columns, and also for r rows and $k - 1$ columns, we prove both theorems for r rows and k columns. Both theorems have been proved for $r = 1$ in § 48.

It is understood that M is a proper module, i.e. the determinants of its basis all vanish for some point whose coordinates are finite, but do not all vanish identically. After proving that M is of rank $\leqslant k - r + 1$ we assume that if M is of rank $k - r + 1$ the module.

$$\begin{pmatrix} u_2 + a_2 u_1, & u_3 + a_3 u_1, & \dots, & u_k + a_k u_1 \\ v_2 + a_2 v_1, & v_3 + a_3 v_1, & \dots, & v_k + a_k v_1 \\ \dots\dots\dots\dots\dots\dots\dots\dots\dots\dots\dots \end{pmatrix},$$

where $a_2, a_3, \dots, a_k$ are suitably chosen constants or polynomials, is of rank $k - r$. This can be proved in a similar way to the corresponding property in § 47. We shall also suppose the matrix to have been so modified beforehand that if the first $s \leqslant k - r$ columns are removed the rank diminishes by s.   It can be shown that the second part of the theorem is true before modification if it is true after.   The same is true of the first part of the theorem, since the modification of the basis does not alter the module.

The general proof will be sufficiently indicated if we suppose M to have 3 rows and 5 columns.   Then

$$M = \begin{pmatrix} u_1 & u_2 & u_3 & u_4 & u_5 \\ v_1 & v_2 & v_3 & v_4 & v_5 \\ w_1 & w_2 & w_3 & w_4 & w_5 \end{pmatrix}$$

and we assume both parts of the theorem for the module

$$M_1 = \begin{pmatrix} u_2 & u_3 & u_4 & u_5 \\ v_2 & v_3 & v_4 & v_5 \\ w_2 & w_3 & w_4 & w_5 \end{pmatrix}$$

and also for
$$M_1' = \begin{pmatrix} u_2 & u_3 & u_4 & u_5 \\ v_2 & v_3 & v_4 & v_5 \end{pmatrix}.$$

If A, B, C are the determinants of the matrix formed by the last two columns of the basis of M, we have

$$A u_i + B v_i + C w_i = D_{i45} \quad (i = 1, 2, 3, 4, 5).$$

Giving to i the values p_1, p_2, p_3 and solving for C (or D_{45}) we have

$$D_{45} D_{p_1 p_2 p_3} = D_{p_2 p_3} D_{p_1 45} + D_{p_3 p_1} D_{p_2 45} + D_{p_1 p_2} D_{p_3 45},$$

where $D_{p_1 p_2}$ denotes the determinant $\begin{vmatrix} u_{p_1} & u_{p_2} \\ v_{p_1} & v_{p_2} \end{vmatrix}$.   This shows that every determinant $D_{p_1 p_2 p_3}$ when multiplied by D_{45} is of the form $X_1 D_{145} + X_2 D_{245} + X_3 D_{345}$.   Hence if there is a point of the module M for which D_{45} does not vanish the module must have a spread of rank $\leqslant 3$ (or $k - r + 1$) through that point.   If however D_{45} contains the whole of the spread of M we move the origin to a point of the spread and modify the last row of the basis by the other rows so as to make the constant terms in the elements of the last row all zero.   After doing this we change u_4, u_5, v_4, v_5 in the first two rows only to $u_4 + a$, $u_5 + b$, $v_4 + c$, $v_5 + d$, where a, b, c, d are constants.   We thus get a new module containing the origin such that the new D_{45} does not contain the origin.   This new module has a spread of rank $\leqslant 3$ through the origin ; and since this is true for general values of a, b, c, d, it is still true when we put $a = b = c = d = 0$; for no diminution in the dimensions of the spread through the origin, i.e. no increase in the rank, could be produced by giving special values to a, b, c, d.   Hence M is of rank $\leqslant 3$; and we have to prove that M is unmixed if its rank is 3.

Consider the equation $\Sigma D_{p_1 p_2 p_3} X_{p_1 p_2 p_3} = 0$ in which we suppose $p_1 < p_2 < p_3$, so that each term occurs once and once only. Multiplying by D_{45} we have

$$\Sigma \left(D_{p_2 p_3} D_{p_1 45} + D_{p_3 p_1} D_{p_2 45} + D_{p_1 p_2} D_{p_3 45} \right) X_{p_1 p_2 p_3} = 0.$$

In this the terms containing D_{145} are obtained by putting $p_1 = 1$ and giving p_2, p_3 the values $(2, 3)$, $(2, 4)$, $(2, 5)$, $(3, 4)$, $(3, 5)$, $(4, 5)$, viz. $D_{145} (D_{23} X_{123} + D_{24} X_{124} + D_{25} X_{125} + D_{34} X_{134} + D_{35} X_{135} + D_{45} X_{145})$, and this is a member of (D_{245}, D_{345}) and therefore of M_1. But M_1 is unmixed and of rank 2, and D_{145} does not contain any of its relevant spreads; for if, after modification of the last two columns of M_1 by the first two, D_{145} contains a relevant spread of M_1 then every $D_{1 p_2 p_3}$ contains the same spread, and consequently M contains the spread and is of rank 2, which is contrary to the data.   Hence

$$\Sigma D_{p_2 p_3} X_{1 p_2 p_3} = 0 \bmod M_1$$
$$= D_{234} W'_{234} + D_{235} W'_{235} + D_{245} W'_{245} + D_{345} W'_{345}$$
$$= (D_{34} w_2 + D_{42} w_3 + D_{23} w_4) W'_{234} + \cdots$$
$$= D_{23} (w_4 W'_{234} + w_5 W'_{235}) + \cdots$$
$$= \Sigma D_{p_2 p_3} (W'_{p_2 p_3 2} w_2 + W'_{p_2 p_3 3} w_3 + W'_{p_2 p_3 4} w_4 + W'_{p_2 p_3 5} w_5);$$

or $\Sigma D_{p_2 p_3} X_{p_2 p_3} = 0$ $(p_2 < p_3 = 2, 3, 4, 5)$,

where $X_{p_2 p_3} = X_{1 p_2 p_3} - \underset{p}{\Sigma} W'_{p_2 p_3 p} w_p$ $(p = 2, 3, 4, 5)$.

The equation $\Sigma D_{p_2 p_3} X_{p_2 p_3} = 0$ stands in the same relation to M_1' as $\Sigma D_{p_1 p_2 p_3} X_{p_1 p_2 p_3} = 0$ to M, and the general solution is

$$X_{p_2 p_3} = \underset{p}{\Sigma} U'_{p_2 p_3 p} u_p + \underset{p}{\Sigma} V'_{p_2 p_3 p} v_p \quad (p = 2, 3, 4, 5)$$

which gives

$$X_{1 p_2 p_3} = \underset{p}{\Sigma} U'_{p_2 p_3 p} u_p + \underset{p}{\Sigma} V'_{p_2 p_3 p} v_p + \underset{p}{\Sigma} W'_{p_2 p_3 p} w_p \quad (p = 2, 3, 4, 5).$$

Substituting these values for $X_{1 p_2 p_3}$ in the equation

$$\Sigma D_{p_1 p_2 p_3} X_{p_1 p_2 p_3} = 0$$

it becomes, after simplifying,

$$D_{234} (X_{234} + U'_{234} u_1 + V'_{234} v_1 + W'_{234} w_1) + \cdots = 0,$$

an equation in reference to M_1 of which the solution is

$$X_{234} = - U'_{234} u_1 - V'_{234} v_1 - W'_{234} w_1 + \underset{p}{\Sigma} U_{234 p} u_p + \cdots + \cdots \quad (p = 2, 3, 4, 5)$$

and similar expressions for X_{235}, X_{245}, X_{345}. If in these and the expressions found for $X_{1 p_2 p_3}$ we put

$$- U'_{p_2 p_3 p} = U_{p_2 p_3 p 1}, \quad - V'_{p_2 p_3 p} = V_{p_2 p_3 p 1}, \quad - W'_{p_2 p_3 p} = W_{p_2 p_3 p 1},$$

we have, for all values of $p_1, p_2, p_3 = 1, 2, 3, 4, 5$,

$$X_{p_1 p_2 p_3} = \sum_p U_{p_1 p_2 p_3 p}\, u_p + \sum_p V_{p_1 p_2 p_3 p}\, v_p + \sum_p W_{p_1 p_2 p_3 p}\, w_p \quad (p = 1, 2, 3, 4, 5),$$

which proves the second part of the theorem for M.

To prove the first part, that M is unmixed, it has to be shown that neither M nor $(M, x_s - a_s, \ldots, x_n - a_n)$ can contain a relevant simple module, where s is any number $\geqslant k - r + 3$ (§ 44).   Let

$$(x_1 - c_1)\, F = 0 \bmod (M, x_s - a_s, \ldots, x_n - a_n)$$

$$= \sum D_{p_1, p_2, \ldots, p_r}\, X_{p_1, p_2, \ldots, p_r} \bmod (x_s - a_s, \ldots, x_n - a_n).$$

Then $\qquad (\sum D_{p_1, p_2, \ldots, p_r}\, X_{p_1, p_2, \ldots, p_r})_{x_1 - c_1 = x_s - a_s = \ldots = x_n - a_n = 0} = 0.$

In putting $x_1 - c_1 = x_s - a_s = \ldots = x_n - a_n = 0$ in M the number of variables is diminished but the rank remains equal to $k - r + 1$.   Hence

$$(X_{p_1, p_2, \ldots, p_r})_{x_1 - c_1 = \ldots = 0} = \left(\sum_p U_{p_1, \ldots, p_r, p}\, u_p + \ldots\right)_{x_1 - c_1 = \ldots = 0};$$

therefore

$$X_{p_1, p_2, \ldots, p_r}$$

$$= \sum_p U_{p_1, \ldots, p_r, p}\, u_p + \ldots + (x_1 - c_1)\, Y_{p_1, p_2, \ldots, p_r} \bmod (x_s - a_s, \ldots, x_n - a_n),$$

and

$$(x_1 - c_1)\, F = (x_1 - c_1) \sum D_{p_1, p_2, \ldots, p_r}\, Y_{p_1, p_2, \ldots, p_r} \bmod (x_s - a_s, \ldots, x_n - a_n).$$

Hence, since $(x_s - a_s, \ldots, x_n - a_n)$ is a module of the principal class, and $x_1 - c_1$ does not contain its spread,

$$F - \sum D_{p_1, p_2, \ldots, p_r}\, Y_{p_1, p_2, \ldots, p_r} = 0 \bmod (x_s - a_s, \ldots, x_n - a_n),$$

and $\qquad\qquad F = 0 \bmod (M, x_s - a_s, \ldots, x_n - a_n).$

Hence $(M, x_s - a_s, \ldots, x_n - a_n)$ cannot contain any relevant simple module, which proves the theorem.

Solution of Homogeneous Linear Equations

54. *Homogeneous linear equations with constants for coefficients.*
In a system of r independent equations with constant coefficients for k
unknowns $X_1, X_2, \ldots, X_k$ there are r' independent solutions, where
$r + r' = k$, and the general solution is expressible in terms of the r'
solutions. The array of the coefficients of the r equations and the
array of the r' solutions together form a square array

$$
\begin{vmatrix}
a_{11} & a_{12} & \ldots & a_{1k} \\
\multicolumn{4}{c}{\cdots\cdots\cdots\cdots} \\
a_{r1} & a_{r2} & \ldots & a_{rk} \\
\hline
b_{11} & b_{12} & \ldots & b_{1k} \\
\multicolumn{4}{c}{\cdots\cdots\cdots\cdots} \\
b_{r'1} & b_{r'2} & \ldots & b_{r'k}
\end{vmatrix}
$$

and the general solution is $X_i = \mu_1 b_{1i} + \mu_2 b_{2i} + \ldots + \mu_{r'} b_{r'i}$ $(i = 1, 2, \ldots, k)$,
where $\mu_1, \mu_2, \ldots, \mu_{r'}$ are arbitrary quantities.

The two arrays are called conjugate arrays; but we shall find it
more convenient to call them *inverse* arrays. Their principal properties
are :—(i) the sum of the products of the elements in any row of one
array with the elements in any row of the other array is zero ; (ii) the
determinants of one array are proportional to the complementary determinants of the other array with a rule as regards sign ; (iii) the
determinant of the combined arrays is not zero if the elements are
real. We shall not have occasion to use either (ii) or (iii) explicitly.

Homogeneous linear equations with polynomials as coefficients
(H, p. 483). Let there be r independent equations, viz.

$$u_1 X_1 + u_2 X_2 + \ldots + u_k X_k = 0,$$

$$v_1 X_1 + v_2 X_2 + \ldots + v_k X_k = 0, \text{ etc.}$$

Then there is an array of solutions

$$
\begin{vmatrix}
f_{11}, & f_{12}, & \ldots, & f_{1k} \\
f_{21}, & f_{22}, & \ldots, & f_{2k} \\
\multicolumn{4}{c}{\cdots\cdots\cdots\cdots} \\
f_{l1}, & f_{l2}, & \ldots, & f_{lk}
\end{vmatrix}
$$

whose elements are polynomials, such that the general solution is

$$X_i = A_1 f_{1i} + A_2 f_{2i} + \ldots + A_l f_{li} \quad (i = 1, 2, \ldots, k)$$

where $A_1, A_2, \ldots, A_k$ are arbitrary polynomials. The rows of this array are not independent.

The general case of r equations can be reduced to that of solving a single equation. Consider first the single equation

$$F_1 X_1 + F_2 X_2 + \ldots + F_k X_k = 0.$$

The conditions imposed by this equation on X_1 are merely that it must be a member of the module $(F_2, F_3, \ldots, F_k)/(F_1)$. Let $(f_{11}, f_{21}, \ldots, f_{l'1})$ be a basis of this module. Then the general solution for X_1 is

$$X_1 = A_1 f_{11} + A_2 f_{21} + \ldots + A_{l'} f_{l'1}.$$

To each separate solution $X_1 = f_{j1}$ there corresponds a solution $f_{j2}, f_{j3}, \ldots, f_{jk}$ for $X_2, X_3, \ldots, X_k$, giving a row $f_{j1}, f_{j2}, \ldots, f_{jk}$ of the array of solutions. The remaining solutions are those for which $X_1 = 0$, when the equation reduces to

$$X_2 F_2 + \ldots + X_k F_k = 0.$$

To each solution for $X_2 = f_{j'2} \ (j' = l' + 1, l' + 2, \ldots, l'')$ there corresponds a row $0, f_{j'2}, f_{j'3}, \ldots, f_{j'k}$ of the array of solutions in which the first element is zero. Similarly there are rows in which the first two elements are zero, and so on. The method may give more rows altogether than are necessary. Any row of the array which can be modified by the other rows so as to become a row of zeros should be omitted.

In the case of r equations we eliminate $X_1, X_2, \ldots, X_{r-1}$, obtaining $D_{1,2,\ldots,r} X_r + D_{1,2,\ldots,r-1,r+1} X_{r+1} + \ldots + D_{1,2,\ldots,r-1,k} X_k = 0$, and find the complete solution of this equation by the method just described. To each solution there is a unique set of values for $X_1, X_2, \ldots, X_{r-1}$ which are in general polynomials. In an exceptional case the unknowns $X_1, X_2, \ldots, X_k$ may be subjected to a linear substitution beforehand.

The principal case. The principal case is that in which the module

$$\begin{pmatrix} u_1 & u_2 \ldots u_k \\ v_1 & v_2 \ldots v_k \\ \ldots\ldots\ldots \end{pmatrix}$$

is of rank $k - r + 1$. In this case it is seen from the equation in $X_r, X_{r+1}, \ldots, X_k$ above that X_k is a member of the module

$$\begin{pmatrix} u_1 & u_2 \ldots u_{k-1} \\ v_1 & v_2 \ldots v_{k-1} \\ \ldots\ldots\ldots\ldots \end{pmatrix}$$

by § 53, and similarly for each unknown. The complete array of solutions is therefore obtained by putting any $k - r - 1$ of the unknowns equal to zero and solving for the ratios of the remaining $r + 1$ unknowns. The $\dfrac{\lfloor k}{\lfloor r + 1 \, \lfloor k - r - 1}$ solutions found in this way are of the type

$$X_{p_1} = D_{p_2, \dots, p_{r+1}}, \; X_{p_2} = - D_{p_1, p_3, \dots, p_{r+1}}, \; \dots \; X_{p_{r+1}} = (-1)^r D_{p_1, p_2, \dots, p_r},$$
$$X_{p_{r+2}} = \dots = X_{p_k} = 0,$$

where $p_1, p_2, \dots, p_k$ is any permutation of $1, 2, \dots, k$.

Noether's Theorem

55. Noether's " fundamental theorem in algebraic functions " (N) furnishes a remarkably direct method of testing whether a given polynomial is a member of a given module or not; but it only attains complete success in its application to a module of rank n. A variation of the method, depending on the same principle, can be applied successfully to any module known to be primary, when the equations to its spread in the form of § 21 have been found (M, p. 88).

Noether proved that if f, ϕ were any two given polynomials in two variables x_1, x_2, without common factor, then the independent linear equations satisfied identically by the coefficients of the power products of x_1, x_2, in $A'f + B'\phi$, where A', B' are ordinary power series with undetermined coefficients, were finite and determinate ; and that any polynomial F whose coefficients satisfied all these identical equations, when the origin was taken successively at each point of (f, ϕ), was a member of (f, ϕ). Thus the conditions which F has to satisfy in order to be a member of (f, ϕ) can be collected locally, so to speak, by going to each point of (f, ϕ) to find them. On going to a point not in (f, ϕ) we get no conditions, for at such a point every polynomial is of the form $A'f + B'\phi$. That the conditions are necessary is evident ; for if $F = 0 \bmod (f, \phi)$ then F is of the form $A'f + B'\phi$ wherever the origin is taken.

König (K, p. 385) proved the theorem for the case of a module $(f_1, f_2, \dots, f_n)$ of rank n in n variables ; and Lasker generalized the theorem in the Lasker-Noether theorem given below.

That the theorem is true for any module of rank n (not merely for a module of the principal class of rank n, the case proved by König) follows from the Hilbert-Netto and Lasker theorems.   For, by Lasker's theorem, the module is the L.C.M. of a finite number of simple modules Q_1, Q_2, ..., Q_l; and if γ is the characteristic number of $Q_i = (f_1, f_2, ..., f_h)$ and the origin is taken at the point of Q_i, we have

$$F = P_1 f_1 + P_2 f_2 + ... + P_h f_h \quad \text{(where } P_1, P_2, ..., P_h \text{ are power series)}$$
$$= X_1 f_1 + X_2 f_2 + ... + X_h f_h \bmod O^\gamma = 0 \bmod Q_i.$$

Thus F contains $[Q_1, Q_2, ..., Q_l]$.

56. The Lasker-Noether Theorem (L, p. 95). *If*

$$M = (F_1, F_2, ..., F_k) \quad and \quad F = P_1 F_1 + P_2 F_2 + ... + P_k F_k,$$

where P_1, P_2, ..., P_k are ordinary power series, there exists a polynomial ϕ not containing the origin such that $F\phi = 0 \bmod M$.

Let Q_1, Q_2, ..., Q_l be the relevant primary modules into which M resolves, and let Q_1, Q_2, ..., $Q_{l'}$ be those which contain the origin, and $Q_{l'+1}$, ..., Q_l those which do not. Then, assuming the theorem to be true, it follows that

$$F = 0 \bmod [Q_1, Q_2, ..., Q_{l'}],$$

since ϕ cannot contain the spread of any of the modules Q_1, Q_2, ..., $Q_{l'}$. Conversely if $F = 0 \bmod [Q_1, Q_2, ..., Q_{l'}]$ and $\phi = 0 \bmod [Q_{l'+1}, ..., Q_l]$, where ϕ does not contain the origin, then $F\phi = 0 \bmod M$. Hence the aggregate of all polynomials F which are of the form

$$P_1 F_1 + P_2 F_2 + ... + P_k F_k$$

constitutes the module $[Q_1, Q_2, ..., Q_{l'}]$.

Definition. A module which resolves into primary modules all of which contain the origin, such as the module $[Q_1, Q_2, ..., Q_{l'}]$ above, will be called a *Noetherian module.*

Thus a Noetherian module, like an H-module, ceases to be such in general when the origin is changed. Moreover an H-module is a particular kind of Noetherian module; for all the primary modules into which an H-module resolves are H-modules and contain the origin.

In order that a polynomial F may be a member of a Noetherian module $(F_1, F_2, ..., F_h)$ it is sufficient that F should be of the form $P_1 F_1 + P_2 F_2 + ... + P_h F_h$.

Proof of the theorem. It is evident that the theorem is true for a module of rank n or dimensions 0 (§ 55). We shall prove the theorem for a module of dimensions $n - r$ assuming it true for a module of dimensions $n - r - 1$. It will be sufficient to prove the theorem for a primary module Q which contains the origin; for it is clear that it will then be true in general.

Let $Q = (f_1, f_2, \ldots, f_h)$, and $f = P_1 f_1 + P_2 f_2 + \ldots + P_h f_h$,

where P_1, P_2, $\ldots$, P_h are power series. Let $Q_O = (f_1', f_2', \ldots, f'_{h'})$ be the module whose members consist of all polynomials of the form of f, and Q_P the like module obtained by moving the origin to P (and then back to O). Choose a point P so near to O as to come within the range of convergency of all the power series P_1, P_2, $\ldots$, P_h for each member f_i' of the basis of Q_O when expressed in the form of f. Then we have $f_i' = 0 \bmod Q_P$, i.e. Q_O contains Q_P. But it does not follow that Q_P contains Q_O however near P may be to O; for O might be a special point of the spread of Q. We assume for the present that O is not a special point of the spread; and we choose P to be another point of the spread so near to O that Q_P contains Q_O. Then $Q_O = Q_P$.

Let u be a fixed arbitrarily chosen linear homogeneous polynomial, and f' any member of Q_O. Then

$$f' = 0 \bmod Q_O = 0 \bmod (Q, u)_O.$$

But (Q, u) is of $n - r - 1$ dimensions; hence, assuming the general theorem as regards (Q, u), there exists a polynomial ϕ not containing O such that

$$f' \phi = 0 \bmod (Q, u) = p u \bmod Q,$$

where p is a polynomial. Hence, since f_1', f_2', $\ldots$, $f'_{h'}$ are members of Q_O,

$$f_i' \phi_i = p_i u \bmod Q \quad (i = 1, 2, \ldots, h');$$

hence $p_i u = 0 \bmod Q_O = 0 \bmod Q_P$;

but u does not contain P, and $\dfrac{1}{u}$ can be expanded as a power series when P is taken as origin; hence

$$p_i = 0 \bmod Q_P = 0 \bmod Q_O$$

$$= p_{i1} f_1' + p_{i2} f_2' + \ldots + p_{ih'} f'_{h'}.$$

Hence

$$f_i' \phi_i = (p_{i1} f_1' + p_{i2} f_2' + \ldots + p_{ih'} f'_{h'}) u \bmod Q \quad (i = 1, 2, \ldots, h').$$

Solving these h' equations for f_1', f_2', $\ldots$, $f'_{h'}$ we have

$$D f_i' = 0 \bmod Q,$$

where

$$D = \begin{vmatrix} p_{11}u - \phi_1 & p_{12}u & \cdots & p_{1h'}u \\ p_{21}u & p_{22}u - \phi_2 & \cdots & p_{2h'}u \\ \cdots\cdots\cdots\cdots\cdots\cdots\cdots\cdots\cdots \\ p_{h'1}u & p_{h'2}u & \cdots & p_{h'h'}u - \phi_{h'} \end{vmatrix} = (-1)^{h'}\phi_1\phi_2\cdots\phi_{h'}\bmod u.$$

Now u contains the origin, but $\phi_1, \phi_2, \ldots, \phi_{h'}$ and consequently D do not; i.e. D does not contain the spread of Q. Hence $f_i' = 0 \bmod Q$. Hence Q_O contains Q, i.e., $Q_O = Q$.

This has been proved for a non-special point O of Q. If O is a special point, choose P a non-special point of Q so near to O that Q_O contains Q_P. Then since $Q_P = Q$ we have again $Q_O = Q$.

The above proof only differs from the proof given by Lasker in the part relating to $Q_O = Q_P$. In this part Lasker's proof seems to be faulty.

IV. THE INVERSE SYSTEM AND MODULAR EQUATIONS

57. A considerable number of the properties proved in this section are to be found in (M); but the introduction of the inverse system is new.

Definitions. The array of the coefficients of a complete linearly independent set of members of a module M of degree $\leqslant t$ arranged under the power products $\omega_1, \omega_2, ..., \omega_\mu$ of degree $\leqslant t$ is called the *dialytic array* of the module M for degree t.

The linear homogeneous equations of which this array is the array of the coefficients are called the *dialytic equations* of M for degree t.

Thus the dialytic equations of M for degree t are represented by equating all members of M of degree $\leqslant t$ to zero and regarding the power products of $x_1, x_2, ..., x_n$ as symbols for the unknowns.

The array inverse (§ 54) to the dialytic array of M for degree t is called the *inverse array* of M for degree t.

The linear homogeneous equations of which this array is the array of the coefficients are called the *modular equations* of M for degree t.

The modular equations for degree t are the equations which are identically satisfied by the coefficients of each and every member of M of degree $\leqslant t$. They may not be independent for members of degree $< t$ and they do not apply to members of degree $> t$ (see § 59).

The sum of the products of the elements in any row of the inverse array for degree t with the inverse power products $\omega_1^{-1}, \omega_2^{-1}, ..., \omega_\mu^{-1}$ is called an *inverse function* of M for degree t.

Thus the modular equations of M for degree t are represented by equating all the inverse functions of M for degree t to zero, taking each negative power product $(x_1^{p_1} x_2^{p_2} ... x_n^{p_n})^{-1}$ as a symbol for " the coefficient of $x_1^{p_1} x_2^{p_2} ... x_n^{p_n}$ in the general member of M of degree t."

We shall also say that a polynomial $F = \Sigma a_{p_1, ..., p_n} x_1^{p_1} ... x_n^{p_n}$ and a finite or infinite negative power series $E = \Sigma c_{q_1, ..., q_n} (x_1^{q_1} ... x_n^{q_n})^{-1}$ are inverse to one another if the constant term of the product FE vanishes, i.e. if $\Sigma a_{p_1, p_2, ..., p_n} c_{p_1, p_2, ..., p_n} = 0$. Thus any member of M of degree $\leqslant t$ and any inverse function of M for degree t are inverse to one another.

Any inverse function of M for degree t can be continued so as to become an inverse function of M for any higher degree (§ 59), and when continued indefinitely becomes an inverse function of M *without limitation in respect to degree.* If all coefficients after a certain stage become zero the inverse function terminates and is a finite negative power series. In the case of an H-module the inverse functions are homogeneous (§ 59) and therefore finite.

In order that a function may be an inverse function of M it is necessary and sufficient that it should be inverse to all members of M; hence if M contains M' any inverse function of M' is an inverse function of M. The whole system of inverse functions of M can therefore be resolved into primary systems corresponding to the primary modules of M. The inverse functions of a Noetherian primary module are all finite (§ 65) but not in general homogeneous. The inverse functions of a non-Noetherian primary module are all infinite power series (§ 65).

We shall regard *inverse function* and *modular equation* as convertible terms, and use that term in each case which seems best suited to the context.

A module is completely determined by its system of modular equations no less than by its system of members. The two systems are alternative representations of the module. Also the properties of the modular equations are very remarkable, and it is necessary to consider them in order to give a complete theory of modular systems.

As there is a one-one correspondence between the members of a module M of degree $\leqslant t$ and the members of the equivalent H-module of degree t, so there is a one-one correspondence between the modular equations of M *for* degree t and the modular equations of the members of the equivalent H-module of degree t. These last are called the modular equations of the H-module *of* (absolute) degree t.

58.   Theorem. *The number of independent modular equations of degree t of an H-module $(F_1, F_2, ..., F_r)$ of rank r is the coefficient of x^t in*

$$(1 - x^{l_1})(1 - x^{l_2}) \dots (1 - x^{l_r})(1 - x)^{-n},$$

where $l_1, l_2, ..., l_r$ are the degrees of $F_1, F_2, ..., F_r$.

Since the whole number of linearly independent polynomials of degree t is the number of power products of degree t, or the coefficient of x^t in $(1 - x)^{-n}$, the theorem will be proved if it is shown that the number $N(r, t)$ of linearly independent members of $(F_1, F_2, ..., F_r)$ of degree t is the coefficient of x^t in

$$\{1 - (1 - x^{l_1})(1 - x^{l_2}) ... (1 - x^{l_r})\}(1 - x)^{-n}.$$

This is easily seen to be true when $r = 1$.

Since any member of $(F_1, F_2, ..., F_r)$ is a linear combination of elementary members, we have

$$N(r, t) = N(r - 1, t) + \rho,$$

where ρ is the number of polynomials $\omega_1 F_r, \omega_2 F_r, ..., \omega_\rho F_r$ of degree t of which no linear combination is a member of $(F_1, F_2, ..., F_{r-1})$, or the number of power products $\omega_1, \omega_2, ..., \omega_\rho$ of degree $t - l_r$ of which no linear combination is a member of $(F_1, F_2, ..., F_{r-1})$, § 48. Hence

$$\rho + N(r - 1, t - l_r) = \text{number of power products of degree } t - l_r$$
$$= \text{coefficient of } x^t \text{ in } x^{l_r}(1 - x)^{-n};$$

and

$$N(r, t) = N(r - 1, t) - N(r - 1, t - l_r) + \text{coefficient of } x^t \text{ in } x^{l_r}(1 - x)^{-n}.$$

Hence, assuming the theorem for $N(r - 1, t)$, it follows that $N(r, t)$ is the coefficient of x^t in

$$\{1 - (1 - x^{l_1}) ... (1 - x^{l_{r-1}})\}(1 - x)^{-n}(1 - x^{l_r}) + x^{l_r}(1 - x)^{-n},$$

or in

$$\{1 - (1 - x^{l_1}) ... (1 - x^{l_{r-1}})(1 - x^{l_r})\}(1 - x)^{-n},$$

which proves the theorem.

This result is independent of the coefficients of $F_1, F_2, ..., F_r$; hence it follows that any member of $(F_1, F_2, ..., F_r)$ is expressible in one way only in the form

$$X^{(0)}F_1 + X^{(1)}F_2 + ... + X^{(r-1)}F_r,$$

where $X^{(i)}$ (as in §§ 6, 7) is a polynomial in which $x_1, x_2, ..., x_i$ occur only to powers as high as $x_1^{l_1-1}, ..., x_i^{l_i-1}$, the variables having been subjected to a substitution beforehand.

The theorem can be applied to any module $(F_1, F_2, ..., F_r)$ of rank r if $(F_1, F_2, ..., F_r)$ is an H-basis, i.e. if the H-module determined by the terms of highest degree in $F_1, F_2, ..., F_r$ is of rank r (§ 49). In this case *the number of independent modular equations for degree t is the coefficient of x^t in $(1 - x^{l_1}) ... (1 - x^{l_r})(1 - x)^{-n-1}$.* An important particular case is the following :

The number of independent modular equations of a module $(F_1, F_2, ..., F_n)$ of rank n such that the resultant of the terms of highest degree in $F_1, F_2, ..., F_n$ does not vanish is $l_1 l_2 ... l_n - 1$ for degree $l - 1$, and $l_1 l_2 ... l_n$ for any degree $\geqslant l$, where

$$l = l_1 + l_2 + ... + l_n - n.$$

This is also true for any H-module $(F_1, F_2, ..., F_n)$ of rank n; but the number of modular equations *for* degree t will be the sum of the numbers of modular equations *of* all degrees $\leqslant t$, so that there is one modular equation of degree l and none of any degree $> l$.

59. *Any inverse function of M for any degree can be continued so as to give an inverse function of M for any higher degree.*

By carrying the continuation on indefinitely we obtain a power

series (finite or infinite) which is an inverse function of M for all degrees without limit.

Let $(F_1, F_2, ..., F_k)$ be an H-basis of M. Then any member F of M is a linear combination of elementary members $\omega_i F_j$ *no one of which is of higher degree than* F. Let l be the lowest degree of any member of M. Write down the dialytic array of M for degree l, viz. the array of the coefficients of such members of the H-basis as are of degree l. Their terms of degree l (corresponding to the compartment l of the diagram) are linearly independent, for if not there would be a member of M of degree $< l$, which is not the case. Next write down the rows of the array representing such members of the basis as are of degree $l + 1$, and members obtained by multiplying members of degree l by $x_1, x_2, ..., x_n$, so as to obtain a complete set of members of degree $l + 1$ linearly independent as regards their terms of degree $l + 1$, these terms corresponding to the compartment $l + 1$ of the diagram. Proceeding in the same way we can obtain the whole dialytic array for any degree.

To obtain the inverse array for the same degree first write down square compartments $0, 1, 2, ..., l - 1$ with arbitrary elements corresponding to degrees $0, 1, 2, ..., l - 1$, and then a compartment l inverse to the compartment l of the dialytic array. Each row of the compartments $0, 1, 2, ..., l - 1$ can be continued so as to be inverse to the dialytic array for degree l, since the determinants of the compartment l do not all vanish. This completes the inverse array for degree l. All its rows can be continued so as to be inverse to the dialytic array for degree $l + 1$, and a compartment $l + 1$ of new rows can be added inverse to the compartment $l + 1$ of the dialytic array. This completes the inverse array for degree $l + 1$; and we can proceed in a similar way to obtain the inverse array for any degree.

This diagram or scheme for the dialytic and inverse arrays of a given module M will be often referred to. The ease with which it can be conceived mentally is due to the fact that it is obtained by working with an H-basis of M. Each pair of corresponding compartments $l + i$ form inverse arrays, and in combination form a square array, showing that the combined complete arrays for any degree have the same number of rows as columns. In the case of a module of rank n the compartments of the dialytic array eventually become square and *the total number of rows of the inverse array is finite*. To a square compartment in either array corresponds no compartment or rows of the other array. In the case of an H-module the compartments are the only parts of the arrays whose elements do not vanish, i.e. the inverse functions are homogeneous.

Definition. The negative power series represented by the rows of the inverse array *continued indefinitely* will be called the *members of the inverse system*, and $E_1, E_2, E_3, ...$ will be used to denote them, just as $F_1, F_2, F_3, ...$ denote members of the module.

The system inverse to (1) has no member.   The system inverse to $(x_1, x_2, ..., x_n)$ has only one member $E = 1$.; and the modular equation $1 = 0$ signifies that the module contains the origin.

60. Properties of the Inverse System.   Before attempting to show in what ways the inverse system may be simplified we consider its general properties.

Definition.   If $E = \overset{\infty}{\Sigma} c_{p_1, p_2, ..., p_n} (x_1^{p_1} x_2^{p_2} ... x_n^{p_n})^{-1}$ is a negative power series (no p_i negative), and A any polynomial, the part of the expanded product AE which consists of a negative power series will be denoted by $A . E$ and called the *A-derivate of E*.   Thus

$$x_1 . (x_1 x_2)^{-1} = (x_2)^{-1}, \quad x_2^2 . (x_1 x_2)^{-1} = 0.$$

A negative power series $E = \overset{\infty}{\Sigma} c_{p_1, p_2, ..., p_n} (x_1^{p_1} x_2^{p_2} ... x_n^{p_n})^{-1}$ is or is not an inverse function of a module M according as every member $F = \Sigma a_{p_1, p_2, ..., p_n} x_1^{p_1} x_2^{p_2} ... x_n^{p_n}$ of M, or not every member of M, is inverse to it, i.e. according as every $\Sigma a_{p_1, p_2, ..., p_n} c_{p_1, p_2, ..., p_n} = 0$ or not.   Suppose E an inverse function and F any member of M.   Then $x_1^{l_1} x_2^{l_2} ... x_n^{l_n} F = \Sigma a_{p_1, p_2, ..., p_n} x_1^{p_1 + l_1} ... x_n^{p_n + l_n}$ is a member inverse to E; hence every $\Sigma a_{p_1, p_2, ..., p_n} c_{p_1 + l_1, ..., p_n + l_n} = 0$, and

$$\Sigma c_{p_1 + l_1, ..., p_n + l_n} (x_1^{p_1} x_2^{p_2} ... x_n^{p_n})^{-1},$$

or $x_1^{l_1} x_2^{l_2} ... x_n^{l_n} . E$, is a member of the inverse system.   *Hence if E is a member of the inverse system of M so also is $x_1^{l_1} x_2^{l_2} ... x_n^{l_n} . E$, and if $E_1, E_2, ..., E_h$ are members so also is $A_1 . E_1 + A_2 . E_2 + ... + A_h . E_h$ a member, where $A_1, A_2, ..., A_h$ are arbitrary polynomials.*

In a slightly modified sense which will be explained later (§ 82) *the inverse system of any module M has a finite basis $[E_1, E_2, ..., E_h]$ such that any member of the inverse system is of the form*

$$X_1 . E_1 + X_2 . E_2 + ... + X_h . E_h,$$

where $X_1, X_2, ..., X_h$ are polynomials.

This theorem is evidently true in the important case in which the total number of linearly independent members of the inverse system is finite, viz. in the case of a module of rank n and in the case of a module of rank r when treated as a module in r variables only, or, in other words, in the case of a module which resolves into simple modules.

Regarding the inverse system as representing the modular equations of M we shall write $M = [E_1, E_2, ..., E_h]$ as well as $M = (F_1, F_2, ..., F_k)$. Here M is the L.C.M. of $[E_1]$, $[E_2]$, ..., $[E_h]$ and the G.C.M. of (F_1), (F_2), ..., (F_k).

Definition. A module M will be called a *principal system* if its inverse system has a basis consisting of a single member, i.e. if $M = [E]$.

A module of the principal class is a principal system (§ 72), but a principal system is not necessarily of the principal class. A principal system is however the residual of a module (F) with respect to any module of the principal class which contains, and is of the same rank as, the principal system (cf. § 62).

61.   *The system inverse to $M = (F_1, F_2, ..., F_k)$ is the system whose F_i-derivates $(i = 1, 2, ..., k)$ vanish identically.*

In other words, in order that E may be a member of the inverse system of M it is necessary and sufficient that $F_i . E$ $(i = 1, 2, ..., k)$ should vanish identically. For if $E = \overset{\infty}{\Sigma} c_{q_1, q_2, ..., q_n} (x_1^{q_1} x_2^{q_2} ... x_n^{q_n})^{-1}$ is any member of the inverse system, and $F_i = \Sigma a_{p_1, p_2, ..., p_n} x_1^{p_1} x_2^{p_2} ... x_n^{p_n}$, then

$$F_i . E = \underset{p}{\Sigma} a_{p_1, p_2, ..., p_n} \underset{q}{\Sigma} c_{p_1+q_1, ..., p_n+q_n} (x_1^{q_1} x_2^{q_2} ... x_n^{q_n})^{-1}$$

$$= \underset{q}{\Sigma} (x_1^{q_1} x_2^{q_2} ... x_n^{q_n})^{-1} \underset{p}{\Sigma} a_{p_1, p_2, ..., p_n} c_{p_1+q_1, ..., p_n+q_n} = 0,$$

since every $\underset{p}{\Sigma} a_{p_1, ..., p_n} c_{p_1+q_1, ..., p_n+q_n}$ vanishes ($x_1^{q_1} ... x_n^{q_n} F_i$ being inverse to E).   Conversely if $F_i . E = 0$, then $\underset{p}{\Sigma} a_{p_1, ..., p_n} c_{p_1+q_1, ..., p_n+q_n} = 0$, i.e. $x_1^{q_1} ... x_n^{q_n} F_i$ is inverse to E, and every member of M is inverse to E, i.e. E is a member of the inverse system.

Similarly if $M = [E_1, E_2, ..., E_h]$ the necessary and sufficient condition that F may be a member of M is that $F . E_j$ $(j = 1, 2, ..., h)$ vanishes identically.

62.   *The modular equations of $M/(F_1, F_2, ..., F_k)$ are the F_i-derivates of the modular equations of M, i.e.*

$$[E_1, E_2, ..., E_h]/(F_1, F_2, ...; F_k) = [..., F_i . E_j, ...].$$

For the necessary and sufficient condition that F may be a member of the residual module is

$$FF_i = 0 \bmod M \quad (i = 1, 2, ..., k)$$

or $$FF_i . E_j = 0 \quad (i = 1, 2, ..., k; \; j = 1, 2, ..., h)$$

or $$F . (F_i . E_j) = 0.$$

Hence $[..., F_i . E_j, ...]$ is the residual module (§ 61).

63. *A system of negative power series with a finite basis* $[E_1, E_2, ..., E_h]$ *of such a nature that all derivates of* $E_1, E_2, ..., E_h$ *belong to the system is an inverse system of a module if* E_i $(i = 1, 2, ..., h)$ *has an* F_i-*derivate which vanishes identically.*

For there are polynomials F such that the F-derivate of each of $E_1, E_2, ..., E_h$ vanishes identically, the product $F_1 F_2 ... F_h$ being one such polynomial. Also the whole aggregate of such polynomials F constitutes a module M; for if F belongs to the aggregate so does AF. Consider the dialytic and inverse arrays of M obtained as in § 59. Since every member of M is inverse to every member of $[E_1, E_2, ..., E_h]$ all members of the latter are represented in the inverse array. If any other power series are represented, viz. if there is a row of the inverse array which does not represent a member of $[E_1, E_2, ..., E_h]$, let it begin in the compartment $l + i$. Then if we omit this row we can add a row to the dialytic array representing a polynomial of degree $l + i$ inverse to all members of $[E_1, E_2, ..., E_h]$ but not a member of M. This is contrary to the fact that M is the whole aggregate of such polynomials. Hence the system inverse to M is $[E_1, E_2, ..., E_h]$.

Thus in order that $E = \overset{\infty}{\Sigma} c_{p_1, p_2, ..., p_n} (x_1^{p_1} x_2^{p_2} ... x_n^{p_n})^{-1}$ may represent a modular equation of a module it is necessary and sufficient that $c_{p_1, p_2, ..., p_n}$ should be a recurrent function of $p_1, p_2, ..., p_n$, that is, a function satisfying some recurrent relation

$$\underset{p}{\Sigma} a_{p_1, p_2, ..., p_n} c_{p_1+l_1, ..., p_n+l_n} = 0$$

for all positive integral values of $l_1, l_2, ..., l_n$, where the $a_{p_1, p_2, ..., p_n}$ are a set of fixed quantities finite in number. It may be that $c_{p_1, p_2, ..., p_n}$ satisfies several such recurrent relations not deducible from one another; but it is sufficient if it satisfies one.

64. *Transformation of the inverse system corresponding to a linear transformation of the modular system.*

If the variables in the modular system M are subjected to a linear non-homogeneous substitution with non-vanishing determinant by which M is transformed to M' it is required to find how the inverse system $[E_1, E_2, ..., E_h]$ is to be transformed so as to be inverse to M'.

In other words, if the negative power series E is inverse to the polynomial F it is required to find a power series E' inverse to the transformed polynomial F'. It will be shown that an E' exists which can be derived from E in a way depending only on the substitution and not on the polynomial F.

Let $F = \Sigma a_{p_1, \dots, p_n} x_1^{p_1} \dots x_n^{p_n}$, $F' = \Sigma a'_{q_1, \dots, q_n} x_1'^{q_1} \dots x_n'^{q_n}$,

and let the coefficients $c_{p_1, p_2, \dots, p_n}$ of E be represented symbolically by $c_1^{p_1} c_2^{p_2} \dots c_n^{p_n}$. Then we have $E = \Sigma c_1^{p_1} \dots c_n^{p_n} (x_1^{p_1} \dots x_n^{p_n})^{-1}$; and

$$\Sigma a_{p_1, p_2, \dots, p_n} c_1^{p_1} c_2^{p_2} \dots c_n^{p_n} = 0,$$

since E, F are inverse to one another. Let the inverse substitution be

$$x_i' = a'_{i1} x_1 + \dots + a'_{in} x_n + a_i' \quad (i = 1, 2, \dots, n).$$

Then $\Sigma a'_{q_1, \dots, q_n} (a'_{11} x_1 + \dots)^{q_1} \dots (a'_{n1} x_1 + \dots)^{q_n} = \Sigma a_{p_1, \dots, p_n} x_1^{p_1} \dots x_n^{p_n}$,

and we have

$\Sigma c_1^{p_1} \dots c_n^{p_n} \times$

{coeff. of $x_1^{p_1} \dots x_n^{p_n}$ in $\Sigma a'_{q_1 \dots q_n} (a'_{11} x_1 + \dots)^{q_1} \dots (a'_{n1} x_1 + \dots)^{q_n}$} = 0,

i.e. $\qquad \Sigma a'_{q_1 \dots q_n} (a'_{11} c_1 + \dots)^{q_1} \dots (a'_{n1} c_1 + \dots)^{q_n} = 0,$

i.e. the power series $E' = \Sigma (a'_{11} c_1 + \dots)^{q_1} \dots (a'_{n1} c_1 + \dots)^{q_n} (x_1^{q_1} \dots x_n^{q_n})^{-1}$ is inverse to the polynomial $F' = \Sigma a'_{q_1, \dots, q_n} x_1^{q_1} \dots x_n^{q_n}$.

Hence the coefficient of $(x_1^{q_1} x_2^{q_2} \dots x_n^{q_n})^{-1}$ in the transformed power series E' is

$$c'_{q_1, q_2, \dots, q_n} = (a'_{11} c_1 + \dots)^{q_1} (a'_{21} c_1 + \dots)^{q_2} \dots (a'_{n1} c_1 + \dots)^{q_n},$$

where, after expanding the right-hand side, $c_1^{p_1} c_2^{p_2} \dots c_n^{p_n}$ is to be put equal to $c_{p_1, p_2, \dots, p_n}$, the coefficient of $(x_1^{p_1} x_2^{p_2} \dots x_n^{p_n})^{-1}$ in E. For such a transformation of F and E, when not inverse to one another, $\Sigma a_{p_1, p_2, \dots, p_n} c_{p_1, p_2, \dots, p_n}$ is an absolute invariant.

The most important transformation is that corresponding to a change of origin only. In this case, if

$$F = \Sigma a_{p_1 \dots p_n} x_1^{p_1} \dots x_n^{p_n} \quad \text{and} \quad E = \Sigma c_1^{p_1} \dots c_n^{p_n} (x_1^{p_1} \dots x_n^{p_n})^{-1},$$

and the new origin is the point $(-a_1, -a_2, \dots, -a_n)$,

then $\qquad F' = \Sigma a_{p_1 \dots p_n} (x_1 - a_1)^{p_1} \dots (x_n - a_n)^{p_n}$

and $\qquad E' = \Sigma (c_1 + a_1)^{p_1} \dots (c_n + a_n)^{p_n} (x_1^{p_1} \dots x_n^{p_n})^{-1}.$

It is to be noticed that if E is a finite power series it nevertheless transforms into an infinite power series E'. In particular if $E = 1$

then $E' = \Sigma a_1^{p_1} \dots a_n^{p_n} (x_1^{p_1} x_2^{p_2} \dots x_n^{p_n})^{-1}$, the inverse function of $(x_1 - a_1, \dots, x_n - a_n)$.

For homogeneous substitutions another way of considering corresponding transformations of F and E can be given, which however *excludes a change of origin.* Represent E by

$$\sum_{}^{\infty} c_{p_1, p_2, \dots, p_n} \frac{u_1^{p_1} u_2^{p_2} \dots u_n^{p_n}}{p_1! \, p_2! \, \dots \, p_n!}$$

instead of $\Sigma c_{p_1, p_2, \dots, p_n} (x_1^{p_1} \dots x_n^{p_n})^{-1}$, and let the new E be defined as inverse (or conjugate) to $F = \Sigma a_{p_1, p_2, \dots, p_n} x_1^{p_1} \dots x_n^{p_n}$ when the same relation $\Sigma a_{p_1, \dots, p_n} c_{p_1, \dots, p_n} = 0$ holds as before. Then for contragredient substitutions of $x_1, x_2, \dots, x_n$ and $u_1, u_2, \dots, u_n$ the polynomial F and power series E will always remain inverse (or conjugate) to one another if they are so originally. Also the members E of the inverse (or conjugate) system of a module M, when expressed in the new form above, are the power series with respect to which the members (of the basis) of the module M are apolar (§ 61).

65. The Noetherian Equations of a Module.

The modular equations $\Sigma c_{p_1, p_2, \dots, p_n} (x_1^{p_1} x_2^{p_2} \dots x_n^{p_n})^{-1} = 0$ of a module M for degree t are finite because they are only applicable to members of degree $\leqslant t$, and the coefficients $(x_1^{p_1} x_2^{p_2} \dots x_n^{p_n})^{-1}$ in the general member of degree t vanish when $p_1 + \dots + p_n > t$. A modular equation may however be finite in itself, i.e. every $c_{p_1, p_2, \dots, p_n}$ for which $p_1 + p_2 + \dots + p_n$ exceeds a certain fixed number l may vanish. If such an equation is applied to a polynomial of degree $> l$ it only affects the coefficients of terms of degree $\leqslant l$.

Definition. The *Noetherian equations* of a module are the modular equations which are finite in themselves.

There are no Noetherian equations if the module does not contain the origin. For if $E = 0$ is a Noetherian equation of absolute degree l, and ω^{-1} a power product of absolute degree l which is present in E, the derivate equation $\omega \cdot E = 0$ is $1 = 0$, showing that the module contains the origin. *Every Noetherian equation has the equation* $1 = 0$ *as a derivate.*

On the other hand Noetherian equations always exist if the module contains the origin, for the equation $1 = 0$ exists, and so does the equation $\omega^{-1} = 0$, where ω is any power product of less degree than any term which occurs in any member of the module.

The whole system of Noetherian equations of a non-Noetherian module M forms only a part of the whole system of modular equations, and is exhibited by a scheme similar to but different from that of § 59, with which it should be compared. In this new scheme the rows of the dialytic array represent the members of the module arranged in order according to their *underdegree* (or degree of their lowest terms) instead of their degree (or degree of their highest terms). The first set of rows represents a complete set of members of underdegree l_1 which are linearly independent as regards their terms of degree l_1,

where l_1 is the lowest underdegree of any member of M. These are obtained from any basis of M, which need not be an H-basis. The next set of rows represents a complete set of members of under-degree $l_1 + 1$ which are linearly independent as regards their terms of degree $l_1 + 1$, obtained partly from the basis of M and partly from the set of members of underdegree l_1 by multiplying them by $x_1, x_2, ..., x_n$; and similarly for succeeding sets. The compartments $l_1, l_1 + 1, ...$ correspond to the terms of lowest degree in the successive sets.

To obtain the corresponding inverse (or Noetherian) array first insert square compartments 0, 1, 2, ..., $l_1 - 1$ with arbitrary elements (or with elements 1 in the diagonal and the remaining elements zero) corresponding to degrees 0, 1, 2, ..., $l_1 - 1$; and then a compartment l_1 inverse to the compartment l_1 of the dialytic array. This completes the array for degree l_1.; all its rows are inverse to all members of M and represent Noetherian equations. Next insert a compartment $l_1 + 1$ inverse to the compartment $l_1 + 1$ of the dialytic array, and continue its rows backwards so as to be inverse to the first set of rows of the dialytic array. This completes the array for degree $l_1 + 1$; and we can proceed similarly to find in theory the whole of the Noetherian array.

The object of the diagram is merely to exhibit the whole system of Noetherian equations, which it evidently does. If F is a polynomial for which all the Noetherian equations for degree t are satisfied, then, up to and inclusive of its terms of degree t, F is a linear combination of members of the module of underdegree $\leqslant t$, i.e. F is expressible as far as degree t in the form $X_1 F_1 + X_2 F_2 + ... + X_k F_k$, where X_1, X_2, ..., X_k are polynomials, and $F = 0 \bmod (M, O^{t+1})$. Consequently if F satisfies the whole system of Noetherian equations it is of the form $P_1 F_1 + P_2 F_2 + ... + P_k F_k$, where P_1, P_2, ..., P_k are power series. Hence $FF_0 = 0 \bmod M$, where F_0 has a non-vanishing constant term (§ 56); and, if M is a Noetherian module, $F = 0 \bmod M$. *Hence the whole system of modular equations of a Noetherian module can be expressed as a system of Noetherian equations.*

66. Modular Equations of Simple Modules.
If in the last article the rows of the compartment $l_1 + i$ of the dialytic array should be equal in number to the power products of degree $l_1 + i$ there will be no Noetherian equations of absolute degree $\geqslant l_1 + i$. In this case the Noetherian equations are finite in number and can be actually determined (at any rate in numerical examples). This can only happen when the module contains the origin as an isolated point, and the Noetherian equations are then the modular equations of the simple Noetherian module contained in the given module. The simple module itself is $(M, O^{l_1 + i})$ and $l_1 + i$ is its characteristic number.

Thus the simple modules at isolated points of a given module M can all be found by moving the origin to each point in succession and finding its Noetherian equations and characteristic number.

Let M have a simple module at the point $(a_1, a_2, ..., a_n)$. Move the origin to the point and find the Noetherian equations. They will be represented by finite negative power series

$$E_1 = E_2 = ... = E_h = 0$$

and all derivates of the same. Also any such system represents a simple module at the origin; the fact that the coefficients of E_1, E_2, ..., E_h are recurrent functions (§ 63) placing no restriction on them when finite in number. Let $E_i = \Sigma c_{p_1, p_2, ..., p_n} (x_1^{p_1} x_2^{p_2} ... x_n^{p_n})^{-1}$ be of absolute degree $\gamma_i - 1$. Moving the origin back to its original position, that is, to the point $(-a_1, -a_2, ..., -a_n)$, the equation $E_i = 0$ becomes (§ 64)

$$\Sigma (c_1 + a_1)^{p_1} (c_2 + a_2)^{p_2} ... (c_n + a_n)^{p_n} (x_1^{p_1} x_2^{p_2} ... x_n^{p_n})^{-1} = 0,$$

where, after expanding $(c_1 + a_1)^{p_1} ... (c_n + a_n)^{p_n}$, each $c_1^{q_1} ... c_n^{q_n}$ is to be put equal to the known constant $c_{q_1, q_2, ..., q_n}$ which it represents. Also $c_{q_1, q_2, ..., q_n} = 0$ if $q_1 + q_2 + ... + q_n \geqslant \gamma_i$. Thus

$$(c_1 + a_1)^{p_1} (c_2 + a_2)^{p_2} ... (c_n + a_n)^{p_n} = \left(1 + \frac{c_1}{a_1}\right)^{p_1} ... \left(1 + \frac{c_n}{a_n}\right)^{p_n} a_1^{p_1} a_2^{p_2} ... a_n^{p_n}$$
$$= k_{p_1, p_2, ..., p_n} a_1^{p_1} a_2^{p_2} ... a_n^{p_n},$$

where $k_{p_1, p_2, ..., p_n}$ is a whole function of $p_1, p_2, ..., p_n$ of degree $\gamma_i - 1$.

Hence the modular equations of any simple module at the point $(a_1, a_2, ..., a_n)$ are represented by power series

$$\overset{\infty}{\Sigma} k_{p_1, p_2, ..., p_n} a_1^{p_1} a_2^{p_2} ... a_n^{p_n} (x_1^{p_1} x_2^{p_2} ... x_n^{p_n})^{-1} = 0$$

and their derivates, where $k_{p_1, p_2, ..., p_n}$ is a whole function of $p_1, p_2, ..., p_n$. Conversely any system of equations (finite in number) of this type with all their derivates is a system of modular equations of a simple module at the point $(a_1, a_2, ..., a_n)$.

The following is a consequence of the above. The general solution for the recurrent function $c_{p_1, p_2, ..., p_n}$ (§ 63) satisfying a set of re-current equations $\underset{p}{\Sigma} a_{p_1, p_2, ..., p_n} c_{p_1+l_1, ..., p_n+l_n} = 0$ for all positive integral values of $l_1, l_2, ..., l_n$, when the corresponding polynomials $\Sigma a_{p_1, p_2, ..., p_n} x_1^{p_1} x_2^{p_2} ... x_n^{p_n}$ have only a finite number of points $(a_1, a_2, ..., a_n)$ in common, is $\Sigma A a_1^{p_1} a_2^{p_2} ... a_n^{p_n}$, where A is a whole function of $p_1, p_2, ..., p_n$ dependent on the point $(a_1, a_2, ..., a_n)$ and involving linear parameters. When the polynomials have an infinite number of points in common there can scarcely be said to be a general solution for $c_{p_1, p_2, ..., p_n}$.

Properties of Simple Modules

67. Theorem. *If the resultant of* $(F_1, F_2, ..., F_n)$ *does not vanish identically the number of Noetherian equations of any simple module of* $(F_1, F_2, ..., F_n)$ *is equal to the multiplicity of the corresponding solution of* $F_1 = F_2 = ... = F_n = 0$ *given by the resultant.*

This theorem is proved for the case $n = 2$ in (M_1, p. 388) and for the general case in (L, p. 98). Both proofs are very complicated; and a simpler proof is given here.

By the resultant of $(F_1, F_2, ..., F_n)$ we shall understand the resultant with respect to $x_1, x_2, ..., x_{n-1}$, viz. a polynomial in x_n, the variables having been subjected to a homogeneous linear substitution beforehand. Move the origin to any point of $(F_1, F_2, ..., F_n)$. Then, if x_n^C is the highest power of x_n which divides the resultant, C is the multiplicity of the solution of $F_1 = F_2 = ... = F_n = 0$ corresponding to the origin. Let Q be the whole simple module of $(F_1, F_2, ..., F_n)$ at the origin, and N the number of its modular equations. We have to prove that $C = N$.

Consider first the specially simple case in which the origin is not a singular point of the curve $(F_2, F_3, ..., F_n)$. The terms of the first degree in $F_2, F_3, ..., F_n$ are then linearly independent. For simplicity we may suppose them to be $x_2, x_3, ..., x_n$. Then F_1 can be modified by $F_2, F_3, ..., F_n$ so that its terms of lowest degree reduce to the single term x_1^p. Hence the modular equations of Q, or Noetherian equations of $(F_1, F_2, ..., F_n)$, are $x_1^{-p+1} = x_1^{-p+2} = ... = x_1^{-1} = 1 = 0$ (§ 65), so that $N = p$. Also the number of points of intersection of $F_1 = F_2 = ... = F_n = 0$ that coincide with the origin is p, so that $C = p$. Hence $C = N$.

Consider now the general case. Let $F_1', F_2', ..., F_n'$ be n polynomials whose coefficients are arbitrary except that they satisfy the N equations of Q. Then $(F_1, F_2, ..., F_n)$ and $(F_1', F_2', ..., F_n')$ have the same simple module Q at the origin, and the same N. It can be proved also that they have the same C. By the Lasker-Noether theorem (§ 56), since $(F_1, F_2, ..., F_n)$ and $(F_1', F_2', ..., F_n')$ have the same Noetherian equations, there exist polynomials $\phi_1, \phi_2, ..., \phi_n$ and $\phi_1', \phi_2', ..., \phi_n'$, none of which vanish at the origin, such that

$$\phi_i F_i = 0 \bmod (F_1', F_2', ..., F_n') \quad \text{and} \quad \phi_i' F_i' = 0 \bmod (F_1, F_2, ..., F_n).$$

Hence the module $(\phi_1 F_1, \phi_2 F_2, ..., \phi_n F_n)$ contains $(F_1', F_2', ..., F_n')$, and the resultant of the former is divisible by that of the latter (§ 11).

But the resultant of $(\phi_1 F_1, \phi_2 F_2, \ldots, \phi_n F_n)$ is the product of 2^n resultants of which one only, the resultant of $(F_1, F_2, \ldots, F_n)$, has x_n as a factor. Hence the resultant of $(F_1, F_2, \ldots, F_n)$ is divisible by as high a power of x_n as the resultant of $(F_1', F_2', \ldots, F_n')$, and *vice versa*; i.e. the two resultants are divisible by the same power of x_n.

Now the resultant of the terms of highest degree $l_1, l_2, \ldots, l_n$ in $F_1', F_2', \ldots, F_n'$ does not vanish, for the coefficients of these terms are absolutely arbitrary if $l_1, l_2, \ldots, l_n$ are all chosen as high as the characteristic number of Q. Hence the equations $F_1' = F_2' = \ldots = F_n' = 0$ have no solutions at infinity, and the number of their finite solutions is $l_1 l_2 \ldots l_n$, taking multiplicity into account. Also the sum of the values of N for all the points of $(F_1', F_2', \ldots, F_n')$ is $l_1 l_2 \ldots l_n$ (end of § 58), i.e. is equal to the sum of the values of C. Also each point of $(F_1', F_2', \ldots, F_n')$ except the origin comes under the simple case considered above; for even if the curve $(F_2', F_3', \ldots, F_n')$ has any singular points other than the origin, F_1' does not pass through them, since the origin is the only fixed point of F_1'. Hence the values of C and N are equal at each point of $(F_1', F_2', \ldots, F_n')$ other than the origin, and are therefore also equal at the origin. This proves the theorem.

68. *Definitions.* The *multiplicity* of a simple module is the number of its independent Noetherian equations.

This number has a geometrical interpretation when the theory of the resultant is applicable; but in general it has only an algebraical interpretation.

The *multiplicity of a primary module* of rank r is the multiplicity of each of the simple modules into which it resolves when regarded as a module in r variables only.

Thus there are four important numbers in connection with any primary module, viz. the rank r, the order d, the characteristic number γ, and the multiplicity μ.

A primary module of rank r will be said to be of the *principal Noetherian class* if there is a module $(F_1, F_2, \ldots, F_r)$ of rank r which contains it and does not contain any primary module of greater multiplicity with the same spread. On moving the origin to any general point of the spread any member of the primary module will be of the form $P_1 F_1 + P_2 F_2 + \ldots + P_r F_r$, where $P_1, P_2, \ldots, P_r$ are power series.

In other words, the primary modules into which a module of the principal class resolves are said to be of the principal Noetherian class.

Any prime module is of the principal Noetherian class ; but in general a primary module is such that any module of the principal class which contains it determines a primary module of greater multiplicity.   For example, O^2 is of multiplicity $n + 1$, but any module of the principal class of rank n containing O^2 contains a simple module at the origin of multiplicity 2^n at least.

If M is a module of rank n the number of its modular equations is finite and equal to the sum $\Sigma\mu$ of the multiplicities of its simple modules.   In order that we may have $F = 0 \bmod M$ the coefficients of F must satisfy the $\Sigma\mu$ equations (which will not be independent unless F is of sufficiently high degree).   Any set of $\Sigma\mu$ linearly independent polynomials such that no linear combination of them is a member of M is called a *complete set of remainders* for M ; and has the property that any polynomial F which is not a member of M is congruent mod M to a unique linear combination of the set of remainders.   The simplest way of choosing a complete set of remainders is to take the polynomial 1 of degree 0, then as many power products of degree 1 as possible, then as many power products of degree 2 as possible, and so on, till a set of $\Sigma\mu$ power products has been obtained of which no linear combination is a member of M.   We shall call any such set a *simple complete set* of remainders for M.

If $M = [E_1, E_2, ..., E_h]$ is a simple Noetherian module no member E of the system $[E_1, E_2, ..., E_h]$ can have the same coefficients (assumed real) as a member F of M ; for if E and F had the same coefficients the sum of their squares would be zero.   Hence if the members of the system $[E_1, E_2, ..., E_h]$ have their power products changed from negative to positive they will form a complete set of remainders for M.

69.   *A Noetherian principal system $[E_1]$ is uniquely expressible as a system $[E]$ such that the polynomial F with the same coefficients as E is a member of the module $[E]/O$.*

Let $E_2, E_3, ..., E_\mu$ be a complete set of linearly independent derivates of E_1 all of less absolute degree than E_1, and let $F_1, F_2, ..., F_\mu$ be the polynomials having the same coefficients as $E_1, E_2, ..., E_\mu$. Then $E_2, E_3, ..., E_\mu$ are the members of the system

$$[E_1]/O = [x_1 . E_1, \ x_2 . E_1, ..., x_n . E_1];$$

and $F_2, F_3, ..., F_\mu$ is a complete set of remainders for the module $[E_1]/O$.   Hence there is a unique F such that

$$F = F_1 + \lambda_2 F_2 + ... + \lambda_\mu F_\mu = 0 \bmod [E_1]/O.$$

The member E of $[E_1]$ with the same coefficients as F is unique, and the system $[E]$ is the same as the system $[E_1]$. A homogeneous Noetherian equation is already in its unique form.

70. *If E is homogeneous and of absolute degree l the numbers of linearly independent derivates of E of degrees l' and $l - l'$ are equal.*

Let $E_1, E_2, \dots, E_N$ be the members of the system $[E]$ of degree l', and $F_1, F_2, \dots, F_L$ the members of the module $[E]$ of degree l', and $G_1, G_2, \dots, G_N$ the polynomials which have the same coefficients as $E_1, E_2, \dots, E_N$; so that $F_1, \dots, F_L, G_1, \dots, G_N$ form a complete set of linearly independent homogeneous polynomials of degree l'. Then the F_1-, F_2-, $\dots$, F_L-derivates of E vanish identically, and the G_1-, G_2-, $\dots$, G_N-derivates are the derivates of degree $l - l'$, and are linearly independent; otherwise some linear combination of $G_1, G_2, \dots, G_N$ would be a member of the module $[E]$. Hence the numbers of derivates of E of degrees l' and $l - l'$ are equal.

71. *The modular equations of a simple module Q of the principal Noetherian class consist of a single equation $E = 0$ and its derivates; that is, a simple module of the principal Noetherian class is a principal system* (M, p. 109).

Take the origin at the point of Q. Then the modular equations of Q are Noetherian, and the characteristic number γ of Q is 1 more than the absolute degree of the highest modular equation. Also since Q is of the principal Noetherian class it is the whole Noetherian module contained in a certain module $M = (F_1, F_2, \dots, F_n)$ of rank n. By choosing the degrees $l_1, l_2, \dots, l_n$ of $F_1, F_2, \dots, F_n$ to be $\geqslant \gamma$ we may assume $(F_1, F_2, \dots, F_n)$ to be an H-basis of M (§ 49).

Now if F is any polynomial of degree $l_1 + l_2 + \dots + l_n - n - 1$ such that $x_1 F, x_2 F, \dots, x_n F$ are all members of M then F itself is a member. We prove this for 2 variables referring for the general proof to (M, p. 110). When $n = 2$, we have

$$x_1 F = A_1 F_1 + A_2 F_2, \quad x_2 F = B_1 F_1 + B_2 F_2,$$

where A_1, B_1 are of degrees $\leqslant l_2 - 2$ and A_2, B_2 of degrees $\leqslant l_1 - 2$.

Hence $$x_2 (A_1 F_1 + A_2 F_2) = x_1 (B_1 F_1 + B_2 F_2),$$

or $$(x_2 A_1 - x_1 B_1) F_1 = (x_1 B_2 - x_2 A_2) F_2,$$

or $$x_2 A_1 - x_1 B_1 = 0 = x_1 B_2 - x_2 A_2,$$

since $x_2 A_1 - x_1 B_1$ is of degree $< l_2$ and cannot be divisible by F_2. Hence A_1, A_2 are both divisible by x_1, and $F = 0 \bmod (F_1, F_2)$.

Suppose $Q = [E_1, E_2, ..., E_h]$, where each E_i is relevant, that is, not a member of the system $[E_1, ..., E_{i-1}, E_{i+1}, ..., E_h]$. Then the conditions that $x_1 F, x_2 F, ..., x_n F$ are to be members of M require only that the coefficients of F should satisfy all the derivates of $E_1 = E_2 = ... = E_h = 0$ (but not these equations themselves) and all the modular equations of the other simple modules of M; i.e. $l_1 l_2 ... l_n - h$ equations in all. But these conditions require $F = 0 \bmod M$, or that the coefficients of F should satisfy all the $l_1 l_2 ... l_n$ modular equations of M, which are equivalent to $l_1 l_2 ... l_n - 1$ independent equations as applied to F (§ 58). Hence the $l_1 l_2 ... l_n - h$ equations as applied to F are equivalent to no less than $l_1 l_2 ... l_n - 1$ independent equations. Hence $h = 1$, and $Q = [E_1]$.

The converse of this theorem, viz. that a simple principal system is of the principal Noetherian class, is true in the case of 2 variables (M_3), but not true in the case of more than 2 variables. Thus

$$[x_1^{-2} + x_2^{-2} + x_3^{-2}] = (x_1^2 - x_2^2,\ x_1^2 - x_3^2,\ x_2 x_3,\ x_3 x_1,\ x_1 x_2)$$

is a principal system which is not of the principal Noetherian class.

72. *A module of the principal class of rank n is a principal system.* Let $[E_1], [E_2], ..., [E_a]$ be the simple modules into which the given module resolves, and $\gamma_1, \gamma_2, ..., \gamma_a$ the characteristic numbers, and $a_1, a_2, ..., a_a$ the x_1-coordinates of the points of $[E_1], [E_2], ..., [E_a]$. The given module $[E_1, E_2, ..., E_a]$ will be proved to be identical with $[E_1 + E_2 + ... + E_a]$.

Since $x_1 - a_i$ contains the spread of $[E_i]$, $(x_1 - a_i)^{\gamma_i}$ is a member of the module $[E_i]$, § 32, and $(x_1 - a_i)^{\gamma_i} . E_i$ vanishes identically (§ 61). Hence from the equation $E_1 + E_2 + ... + E_a = 0$ we have

$$(x_1 - a_2)^{\gamma_2} (x_1 - a_3)^{\gamma_3} ... (x_1 - a_a)^{\gamma_a} . E_1 = 0.$$

The operator on the left hand is a polynomial in $x_1 - a_1$ in which the constant term does not vanish ; hence if we apply the inverse operator $(x_1 - a_2)^{-\gamma_2} ... (x_1 - a_a)^{-\gamma_a}$ expanded in powers of $(x_1 - a_1)$ as far as $(x_1 - a_1)^{\gamma_1 - 1}$ we shall obtain $E_1 = 0$; since $(x_1 - a_1)^l . E_1$ vanishes identically when $l \geqslant \gamma_1$.

Hence E_1, and similarly $E_2, E_3, ..., E_a$, are all derivates of $E_1 + E_2 + ... + E_a$ and the given module $[E_1, E_2, ..., E_a] = [E_1 + E_2 + ... + E_a]$.

If M is a module of the principal class of rank r then $M^{(r)}$ and all its simple modules are principal systems. *Hence any module of the principal class, and its primary modules, are principal systems* (§ 82).

73. *If a simple module M_μ of multiplicity μ is a principal system* *$[E]$, and $M'_{\mu'}$ is a simple module of multiplicity μ' contained in M_μ, and* *$M_\mu/M'_{\mu'} = M''_{\mu''}$, then $M_\mu/M''_{\mu''} = M'_{\mu'}$, and $\mu' + \mu'' = \mu$ (M, p. 111).*

The modular equations of $M_\mu/M'_{\mu'}$ are the F-derivates of $E = 0$, where F is any member of $M'_{\mu'}$ (§ 62). Let $F_1, F_2, \ldots, F_{\mu'}$ be a complete set of remainders for $M'_{\mu'}$. To these can be added $F_{\mu'+1}, \ldots, F_\mu$ so that $F_1, F_2, \ldots, F_\mu$ is a complete set of remainders for M_μ. Also each of $F_{\mu'+1}, \ldots, F_\mu$ can be modified by a linear combination of $F_1, F_2, \ldots, F_{\mu'}$ so as to become a member of $M'_{\mu'}$; and we will suppose this to have been done. Then the $F_{\mu'+1}, \ldots, F_\mu$-derivates of $E = 0$ are modular equations of $M''_{\mu''}$, and are linearly independent, since no linear combination of $F_{\mu'+1}, \ldots, F_\mu$ is a member of M_μ. Also any other F-derivate of $E = 0$, where F is a member of $M'_{\mu'}$, is dependent on the $\mu - \mu'$ equations already found, since

$$F = \lambda_1 F_1 + \lambda_2 F_2 + \ldots + \lambda_\mu F_\mu \bmod M_\mu,$$

which requires, since $F = 0 \bmod M'_{\mu'}$,

$$\lambda_1 F_1 + \lambda_2 F_2 + \ldots + \lambda_{\mu'} F_{\mu'} = 0 \bmod M'_{\mu'},$$

or $$\lambda_1 = \lambda_2 = \ldots = \lambda_{\mu'} = 0.$$

Hence the F-derivate of $E = 0$ is the $(\lambda_{\mu'+1} F_{\mu'+1} + \ldots + \lambda_\mu F_\mu)$-derivate, and the number of modular equations of $M''_{\mu''}$ is $\mu - \mu'$, i.e. $\mu = \mu' + \mu''$.

Also since $M'_{\mu'} M''_{\mu''}$ contains M_μ, $M'_{\mu'}$ contains $M_\mu/M''_{\mu''}$ which is of multiplicity $\mu - \mu'' = \mu'$. Hence $M'_{\mu'} = M_\mu/M''_{\mu''}$.

It is true in general for unmixed modules of the same rank that if M is a principal system containing M', and $M/M' = M''$, then M', M'' are mutually residual with respect to M (cf. § 24, Ex. ii).

In (M, p. 112) the opinion is expressed that if M_μ is any simple module of multiplicity μ, and $M'_{\mu'}$ any module contained in M_μ, then the multiplicity of $M_\mu/M'_{\mu'}$ cannot exceed $\mu - \mu'$. This is not correct, as the following example shows.

Example. Let

$$M_\mu = [E_1, E_2] = [(x_1 x_3)^{-1} + (x_2 x_4)^{-1}, (x_1 x_5)^{-1} + (x_2 x_6)^{-1}],$$

and $$M'_{\mu'} = (x_1, x_2, O^2) = [x_3^{-1}, x_4^{-1}, x_5^{-1}, x_6^{-1}],$$

so that $$\mu = 2 + 6 + 1 = 9, \quad \mu' = 4 + 1 = 5.$$

Then $$M_\mu/M'_{\mu'} = [E_1, E_2]/(x_1, x_2) = [x_1 . E_1, x_2 . E_1, x_1 . E_2, x_2 . E_2]$$
$$= [x_3^{-1}, x_4^{-1}, x_5^{-1}, x_6^{-1}] = M'_{\mu'}.$$

Hence (since $M_\mu/M'_{\mu'} = M'_{\mu'}$) $M'_{\mu'}$ and $M'_{\mu'}$ are mutually residual with respect to M_μ; and the multiplicity of $M_\mu/M'_{\mu'}$ is $\mu' > \mu - \mu'$.

It can be proved that if M_μ is simple and contains $M'_{\mu'}$ the multiplicity of $M_\mu/M'_{\mu'}$ cannot exceed $1 + \frac{1}{4}(\mu - \mu')^2$ or $\frac{3}{4} + \frac{1}{4}(\mu - \mu')^2$ according as $\mu - \mu'$ is even or odd.

74. *If a simple H-module M_μ of multiplicity μ is a principal system $[E]$ with characteristic number γ, and if $M'_{\mu'}$, $M''_{\mu''}$ are mutually residual with respect to M_μ, and μ_l, μ'_l, μ''_l are the numbers of linearly independent modular equations of M_μ, $M'_{\mu'}$, $M''_{\mu''}$ of degree l, then $\mu'_{l'} + \mu''_{l''} = \mu_{l'} = \mu_{l''}$, where $l' + l'' = \gamma - 1$* (M, p. 112).

Here E is homogeneous and of absolute degree $\gamma - 1$; and we have already shown that $\mu_{l'} = \mu_{l''}$ (§ 70). The $\mu''_{l''}$ modular equations of $M''_{\mu''}$ of degree l'' are F'-derivates of $E = 0$, where F' is a member of $M'_{\mu'}$ of degree l'. Hence $\mu''_{l''}$ is the number of members F' of $M'_{\mu'}$ of degree l' of which no linear combination is a member F of M_μ; for $F.E$ vanishes identically. There are $\mu_{l'}$ polynomials in all of degree l' of which no linear combination is a member of M_μ, and $\mu'_{l'}$ of these are such that no linear combination of them is a member of $M'_{\mu'}$, while the remainder $\mu_{l'} - \mu'_{l'}$ can be modified by the $\mu'_{l'}$ so as to be members of $M'_{\mu'}$. Hence

$$\mu''_{l''} = \mu_{l'} - \mu'_{l'}, \quad \text{or} \quad \mu'_{l'} + \mu''_{l''} = \mu_{l'} = \mu_{l''}.$$

Thus the values of μ''_l are known for all values of l in terms of the values of μ_l and μ'_l for all values of l.

75. *If M is any module of rank n in $x_1, x_2, \ldots, x_n$, and M_0 the equivalent H-module in $x_1, \ldots, x_n, x_0$, and μ_m the number of modular equations of $(M_0)_{x_0 = 0}$ of degree m, then the number of modular equations of M for degree m is*

$$H_m = 1 + \mu_1 + \mu_2 + \ldots + \mu_m.$$

This is immediately seen by considering the scheme of § 59 carried as far as degree m. The number of rows in the compartments $0, 1, 2, \ldots, l-1$ of the inverse array is the number of power products of degree $\leqslant l - 1$, and each such power product inverted represents a modular equation of $(M_0)_{x_0 = 0}$. This number is therefore $1 + \mu_1 + \mu_2 + \ldots + \mu_{l-1}$. The numbers of rows in the succeeding compartments are μ_l, μ_{l+1}, $\ldots$, μ_m; and H_m is the total number of rows, viz. $1 + \mu_1 + \mu_2 + \ldots + \mu_m$.

Also the total number of modular equations of M, or the sum of the multiplicities of its simple modules, is equal to the multiplicity of $(M_0)_{x_0 = 0}$.

76.   If M' is any module of rank n and μ' the sum of the multiplicities of its simple modules, we can choose n members $F_1, F_2, ..., F_n$ of M' such that the resultant of their terms of highest degree does not vanish.   If then the sum of the multiplicities of the simple modules of $M = (F_1, F_2, ..., F_n)$ is μ the sum of the multiplicities of the simple modules of M/M' is $\mu - \mu'$ (§§ 71, 73), and if $M/M' = M''$ then $M/M'' = M'$.   The important point is that M' is unrestricted except that it is composed of simple modules.   The simple modules of M are principal systems, but not those of M'.   These remarks are intended to point out the generality of the following theorem.

If $(F_1, F_2, ..., F_n)$ is an H-basis of a module M of rank n, and M' any module contained in M, and M'' the residual module M/M', then M', M'' are mutually residual with respect to M, and

$$H'_{l'} - H''_{l''} = H'_{l'+l''} - H_{l''} = H_{l'} - H''_{l'+l''},$$

where $l' + l'' + n + 1$ is the sum of the degrees of $F_1, F_2, ..., F_n$, and H_l, H'_l, H''_l are the numbers of modular equations of M, M', M'' for degree l.

This gives the values of H''_l for all values of l in terms of the values of H'_l for all values of l; for H_l is known by § 58.

The theorem is a generalization of the Brill-Noether reciprocity theorem (BN, p. 280, § 5, " Der Riemann-Roch'sche Satz").   It expresses the reciprocal relations between the numbers of the conditions which must be satisfied by members of M' and M'' in order that the product $M'M''$ may contain M.

A somewhat more general theorem is the following :

If $(F_1, F_2, ..., F_k)$ is an H-basis of a module M of rank n such that the H-module determined by the terms of highest degree in $F_1, F_2, ..., F_k$ is a principal system with characteristic number γ, and if M' is any module contained in M, and M'' the residual module M/M', then M', M'' are mutually residual with respect to M, and

$$H'_{l'} - H''_{l''} = H'_{l'+l''} - H_{l''} = H_{l'} - H''_{l'+l''}, \text{ where } l' + l'' = \gamma - 2.$$

We shall prove this more general theorem which includes the other. We must prove first that the simple modules of M are all principal systems*.   Let M_0, M_0', M_0'' be the H-modules in $x_1, x_2, ..., x_n, x_0$ equivalent to M, M', M''.   Then $(M_0)_{x_0=0}$ is a principal system ; and

---

* The converse that if M is a module of rank n whose simple modules are all principal systems $(M_0)_{x_0=0}$ is a principal system is not true.   For example, if M is the module in 2 variables determined by 3 points in a plane, then $(M_0)_{x_0=0}$ has the modular equations $x_1^{-1} = x_2^{-1} = 1 = 0$, and is not a principal system.

the multiplicities μ, μ', μ'' of $(M_0)_{x_0=0}$, $(M_0')_{x_0=0}$, $(M_0'')_{x_0=0}$ are the sums of the multiplicities of the simple modules of M, M', M'' (§ 75). Let Q' be the module determined by the a points forming the spread of M, and Q'' the residual module M/Q'. Also let Q_0', Q_0'' be the H-modules equivalent to Q', Q''. Then, since $Q'Q''$ contains M, $Q_0'Q_0''$ contains M_0, and $(Q_0'Q_0'')_{x_0=0}$ contains $(M_0)_{x_0=0}$, which is a principal system. Hence also $(Q_0'')_{x_0=0}$ contains $(M_0)_{x_0=0}/(Q_0')_{x_0=0}$ whose multiplicity is $\mu - a$; i.e. the sum of the multiplicities of the simple modules of $Q'' \geqslant \mu - a$. This is only possible when the simple modules of M are all principal systems; for if $[E_1, ..., E_h]$ is the simple module of M at the point P (say), the corresponding simple modules of Q', Q'' are P and $[E_1, E_2, ..., E_h]/P$, and the multiplicity of the latter is h less than that of $[E_1, E_2, ..., E_h]$; so that $\mu - \Sigma h \geqslant \mu - a$, $\Sigma h \leqslant a = a$, and $h = 1$. It follows that M' and M'' are mutually residual with respect to M.

It also follows that $\mu = \mu' + \mu''$, and that $(M_0')_{x_0=0}$ and $(M_0'')_{x_0=0}$ are mutually residual with respect to $(M_0)_{x_0=0}$. Hence $\mu'_{l'+1} + \mu''_{l''} = \mu_{l'+1} = \mu_{l''}$ (§ 74). Also $H'_{l'} = 1 + \mu_1' + \mu_2' + ... + \mu'_{l'}$ (§ 75). Hence

$$(H'_{l'+l''} - H'_{l'}) + H''_{l''}$$

$$= (\mu'_{l'+1} + \mu'_{l'+2} + ... + \mu'_{l'+l''}) + (1 + \mu_1'' + \mu_2'' + ... + \mu''_{l''})$$

$$= 1 + (\mu'_{l'+l''} + \mu_1'') + (\mu'_{l'+l''-1} + \mu_2'') + ... + (\mu'_{l'+1} + \mu''_{l''})$$

$$= 1 + \mu_1 + \mu_2 + ... + \mu_{l''} = H_{l''};$$

i.e. $$H'_{l'} - H''_{l''} = H'_{l'+l''} - H_{l''} = H_{l'} - H''_{l'+l''}.$$

Modular Equations of Unmixed Modules

77. We have hitherto specially considered modules of rank n, that is, modules which resolve into simple modules. The H-module of rank n is of a special type, since it is itself a simple module, and its equations are homogeneous. The general case of a module of rank n is therefore that of a module which is not an H-module. When however we consider a module of rank $< n$ it is of some advantage to replace it by its equivalent H-module, which is of the same rank but of greater dimensions by 1. We shall not avoid by this means the consideration of modules which are not H-modules, but the results obtained will be expressed more conveniently. We shall therefore assume that the given module M whose modular equations and properties are to be discussed is an H-module in n variables x_1, x_2, ..., x_n.

By treating any H-module M of rank r (whether mixed or unmixed) as a module $M^{(r)}$ in r variables $x_1, x_2, \ldots, x_r$ it will resolve into simple modules and have only a finite number of modular equations, viz. a number μ equal to the sum of the multiplicities of its simple modules. The unknowns in the modular equations will be represented by negative power products of $x_1, x_2, \ldots, x_r$ while the coefficients will be whole functions of the parameters $x_{r+1}, \ldots, x_n$. The module determined by these modular equations will be unmixed, viz. the L.C.M. of all the primary modules of M of rank r (§ 43); and will be the module M itself if M is unmixed. We proceed to discuss these equations and shall call them the *r-dimensional modular equations* of M (or the modular equations of $M^{(r)}$) since they are obtained by regarding the module M as a module $M^{(r)}$ in space of r dimensions. $M^{(r)}$ is not an H-module.

The dialytic array of $M^{(r)}$. We choose any basis $(F_1, F_2, \ldots, F_k)$ of M as the basis of $M^{(r)}$. This is not in general an H-basis of $M^{(r)}$. The module $M_{x_{r+1}=\ldots=x_n=0}$ determined by the highest terms of the members of the basis of $M^{(r)}$ is of rank r (assuming that $x_1, x_2, \ldots, x_n$ have been subjected to a linear homogeneous substitution beforehand) and is therefore a simple H-module whose characteristic number will be denoted by γ.

Construct a dialytic array for $M^{(r)}$ whose elements are whole functions of $x_{r+1}, \ldots, x_n$ in which each row represents an elementary member $\omega_i F_j$ of $M^{(r)}$, where ω_i is a power product of $x_1, x_2, \ldots, x_r$ (cf. § 59). The first set of rows will represent the members of the basis which are of lowest degree l, the next set a complete set of elementary members of degree $l+1$ which are linearly independent of one another and of the complete rows in the first set, the next set a complete set of elementary members of degree $l+2$ linearly independent of one another and of the complete rows in the first two sets, and so on.

In comparing this with the scheme of § 59 there is the obvious difference that the elements of the array are whole functions of $x_{r+1}, \ldots, x_n$ instead of pure constants; and there is the more important difference that *the compartments $l, l+1, \ldots$ do not necessarily consist of independent rows*, because the array is not constructed from an H-basis of $M^{(r)}$. It is only the complete rows of the array that are independent. *The elements in the compartments are all pure constants independent of $x_{r+1}, \ldots, x_n$.* The diagram of § 59 serves perfectly well to illustrate the dialytic array although its properties are now different.

In each compartment we choose a set of independent rows such that all the remaining rows of the compartment are dependent on them, and we name them *regular* rows and *extra* rows respectively, and apply the same terms to the complete rows of which they form part. In the compartment γ the regular rows will form a square array, and the same will be true of the compartments $\gamma + 1$, $\gamma + 2$, ... Eventually a compartment $\delta \geqslant \gamma$ will be reached such that the number of rows in the whole array for degree δ is exactly μ less than the whole number of columns, where μ is the number of modular equations of $M^{(r)}$ as mentioned above. After this all succeeding compartments $\delta + 1$, $\delta + 2$, ... will consist of square arrays only without any extra rows.

We can now modify any extra row of the array by regular rows so as to make all its elements which project beyond the columns of degree $\gamma - 1$ vanish, and this leaves its elements in the columns up to degree $\gamma - 1$ whole functions of $x_{r+1}, \ldots, x_n$ of the same degrees as they were before. If this is done with all the extra rows projecting beyond the columns of degree $\gamma - 1$ the array may be said to be brought to its *regular form* in which the whole number of rows of the array for degree $\gamma - 1$ is μ less than the whole number of columns, and all the compartments γ, $\gamma + 1$, ... are made square. The extra rows, modified so as to end at the columns of degree $\gamma - 1$, represent members of $M^{(r)}$ of degree $\gamma - 1$ which are not elementary members $\omega_i F_j$.

We may further modify the *regular form* of the complete array for degree $\gamma - 1$ so as to reduce the number of rows in each compartment $\gamma - 1$, $\gamma - 2$, ... successively to independent rows. The elements of some of the rows of the array for degree $\gamma - 1$ may thus become fractional in $x_{r+1}, \ldots, x_n$, and the whole number of compartments will in general be increased, so that the last (or first) compartment will be numbered $l' < l$. Supposing this to be done we can choose a *simple* complete set of remainders for $M^{(r)}$ consisting of all power products of $x_1, x_2, \ldots, x_r$ of degree $< l'$ and as many power products of each degree $l'' \geqslant l'$ as the number of columns of the compartment l'' exceeds the number of rows of the same. We denote these power products in ascending degree by $\omega_1, \omega_2, \ldots, \omega_\mu$ (so that $\omega_1 = 1$) and all remaining power products to infinity in ascending degree by $\omega_{\mu+1}, \omega_{\mu+2}, \ldots$. The two series $\omega_1, \omega_2, \ldots, \omega_\mu$ and $\omega_{\mu+1}, \omega_{\mu+2}, \ldots$ overlap in respect to the degrees of their terms.

The basis of M used for constructing the dialytic array of $M^{(r)}$ must be one in which each member is of the same degree in $x_1, x_2, \ldots, x_r$ as in $x_1, x_2, \ldots, x_n$. We shall say that M is a *perfect* module if the array of $M^{(r)}$ as originally constructed has no extra rows, i.e. if the basis $(F_1, F_2, ..., F_k)$ is an H-basis of $M^{(r)}$.

78.   Solution of the dialytic equations of $M^{(r)}$.   We return to what has been called above the regular form of the dialytic array of $M^{(r)}$. Each row represents a member of $M^{(r)}$ and supplies a congruence equation mod $M^{(r)}$. Solving these equations, regarding $\omega_{\mu+1}, \omega_{\mu+2}, ...$ as the unknowns, we have

$$D\omega_p + D_{p1}\omega_1 + D_{p2}\omega_2 + ... + D_{p\mu}\omega_\mu = 0 \bmod M^{(r)} \quad (p = \mu + 1, \mu + 2, ...).$$

There are two slightly different cases according as the degree of $\omega_p < \gamma$ or $\geqslant \gamma$. If ω_p is of degree $< \gamma$ we use the regular form of the array for degree $\gamma - 1$ for solving for ω_p. D is then the determinant of this array formed from the columns corresponding to $\omega_{\mu+1}, \omega_{\mu+2}, ...,$ and D_{pi} the determinant formed from the columns corresponding to $\omega_{\mu+1}, ..., \omega_{p-1}, \omega_i, \omega_{p+1}, ...$ If ω_p is of degree $\geqslant \gamma$ we must use the array up to the degree of ω_p in order to solve for ω_p. D is the same as in the former case except for a factor independent of $x_{r+1}, ..., x_n$ (since the compartments $\gamma, \gamma + 1, ...$ are square and all their elements are pure constants) by which the equation can be divided. Also D_{pi} is a sum of products of determinants of the regular form of the array for degree $\gamma - 1$ with determinants from the remaining rows of the larger array, so that the H.C.F. of the determinants of the array for degree $\gamma - 1$ can be divided out, and we obtain in both cases

(A) $R\omega_p + R_{p1}\omega_1 + ... + R_{p\mu}\omega_\mu = 0 \bmod M^{(r)} \quad (p = \mu + 1, \mu + 2, ...).$

This equation is homogeneous in $x_1, x_2, ..., x_n$, and each R_{pi} is homogeneous in $x_{r+1}, ..., x_n$. Also, owing to the fact that the remainders $\omega_1, \omega_2, ..., \omega_\mu$ are a *simple* set, each ω_p is congruent mod $M^{(r)}$ to a linear combination of those power products $\omega_1, \omega_2, ..., \omega_\mu$ which are of equal or less degree than ω_p. *Hence R_{pi} vanishes if the degree of ω_i exceeds the degree of ω_p. Also $R = 1$ if M is perfect* (cf. § 81).

79.   The modular equations of $M^{(r)}$.   If the coefficient of $\omega_p = x_1^{p_1} x_2^{p_2} ... x_r^{p_r}$ in the general member of $M^{(r)}$ of any degree is represented by $\omega_{-p} = (x_1^{p_1} x_2^{p_2} ... x_r^{p_r})^{-1}$ we have

$$\omega_{-1}\omega_1 + \omega_{-2}\omega_2 + ... + \omega_{-p}\omega_p + ... = 0 \bmod M^{(r)},$$

and, by (A),

$$R(\omega_{-1}\omega_1 + ... + \omega_{-\mu}\omega_\mu) = \sum_{p=\mu+1}^{\infty} \omega_{-p}(R_{p1}\omega_1 + R_{p2}\omega_2 + ... + R_{p\mu}\omega_\mu) \bmod M^{(r)}.$$

Here coefficients of ω_1, ω_2, ..., ω_μ on both sides are equal, i.e.

(B) $$R\omega_{-i} = \sum_{p=\mu+1}^{\infty} R_{pi}\omega_{-p} \quad (i = 1, 2, ..., \mu).$$

This is the complete system of modular equations of $M^{(r)}$, or r-dimensional modular equations of M, and the system includes all its own derivates. R *and all the* R_{pi} *are definite whole functions of* x_{r+1}, ..., x_n. If any other complete system were given and solved for ω_{-1}, ω_{-2}, ..., $\omega_{-\mu}$ in terms of $\omega_{-\mu-1}$, $\omega_{-\mu-2}$, ... the result would be the unique system (B).

Since in (A) $R\omega_p$ and $R_{pi}\omega_i$ are of the same degree in x_1, x_2, ..., x_n, so in (B), $R\omega_{-i}$ and $R_{pi}\omega_{-p}$ are of the same degree, i.e. all terms in one equation (B) are of the same degree in x_1, x_2, ..., x_n. Also since (§ 78) R_{pi} vanishes if the degree of ω_i exceeds the degree of ω_p *there is no* ω_{-p} *on the right-hand side of* (B) *of less absolute degree than* ω_{-i}; but every ω_{-p} of the same degree as ω_{-i} and not among ω_{-1}, ω_{-2}, ..., $\omega_{-\mu}$ will appear on the right-hand side of (B).

(B) is the complete system of r-dimensional equations of the L.C.M. of all the primary modules of M of rank r; and will decompose into separate distinct systems corresponding to the separate primary modules of rank r if M has more than one irreducible spread of rank r.

The n-dimensional equations. We can obtain the whole system of n-dimensional equations of M corresponding to the system (B) as follows: ω_{-p} or $(x_1^{p_1} x_2^{p_2} \ldots x_r^{p_r})^{-1}$ represents the whole coefficient of $x_1^{p_1} x_2^{p_2} \ldots x_r^{p_r}$ in the general member of $M^{(r)}$, i.e. it stands for

$$\Sigma \, (x_1^{p_1} \ldots x_n^{p_n})^{-1} \, x_{r+1}^{p_{r+1}} \ldots x_n^{p_n},$$

the summation extending to all values of p_{r+1}, ..., p_n only. If this be substituted for each $(x_1^{p_1} \ldots x_r^{p_r})^{-1}$ in each of the equations (B) the whole coefficients of the power products of x_{r+1}, ..., x_n will represent the n-dimensional equations. *This will be the whole system of n-dimensional equations of M if M is unmixed, as we shall assume hereafter is the case.*

The whole system of modular equations of a mixed module may be regarded as consisting of the separate systems corresponding to the primary modules into which it resolves.

80.   *The system of homogeneous equations*

(C) $$R\omega_{-i} = \Sigma R_{pi}\omega_{-p} \quad (i = 1, 2, ..., \mu)$$

obtained from the system (B) *by retaining only those terms on the right hand in which R_{pi} and ω_{-p} are of the same degrees as R and ω_{-i}*

respectively is the complete system of equations of the simple H-module determined by the highest terms in x_1, x_2, ..., x_r of the members of an H-basis of $M^{(r)}$.

This can be seen by considering the diagram of § 59 assuming that it had been constructed from an H-basis of $M^{(r)}$. The compartments l, $l+1$, $l+2$, ... in the two arrays in § 59 are the dialytic and inverse arrays of the simple H-module determined by the highest terms of the members of the H-basis; and the modular equations of this simple H-module are represented by the compartments 0, 1, ..., l, $l+1$, ... of the inverse array. The system (C) is that which is represented by the compartments of the inverse array.

81. *If $R = 1$ the module M (assumed unmixed) is perfect.* Since M is unmixed every whole member of $M^{(r)}$ is a member of M (§ 43). Also, since $R = 1$, there is an inverse array of $M^{(r)}$ each of whose compartments consists of independent rows in which all the elements are pure constants. Hence there is a corresponding dialytic array having the same property. From this it follows that M is perfect (§ 77).

82. The r-dimensional and n-dimensional equations of M.

If the system (B) is a principal system, i.e. if all its equations are derivates of a single one of them, each simple module of $M^{(r)}$ is a principal system; for if F is a polynomial containing all the simple modules of $M^{(r)}$ except one, then $M^{(r)}/(F)$ is the last one, and is a principal system (§ 62). The converse is also true (see § 72). Also the unmixed module M in n variables is a principal system, as we proceed to prove.

Let the r-dimensional equation of which all the equations of the system (B) are derivates be

$$\sum_{\infty} R_{p_1, p_2, ..., p_r}(x_1^{p_1} x_2^{p_2} ... x_r^{p_r})^{-1} = 0,$$

where $R_{p_1, p_2, ..., p_r}$ is a homogeneous polynomial in x_{r+1}, ..., x_n of degree $p_1 + p_2 + ... + p_r + \delta$. The integer δ may be negative, but the more unfavourable case for the proof is that in which it is positive. Let $c_{p_1, p_2, ..., p_n}$ be the coefficient of $x_{r+1}^{p_{r+1}} ... x_n^{p_n}$ in $R_{p_1, p_2, ..., p_r}$, so that $p_{r+1} + ... + p_n = p_1 + ... + p_r + \delta$. To convert the equation into an n-dimensional equation we put

$$(x_1^{p_1} x_2^{p_2} ... x_r^{p_r})^{-1} = \sum_{q}^{\infty} x_{r+1}^{q_{r+1}} ... x_n^{q_n} (x_1^{p_1} ... x_r^{p_r} x_{r+1}^{q_{r+1}} ... x_n^{q_n})^{-1}$$

as in § 79, and we have

$$\underset{p}{\Sigma} c_{p_1,\dots,p_n} x_{r+1}^{p_{r+1}} \dots x_n^{p_n} \underset{q}{\Sigma} x_{r+1}^{q_{r+1}} \dots x_n^{q_n} (x_1^{p_1} \dots x_r^{p_r} x_{r+1}^{q_{r+1}} \dots x_n^{q_n})^{-1} = 0, \quad \dots (1)$$

or, equating the whole coefficient of $x_{r+1}^{l_{r+1}} \dots x_n^{l_n}$ to zero,

$$\underset{p}{\Sigma} c_{p_1, p_2, \dots, p_n} (x_1^{p_1} \dots x_r^{p_r} x_{r+1}^{l_{r+1} - p_{r+1}} \dots x_n^{l_n - p_n})^{-1} = 0, \quad \dots \dots (2)$$

which is homogeneous and of absolute degree $l_{r+1} + \dots + l_n - \delta$. Similarly the general n-dimensional equation obtained from the coefficient of $x_{r+1}^{m_{r+1}} \dots x_n^{m_n}$ in the $x_1^{t_1} \dots x_r^{t_r}$-derivate of (1) is

$$\underset{p}{\Sigma} c_{p_1, p_2, \dots, p_n} (x_1^{p_1 - t_1} \dots x_r^{p_r - t_r} x_{r+1}^{m_{r+1} - p_{r+1}} \dots x_n^{m_n - p_n})^{-1} = 0, \quad \dots \dots (3)$$

where $t_1, \dots, t_r, m_{r+1}, \dots, m_n$ are any n fixed positive integers (including zeros) such that $t_1 + \dots + t_r \leqslant$ a fixed limit τ (since there are only a finite number of linearly independent derivates of the original r-dimensional equation) and $(x_1^{p_1 - t_1} \dots x_r^{p_r - t_r} x_{r+1}^{m_{r+1} - p_{r+1}} \dots x_n^{m_n - p_n})^{-1}$ is zero if any one of the indices $p_1 - t_1, \dots, p_r - t_r, m_{r+1} - p_{r+1}, \dots, m_n - p_n$ is negative.

Consider all the n-dimensional modular equations of degree l, that is, all the equations of the system (3) of absolute degree l. The absolute degree of (3) is

$$m_{r+1} + \dots + m_n - \delta - t_1 - \dots - t_r = l.$$

Hence each of $m_{r+1}, \dots, m_n$ is equal to or less than $l + \delta + \tau$; and every equation (3) of absolute degree l is a derivate of the single equation (2) if $l_{r+1}, \dots, l_n$ are all chosen as high as $l + \delta + \tau$. Hence there is a single equation of which all the modular equations of M of degree l are derivates, and any equation (2) in which $l_{r+1}, \dots, l_n$ are not numerically specified will serve for the single equation.

It follows that *the inverse system of any module M has a finite basis* $[E_1, E_2, \dots, E_h]$; for M resolves into a finite number of primary modules of the same or of different ranks, and each primary module of rank r has a finite number of r-dimensional equations, and a smaller number of r-dimensional equations of which all the others are derivates, and an equal or still smaller number of n-dimensional equations of which all the others are derivates.

83.   If (B) is a principal system it does not follow that (C) is a principal system (footnote § 76). *If however* (C) *is a principal system*

(B) *is a principal system.* For the basis equation of the system (C) must be the homogeneous equation

$$R\omega_{-\mu} = \Sigma R_{p\mu}\omega_{-p},$$

and all the other equations of (C) must be of less absolute degree. Now the system (B) is unique and any equation obtained from it

$$R_1\omega_{-1} + R_2\omega_{-2} + \ldots + R_p\omega_{-p} + \ldots = 0$$

must be the result of multiplying the equations of (B) by $R_\mu, R_{\mu-1}, \ldots, R_1$ and adding and dividing out R. Hence the equation

$$R\omega_{-i} = \overset{\infty}{\Sigma} R_{pi}\omega_{-p}$$

is exactly the same derivate of $R\omega_{-\mu} = \overset{\infty}{\Sigma} R_{p\mu}\omega_{-p}$ as the corresponding homogeneous equation $R'\omega_{-i} = \Sigma R_{pi}\omega_{-p}$ is of $R\omega_{-\mu} = \Sigma R_{p\mu}\omega_{-p}$.

If (C) is a principal system the formulae of § 76 apply to any two modules M', M'' mutually residual with respect to M when regarded as modules in r variables. If (B) is a principal system, but not (C), the formula $\mu = \mu' + \mu''$ applies, where μ, μ', μ'' are the numbers of equations in the systems (B), (B'), (B'') for M, M', M''. This follows from § 73 by summing for all the simple modules of $M^{(r)}$.

84. Modular equations of an *H*-module of the principal class.

·In the case of an H-module $(F_1, F_2, \ldots, F_r)$ of rank r (C) is a principal system (§ 71); and $R = 1$, since $(F_1, F_2, \ldots, F_r)$ is an H-basis of $M^{(r)}$ (§ 49). Also, if $F_1, F_2, \ldots, F_r$ are of degrees $l_1, l_2, \ldots, l_r$, a complete set of remainders for $M^{(r)}$ consists of the $l_1 l_2 \ldots l_r$ factors of $x_1^{l_1-1} x_2^{l_2-1} \ldots x_r^{l_r-1}$, since this is a complete set of remainders for $(x_1^{l_1}, x_2^{l_2}, \ldots, x_r^{l_r})$, cf. § 58. Hence the system (B) for M consists of the single equation

$$(x_1^{l_1-1} \ldots x_r^{l_r-1})^{-1} = \overset{\infty}{\Sigma} R_{p_1, p_2, \ldots, p_r}(x_1^{p_1} x_2^{p_2} \ldots x_r^{p_r})^{-1} \quad \ldots\ldots\ldots(4)$$

and its derivates, where $p_1 + \ldots + p_r \geqslant l_1 + \ldots + l_r - r$, and consequently $p_i \geqslant l_i$ for one value at least of i. The corresponding n-dimensional equation is (§ 82)

$$\underset{q}{\Sigma} x_{r+1}^{q_{r+1}} \ldots x_n^{q_n} (x_1^{l_1-1} \ldots x_r^{l_r-1} x_{r+1}^{q_{r+1}} \ldots x_n^{q_n})^{-1}$$
$$= \underset{p}{\Sigma} c_{p_1, \ldots, p_n} x_{r+1}^{p_{r+1}} \ldots x_n^{p_n} \underset{q}{\Sigma} x_{r+1}^{q_{r+1}} \ldots x_n^{q_n} (x_1^{p_1} \ldots x_r^{p_r} x_{r+1}^{q_{r+1}} \ldots x_n^{q_n})^{-1},$$

or, by equating coefficients of $x_{r+1}^{l_{r+1}-1} \ldots x_n^{l_n-1}$ on both sides,

$$(x_1^{l_1-1} x_2^{l_2-1} \ldots x_n^{l_n-1})^{-1} = \underset{p}{\Sigma} c_{p_1, p_2, \ldots, p_n}(x_1^{p_1} \ldots x_r^{p_r} x_{r+1}^{l_{r+1}-1-p_{r+1}} \ldots x_n^{l_n-1-p_n})^{-1}.$$

When F_1, F_2, ..., F_r are general with letters for coefficients, the $c_{p_1, p_2, ..., p_n}$ are rational functions of the coefficients and on multiplying up by their common denominator K we can write the equation

$$K \left(x_1^{l_1-1} x_2^{l_2-1} \ldots x_n^{l_n-1}\right)^{-1} = \underset{p}{\Sigma} K_{p_1, p_2, ..., p_n} \left(x_1^{p_1} x_2^{p_2} \ldots x_n^{p_n}\right)^{-1}, \quad \ldots(5)$$

where $p_1 + p_2 + \ldots + p_n = l_1 + l_2 + \ldots + l_n - n$, and at least one $p_i \geqq l_i$ $(i = 1, 2, ..., r)$ and every $p_j < l_j$ $(j = r+1, ..., n)$. This is the n-dimensional modular equation of $(F_1, F_2, ..., F_r)$ of which all others are derivates, $l_{r+1}, ..., l_n$ being unspecified numerically. More explicitly it is the unique modular equation of the simple module $(F_1, F_2, ..., F_r, x_{r+1}^{l_{r+1}}, ..., x_n^{l_n})$; for it is a relation satisfied by the coefficients of the general member of $(F_1, F_2, ..., F_r)$ of degree $l_1 + l_2 + \ldots + l_n - n$ in which $p_j < l_j$ $(j = r+1, ..., n)$, i.e. it is the unique relation (§ 58) satisfied by the coefficients of the general member of

$$(F_1, ..., F_r, x_{r+1}^{l_{r+1}}, ..., x_n^{l_n})$$

of degree $l_1 + \ldots + l_n - n$. The coefficients $K_{p_1, p_2, ..., p_n}$ are whole functions of the coefficients of F_1, F_2, ..., F_r of a similar kind to the resultant of $(F_1, ..., F_r, x_{r+1}^{l_{r+1}}, ..., x_n^{l_n})$ and of degree 1 less than this resultant in the coefficients of each of F_1, F_2, ..., F_r, viz. of degree $L_i - 1$ in the coefficients of F_i where $L_i l_i = l_1 l_2 \ldots l_n = L$. The vanishing of $K_{p_1, p_2, ..., p_n}$ is the condition that

$$x_1^{p_1} x_2^{p_2} \ldots x_n^{p_n} = 0 \bmod \left(F_1, F_2, ..., F_r, x_{r+1}^{l_{r+1}}, ..., x_n^{l_n}\right)$$

(§ 61, since the $x_1^{p_1} x_2^{p_2} \ldots x_n^{p_n}$-derivate of (5) then vanishes), whereas the non-vanishing of the resultant is the condition that every power product of degree $l_1 + \ldots + l_n - n + 1$ is a member of the module. It is probable that some of the quantities $K_{p_1, p_2, ..., p_n}$ factorise but that they have not all a common factor. The resultant of

$$(F_1, F_2, ..., F_r, x_{r+1}^{l_{r+1}}, ..., x_n^{l_n})$$

is $R_{r+1}^{l_{r+1} \ldots l_n}$ (§ 8).

85. Whole basis of the system inverse to $M^{(r)}$. The simplest *whole* basis $[E_1, E_2, ..., E_h]$ of the r-dimensional system inverse to an unmixed H-module M of rank r, or the simplest expression for the system of equations (B), satisfies the following conditions: (i) each E_i $(i = 1, 2, ..., h)$ is a *whole* member of the inverse system, i.e. its coefficients are whole functions of the parameters $x_{r+1}, ..., x_n$;

(ii) all the members E_1, E_2, ..., E_h are relevant ; (iii) any whole member of the system $[E_1, E_2, ..., E_h]$ is of the form

$$X_1 . E_1 + X_2 . E_2 + ... + X_h . E_h,$$

where X_1, X_2, ..., X_h are whole functions of x_{r+1}, ..., x_n as well as of x_1, x_2, ... x_r; (iv) E_1, E_2, ..., E_h have as high absolute under-degrees in x_1, x_2, ..., x_r as possible. A whole basis, as distinguished from a simplest whole basis, is defined by (i) and (iii).

A basis $(F_1, F_2, ..., F_k)$ of M furnishes a whole basis of $M^{(r)}$, and any whole basis of $M^{(r)}$ satisfying the condition corresponding to (iii) above is a basis of M. A simplest whole basis* of $M^{(r)}$ is one in which the degrees of F_1, F_2, ..., F_k in x_1, x_2, ..., x_r are as low as possible.

If $(F_1, F_2, ..., F_r)$ is any module of rank r containing M such that $(F_1, F_2, ..., F_r)_{x_{r+1}=...=x_n=0}$ is of rank r, and $M = (F_1, F_2, ..., F_{k'})$, and the degrees of F_{r+1}, ..., $F_{k'}$ in x_1, x_2, ..., x_r are as low as possible, the basis $(F_1, F_2, ..., F_{k'})$ will be called *a whole basis of* $M^{(r)}$ *in reference to* $(F_1, F_2, ..., F_r)$. All of F_{r+1}, ..., $F_{k'}$ are to be relevant, but some or all of F_1, F_2, ..., F_r may be irrelevant for a basis of M.

86. Properties of H-modules mutually residual with respect to an H-module of the principal class.

Let F_1, F_2, ..., F_r, of degrees l_1, l_2, ..., l_r, be any r members of the unmixed H-module M of rank r such that

$$(F_1, F_2, ..., F_r)_{x_{r+1}=...=x_n=0}$$

is of rank r ; and let M' be the residual module $(F_1, F_2, ..., F_r)/M$. Also let $(F_1, ..., F_r, F'_{r+1}, ..., F'_{r+h})$ be a whole basis of $M'^{(r)}$ in reference to $(F_1, F_2, ..., F_r) = [E]$. Since F'_{r+i} is of as low degree in x_1, x_2, ..., x_r as possible the terms of F'_{r+i} of highest degree in x_1, x_2, ..., x_r do not form a member of the module

$$(F_1, F_2, ..., F_r)_{x_{r+1}=...=x_n=0},$$

and are therefore of degree $l'_{r+i} \leqslant l_1 + l_2 + ... + l_r - r$ in x_1, x_2, ..., x_r. Also, since E begins with terms which represent the modular equation

---

* A simplest whole basis of $M^{(r)}$ is a whole basis which approaches most nearly to an H-basis; but is not necessarily an H-basis. For example,

$$(x_1^4,\ x_1^3 x_2,\ x_1 x_2^3,\ x_2^4,\ x_1^3 x_3^2 + x_1^2 x_2^2 x_4,\ x_2^3 x_4^2 + x_1^2 x_2^2 x_3)$$

is the basis of a module M of rank 2, and a simplest whole basis of $M^{(2)}$, but not an H-basis of $M^{(2)}$; since $x_1^3 x_3^3 - x_2^3 x_4^3$ is needed for an H-basis of $M^{(2)}$, but is irrelevant for a basis of M or whole basis of $M^{(2)}$.

of $(F_1, F_2, \ldots, F_r)_{x_{r+1}=\ldots=x_n=0}$ of degree $l_1 + l_2 + \ldots + l_r - r$, $F'_{r+i} \cdot E$ will begin with terms of absolute degree $l_1 + \ldots + l_r - r - l'_{r+i}$ in $x_1, x_2, \ldots, x_r$ which do not vanish identically.

Now M, M' are mutually residual with respect to $(F_1, \ldots, F_r)$ or $[E]$. Hence

$$M = [E]/M' = [E]/(F_1, \ldots, F_r, F'_{r+1}, \ldots, F'_{r+h})$$
$$= [F'_{r+1} \cdot E, F'_{r+2} \cdot E, \ldots, F'_{r+h} \cdot E].$$

This basis of the r-dimensional system inverse to M is a simplest whole basis $[E_1, E_2, \ldots, E_h]$ as defined in § 85. All its members are relevant, for if (say)

$$F'_{r+h} \cdot E = (X_1 F'_{r+1} + \ldots + X_{h-1} F'_{r+h-1}) \cdot E,$$
then
$$F'_{r+h} - X_1 F'_{r+1} - \ldots - X_{h-1} F'_{r+h-1} = 0 \bmod (F_1, F_2, \ldots, F_r),$$

which is not the case. Also any r-dimensional modular equation of M is a derivate of $E = 0$, and if a whole equation, is $F' \cdot E = 0$, where F' is a whole function of $x_1, x_2, \ldots, x_n$, since $[E]$ is a whole basis; and if F is any member of M, $FF' \cdot E$ vanishes identically, i.e.

$$FF' = 0 \bmod (F_1, F_2, \ldots, F_r)$$
and
$$F' = 0 \bmod M' = X_1 F'_{r+1} + \ldots + X_h F'_{r+h} \bmod (F_1, F_2, \ldots, F_r),$$
and
$$F' \cdot E = X_1 \cdot E_1 + X_2 \cdot E_2 + \ldots + X_h \cdot E_h.$$

Finally the absolute underdegrees of $E_1, E_2, \ldots, E_h$ are as high as possible since the degrees of $F'_{r+1}, \ldots, F'_{r+h}$ in $x_1, x_2, \ldots, x_r$ are as low as possible. The coefficients of the terms in E_i and F'_{r+i} which involve the parameters $x_{r+1}, \ldots, x_n$ to the least degree involve them to the same degree, so that $E_1, E_2, \ldots, E_h$ and $F'_{r+1}, F'_{r+2}, \ldots, F'_{r+h}$ are of the same degree of complexity in this respect.

It follows from the above that if M' is the residual of a given unmixed H-module M of rank r with respect to any H-module $(F_1, F_2, \ldots, F_r)$ of rank r containing M, and if

$$M' = (F_1, F_2, \ldots, F_r, F'_{r+1}, \ldots, F'_{r+h}),$$

where $F'_{r+1}, \ldots, F'_{r+h}$ are all relevant, then h is a fixed number independent of the choice of $F_1, F_2, \ldots, F_r$, viz. the number of members in a simplest whole basis $[E_1, E_2, \ldots, E_h]$ of the system inverse to $M^{(r)}$. Also if the degrees of $F'_{r+1}, \ldots, F'_{r+h}$ in respect to $x_1, x_2, \ldots, x_r$ are made as low as possible the degree of F'_{r+i} in respect to $x_1, x_2, \ldots, x_r$

is $l - a_i$ and in respect to x_1, x_2, ..., x_n is $l - a_i + \beta_i$, where l is the sum of the degrees of F_1, F_2, ..., F_r diminished by r, a_i is the absolute degree of the terms with which E_i begins, and β_i is the degree of the coefficients of these terms in x_{r+1}, ..., x_n.

87. The Theorem of Residuation. As in the last article let M be any unmixed H-module of rank r, and $(F_1, F_2, ..., F_r)$ any module of rank r containing M, and M' the residual module $(F_1, F_2, ..., F_r)/M$, so that M, M' are mutually residual with respect to $(F_1, F_2, ..., F_r)$. In geometrical terminology M, M' are residuals on $(F_2, F_3, ..., F_r)$ determined by the section F_1. Replace F_1 by another member F_1' of M, which we will suppose to be of the same degree as F_1, giving another section of $(F_2, F_3, ..., F_r)$ through M, and let $M_1' = (F_1', F_2, ..., F_r)/M$ be the residual section or module.

Also let F' be a section through M', F' being of the same degree as F_1, and $M_1 = (F', F_2, ..., F_r)/M'$ the residual section or module. Then M', M_1' are coresidual on $(F_2, F_3, ..., F_r)$ having a common residual M; and M_1 is any other residual of M'. *The theorem of residuation says that every*

residual M_1 of M' on $(F_2, F_3, ..., F_r)$ is also a residual of M_1', i.e. to every section F' through M' there corresponds a section F through M_1' having the same residual section on $(F_2, F_3, ..., F_r)$. This theorem is a generalization of Sylvester's theory of residuation (Salmon's *Higher Plane Curves*, Chap. v) and the *Restsatz* of Brill and Noether* (BN, p. 271). Besides this relation of M' to M_1' there are properties connecting them both with M which are proved in the last article, viz. the number of members over and above F_1, F_2, ..., F_r (or F_1', F_2, ..., F_r) required for a basis of M' (or M_1') is equal to the number of members required for a whole basis of the system inverse to $M^{(r)}$; and the number of members required for a whole basis of the system inverse to $M'^{(r)}$ (or $M_1'^{(r)}$) is equal to the number of members over and above F_1, F_2, ..., F_r (or F_1', F_2, ..., F_r) required for a basis of M.

---

* It would be more correct to say that the *Restsatz* can be deduced from the theorem proved here; but not such extensions of it as have been made to surfaces etc., because these bring in mixed modules. The module M may be composed of *any* primary modules of rank r; and corresponding to each one which is not of the principal Noetherian class M' must contain a residual primary module with the same spread.

The polynomials F_1, F_1', F' and the modules M, M', M_1, M_1' having been defined as above it is required to prove that there exists a polynomial F such that M_1, M_1' are mutually residual with respect to $(F, F_2, ..., F_r)$.   Let μ, μ', μ_1, μ_1' be the numbers of r-dimensional modular equations of M, M', M_1, M_1' ; then

$$\mu + \mu' = \mu + \mu_1' = \mu' + \mu_1 = l_1 l_2 ... l_r$$

and therefore each equals $\mu_1 + \mu_1'$.   Let ϕ, ϕ', ϕ_1, ϕ_1' be general members of M, M', M_1, M_1' with coefficients involving linear parameters. Then

$$F'F_1' = 0 \bmod MM' = 0 \bmod (F_1, F_2, ..., F_r) = FF_1 \bmod (F_2, ..., F_r),$$
$$......(1)$$

where F is a polynomial of the same degree as F_1, F_1', F'.   Also

$$F_1\phi_1' = 0 \bmod MM_1' = X_1'F_1' \bmod (F_2, ..., F_r), \quad ......(2)$$

and $\qquad \phi\phi_1' = 0 \bmod MM_1' = XF_1' \bmod (F_2, ..., F_r)$;

hence by cross multiplying and dividing out $\phi_1'F_1'$,

$$X_1'\phi = XF_1 \bmod (F_2, ..., F_r) = 0 \bmod (F_1, F_2, ..., F_r),$$
$$\therefore \ X_1' = 0 \bmod (F_1, F_2, ..., F_r)/M = 0 \bmod M'.$$

Similarly $\qquad F_1\phi_1 = 0 \bmod M'M_1 = X'F' \bmod (F_2, ..., F_r), \quad ......(3)$

where $X' = 0 \bmod M$;

$$\therefore \ X'X_1' = 0 \bmod MM' = X_1F_1 \bmod (F_2, ..., F_r). \quad ......(4)$$

Multiplying (1), (2), (3), (4), and dividing out $F'F_1'F_1^2X'X_1'$,

$$\phi_1\phi_1' = X_1F \bmod (F_2, ..., F_r) = 0 \bmod (F, F_2, ..., F_r).$$

Hence M_1M_1' contains $(F, F_2, ..., F_r)$; and since M_1, M_1' have only μ_1, μ_1' r-dimensional modular equations, while $(F, F_2, ..., F_r)$ has $\mu_1 + \mu_1'$ and is a principal system, it follows that $M_1^{(r)}$, $M_1'^{(r)}$, and consequently M_1, M_1', are mutually residual with respect to $(F, F_2, ..., F_r)$.

The theorem has been proved on the supposition that the modules are H-modules and the degrees of F_1, F_1', F' are equal; but it is true without any of these restrictions.   In the case of modules which are not H-modules the region at infinity must be regarded as nonexistent and the usual conception of residual and coresidual must be slightly extended.   Thus if through a point P on a plane cubic curve two lines are drawn parallel to two asymptotes cutting the curve again in Q, R, then P is residual to Q and R, and Q, R are coresidual.   If through Q a line is drawn cutting the curve again in two points these two are residual to R, i.e. a curve (viz. a conic) can be drawn through them and R which does not meet the curve again except at infinity.

As an illustration of the general theorem we may suppose M to be any unmixed module of rank 2 in space of three dimensions. Then F_1, F_2 are any two surfaces containing M whose whole intersection consists of a finite number of irreducible spreads (excluding infinity); and to each spread or curve corresponds a primary principal system of (F_1, F_2). M contains a certain part of some of these principal systems and no part of others; M' has to contain the whole of the latter and the residual part of each of the former. These conditions determine M', and similarly for M_1 and M_1'.

88. Perfect Modules. *Definition.* If a module M of rank r in n variables and the corresponding module $M^{(r)}$ in r variables have a common H-basis of which each member is of the *same degree in the r variables as in the n variables* then M is called a *perfect module.*

Any module of rank n is perfect, by definition.

An unmixed H-module of rank $n-1$ is perfect; for its basis is an H-basis of $M^{(n-1)}$.

An H-module of the principal class is perfect (§ 49).

A module of the principal class which is not an H-module is not necessarily perfect. For example, the module $(x_1{}^2, \ x_2 + x_1 x_3)$ whose H-basis is $(x_1{}^2, \ x_1 x_2, \ x_2{}^2, \ x_2 + x_1 x_3)$, § 38, is not perfect since $x_2 + x_1 x_3$ is of less degree in x_1, x_2 than in x_1, x_2, x_3.

A prime module is not necessarily perfect. For example, the prime module of rank 2 whose spread is given by $u = \lambda u_1 = \lambda^3 u_3 = \lambda^4 u_4$, where u, u_1, u_3, u_4 are linear, has an H-basis

$$(uu_4 - u_1 u_3, \ u_1{}^3 - u^2 u_3, \ u_1{}^2 u_4 - u u_3{}^2, \ u_1 u_4{}^2 - u_3{}^3) = (f, f_1, f_2, f_3)$$

and no other member than $uu_4 - u_1 u_3$ of degree 2.   But it has a second member $\lambda_1 f_1 + \lambda_2 f_2 + \lambda_3 f_3 + (\lambda_4 x_1 + \lambda_5 x_2) f$ which can be made of degree 2 in x_1, x_2; hence it is not perfect.

89. *An H-module M of rank r is perfect or not according as the multiplicity of the simple module $M_{x_{r+1}=\ldots=x_n=0}$ is equal to or greater than the number of modular equations of $M^{(r)}$ or of $M^{(r)}{}_{x_{r+2}=\ldots=x_n=0}$.* The difference between the two numbers when M is unmixed is the total number of *extra* rows of the dialytic array of $M^{(r)}$ when carried as far as degree δ (§ 77), and when M is mixed is still greater. The property affords the simplest test for deciding whether a given module is perfect or not; for the two numbers can generally be found. For example, the prime module M in § 88 is of rank 2 and order 4, while the multiplicity of $M_{x_3=\ldots=x_n=0}$ is 5, so that M is not perfect. The property may also be stated in the form that *an H-module M of rank r is perfect or not according as* $M^{(r)}{}_{x_{r+2}=\ldots=x_n=0}$ *is perfect (i.e. unmixed) or not.*

90. *A perfect module is unmixed.* If M is perfect the module $M^{(r)}$ has an H-basis of which each member has its highest terms independent of the parameters $x_{r+1}, \ldots, x_n$. Hence the dialytic array of $M^{(r)}$ constructed from an H-basis has pure constants for the elements in all its compartments; and a non-vanishing determinant D can be selected from the array for any degree t which is a pure constant. Let ϕF be a member of M, where ϕ is a whole function of the parameters only. Then F is a member of $M^{(r)}$ and if we insert a row in the array representing F it will be dependent on the rest, i.e.

$$F = \lambda_1 F_1 + \lambda_2 F_2 + \ldots + \lambda_\rho F_\rho,$$

where $F_1, F_2, \ldots, F_\rho$ are the members of $M^{(r)}$ represented by the rows of the array, and $\lambda_1, \lambda_2, \ldots, \lambda_\rho$ are rational functions of $x_{r+1}, \ldots, x_n$. Equating coefficients on the two sides of power products of $x_1, x_2, \ldots, x_r$ corresponding to the columns of the determinant D mentioned above, and solving for $\lambda_1, \lambda_2, \ldots, \lambda_\rho$, we see that $\lambda_i D$ and consequently λ_i is a whole function of $x_{r+1}, \ldots, x_n$. Hence F is a member of M, since $F_1, F_2, \ldots, F_\rho$ are all members of M; and $\phi F = 0 \bmod M$ requires $F = 0 \bmod M$. Hence M is unmixed.

If M is a perfect module of rank r and M' a module in $x_{r+1}, \ldots, x_n$ (independent of $x_1, x_2, \ldots, x_r$) the L.C.M. *of M, M' is the same as their product MM'.* For if the F above is a member of the L.C.M. of M, M' the elements in the row representing F are all members of M', and the λ_i are linear functions of them and therefore also members of M'. Hence

$$F = \Sigma \lambda_i F_i = 0 \bmod MM', \quad \text{i.e.} \quad [M, M'] = MM',$$

since $\lambda_i = 0 \bmod M'$ and $F_i = 0 \bmod M$.

91. *The number H_l of modular equations of degree l of a perfect H-module M of rank r is the coefficient of x^l in*

$$(1 + \mu_1 x + \mu_2 x^2 + \ldots + \mu_{\gamma-1} x^{\gamma-1}) (1 - x)^{r-n},$$

where γ is the characteristic number, and μ_m the number of modular equations of degree m, of the simple module $M_{x_{r+1}=\ldots=x_n=0}$.

For the general member of M of degree l is (§ 90)

$$\lambda_1 F_1 + \lambda_2 F_2 + \ldots + \lambda_\rho F_\rho,$$

where $\lambda_1, \lambda_2, \ldots, \lambda_\rho$ are whole functions of $x_{r+1}, \ldots, x_n$, and cannot vanish identically unless $\lambda_1, \lambda_2, \ldots, \lambda_\rho$ all vanish identically. Hence the number of linearly independent members of M of degree l is the total number of terms in λ_1, λ_2, ..., λ_ρ. Now the number of the polynomials F_1, F_2, ..., F_ρ which are of degree m is μ_m less than the number of power products of x_1, x_2, ..., x_r of degree m, and the number of terms in each corresponding λ (of degree $l-m$) is the coefficient of x^l in $x^m (1-x)^{r-n}$. Hence the number of linearly independent members of M of degree l is less than the number of power products of x_1, x_2, ..., x_n of degree l by the coefficient of x^l in

$$(1 + \mu_1 x + \mu_2 x^2 + \ldots + \mu_l x^l) (1 - x)^{r-n} ;$$

and this coefficient is the value of H_l.   § 75 is a particular case.

92.   *If M is a perfect H-module of rank r such that the simple module $M_{x_{r+1}=\ldots=x_n=0}$ is a principal system, and M' a perfect H-module of rank r contained in M, the module M/M' is perfect.*

The μ and μ' r-dimensional modular equations of M and M' begin with the μ and μ' modular equations of $M_{x_{r+1}=\ldots=x_n=0}$ and $M'_{x_{r+1}=\ldots=x_n=0}$. Also the $\mu - \mu'$ r-dimensional modular equations of M/M' are the F'-derivates of the modular equations of M, where F' is any member of M', and begin with the $F'_{x_{r+1}=\ldots=x_n=0}$-derivates of the modular equations of $M_{x_{r+1}=\ldots=x_n=0}$, that is, with the modular equations of $M_{x_{r+1}=\ldots=x_n=0}/M'_{x_{r+1}=\ldots=x_n=0}$. These are $\mu - \mu'$ in number, since $M_{x_{r+1}=\ldots=x_n=0}$ is a principal system containing $M'_{x_{r+1}=\ldots=x_n=0}$. Hence M/M' is perfect (§ 81).

93.   We may sum up some of the relations between different kinds of modules.

A module of the principal class is unmixed and a principal system, and in the case of an H-module is perfect.

Any power of a module of the principal class is unmixed, and in the case of an H-module is perfect (§ 89, end), but is not a principal system ; e.g. $(x_1, x_2)^2$ is not a principal system.

A module of rank $k - r + 1$ whose basis is a matrix with r rows and k columns is unmixed, and in the case of an H-module is perfect (§ 89, end), but is not a principal system ; e.g. the module $\begin{pmatrix} 0 & x_1 & x_2 \\ x_1 & x_2 & 0 \end{pmatrix}$ is not a principal system.

A primary module of the principal Noetherian class is a principal system, but not perfect.

NOTE ON THE THEORY OF IDEALS

The following is a brief explanation of the theory of ideals of algebraic numbers* and functions and the relation in which the theory given in the preceding pages stands with respect to it.

Gauss (*Disquisitiones Arithmeticae* (1801)) was the first to consider the laws of factorisation in a domain of whole numbers other than that of rational whole numbers $0, \pm 1, \pm 2, \ldots$. He proved that two given complex whole numbers $a + b\sqrt{-1}$, $c + d\sqrt{-1}$ (a, b, c, d rational integers) have always an H.C.F. and that any such number is a unique product of prime factors. Kummer (*J. reine angew. Math.* 35 (1847), 40 (1850), 53 (1857)) in extending the research to a larger class of whole numbers found that these properties were no longer absolutely true. Nevertheless he succeeded in making such numbers amenable to all the simpler laws of rational integers by introducing certain *ideal numbers* not existing in the domain considered ; and thus laid the foundation of the theory of factorisation of whole algebraic numbers. Finally Dedekind (D), by using *ideals* instead of ideal numbers, extended the theory to the whole numbers of any algebraic corpus and to whole algebraic functions of one variable (DW); while Kronecker (Kr) extended the same theory of factorisation to algebraic functions in general. Kronecker went still further ; he gave the first steps of a *general* theory of ideals of algebraic functions (Kr, p. 77) under the name of *modular systems*. In this general theory factorisation plays only a subsidiary part, since an ideal which is not prime is not in general a product of prime ideals.

Modules of whole rational functions (as defined pp. 1, 2 above) are ideals and modules in the sense of Dedekind ; and the theory of such modules is the necessary starting point of the general theory of ideals.

An *algebraic number* is any root a of an algebraic equation

$$a_0 x^m + a_1 x^{m-1} + \ldots + a_m = 0$$

---

* The following are notable general accounts of the theory of algebraic numbers :

D. Hilbert. "Bericht über die Theorie der algebraischen Zahlkörper" (*Jahresb. d. deutschen Math.-Verein.*, Berlin (1897), Bd. IV).

H. Weber. *Lehrbuch der Algebra* (Brunswick, 2nd ed. (1899), Bd. II, p. 553).

G. B. Mathews. "Number" (*Ency. Brit.*, Cambridge, 11th ed. (1911), Vol. 19, p. 847).

For other references to the arithmetic theory of algebraic numbers and functions see (D), (DW), (K), and (Kr), p. xiii.

in which the coefficients $a_0, a_1, \ldots, a_m$ are rational integers. We may suppose that a_0 is positive, and that $a_0, a_1, \ldots, a_m$ have no common factor other than 1, and that the equation is irreducible in the rational domain. There is only one set of values of $a_0, a_1, \ldots, a_m$ satisfying these conditions for an assigned a.

a is called a *whole* (algebraic) number if $a_0 = 1$, and is called a *fractional* number if $a_0 \neq 1$. Thus an algebraic (as well as a rational) number is integral or fractional, but cannot be both. In any case $a_0 a$ is a whole number β, and $a = \beta/a_0$, i.e. the denominator of any fractional algebraic number a can be rationalized, while the numerator remains a whole algebraic number β.

All roots of any equation $x^n + c_1 x^{n-1} + \ldots + c_n = 0$ (whether reducible or not) in which $c_1, c_2, \ldots, c_n$ are rational integers are whole algebraic numbers. For all irreducible factors of the left-hand side are of the type

$$x^m + a_1 x^{m-1} + \ldots + a_m.$$

We omit the proof of this as of most other properties to be stated. Hence any number is whole if it satisfies any equation of this type.

If $a, \beta, \gamma, \ldots$ are whole numbers $a \pm \beta$ and $a\beta$ are also whole numbers (D, p. 145); and so also is any whole rational function of $a, \beta, \gamma, \ldots$ with rational integral coefficients.

A whole number a is said to have another β as a factor, or to be divisible by β, if $a = \beta\gamma$, where γ is a whole number.

A whole number ϵ is called a *unit* if it is a factor of 1; or ϵ is a unit if ϵ and $1/\epsilon$ are both whole numbers. Thus if in the above equation $a_0 = \pm a_m = 1$ all its roots are units.

Two whole numbers a, β are said to be *equivalent* (as regards divisibility) if $a = \epsilon\beta$ where ϵ is a unit; for then any whole number which divides either a or β divides the other. Such equivalence of a, β is denoted by $a \sim \beta$.

A *corpus* of algebraic numbers is the aggregate of all rational functions (with rational coefficients) of any finite set of given algebraic numbers $a_1, a_2, \ldots, a_k$. All numbers of the corpus are rational functions of a single element

$$a = c_1 a_1 + c_2 a_2 + \ldots + c_k a_k,$$

where $c_1, c_2, \ldots, c_k$ are rational integers so chosen as not to be connected by special relations.

The corpus generated by a is denoted by $\Omega(a)$ and the aggregate of algebraic integers included in the corpus by $\omega(a)$. The *order* of the corpus and of a is the degree of the irreducible equation of which a is a root.

Thus $\Omega(1)$ is the corpus of rational numbers and $\omega(1)$ the aggregate of rational integers.

Any rational function of any finite number of elements of $\Omega(a)$ is an element of $\Omega(a)$, and any whole rational function with rational integral coefficients of any finite number of elements of $\omega(a)$ is an element of $\omega(a)$.

Any corpus $\Omega(a)$ includes $\Omega(1)$, for $a/a = 1$.

If $a_0 x^m + a_1 x^{m-1} + \ldots + a_m = 0$ is the irreducible equation of which the element a of the corpus $\Omega(a)$ is a root, the other roots $a', a'', \ldots, a^{(m-1)}$ are called the *conjugates* of a, and $\Omega\,(a'), \ldots, \Omega\,(a^{(m-1)})$ the conjugates of $\Omega\,(a)$. If a' is an element of $\Omega\,(a)$ then $\Omega\,(a')$ is the same as $\Omega\,(a)$, and if not, not. The corpus generated by $a, a', \ldots, a^{(m-1)}$ is called the Galoisian domain corresponding to $\Omega\,(a)$. The conjugates of any number $\beta = f(a)$ of $\Omega\,(a)$ are

$$\beta' = f(a'), \ldots, \beta^{(m-1)} = f(a^{(m-1)}).$$

The product $\beta\,\beta' \ldots \beta^{(m-1)}$ is a rational number (being a symmetric function of $a, a', \ldots, a^{(m-1)}$) and is called the *norm* of β and written norm β.

Since β and norm β are both numbers in $\Omega\,(a)$, norm β/β is a number in $\Omega\,(a)$. Moreover if β is a number in $\omega\,(a)$, then $\beta', \ldots, \beta^{(m-1)}$ are whole algebraic numbers, and norm β/β is a number in $\omega\,(a)$. If β is a unit, $\beta', \beta'', \ldots, \beta^{(m-1)}$ are all algebraic units, and norm $\beta = \pm 1$. Conversely, if β is a number in $\omega\,(a)$ such that norm $\beta = \pm 1$, β is a unit in $\omega\,(a)$. Norm $(au + \beta v + \ldots)$ is defined as $\prod\limits_{i=0}^{m-1} (a^{(i)}u + \beta^{(i)}v + \ldots)$, $u, v, \ldots$ being indeterminates.

$\Omega\,(a)$ is a domain of rationality. $\omega\,(a)$ is called a *proper holoid* domain (König), that is, a domain in which every sum, difference and product, but not every quotient, of two elements is an element of the domain. A proper holoid domain in which every pair of elements a, β have an H.C.F. in the domain (defined as a factor δ of a and of β such that every common factor of a, β is a factor of δ) is called a *complete* holoid domain. $\omega\,(a)$ is not necessarily *complete*.

The simplest example of this last statement is the domain $\omega\,(\sqrt{-5})$ which is fully discussed by Dedekind (D, p. 73). If $x = a + b\,\sqrt{-5}$ $(a, b$ rational) then $(x - a)^2 + 5b^2 = 0$, and in order that x may be whole $2a$ and $a^2 + 5b^2$ must be rational integers, i.e. a and b must be integers. Consider the two whole numbers $9, 3\,(1 + \sqrt{-5})$. If these have an H.C.F. in $\omega\,(\sqrt{-5})$ it must be 3δ, where δ is a whole number in $\omega\,(\sqrt{-5})$ which divides 3 and $1 + \sqrt{-5}$. But 3 and $1 + \sqrt{-5}$ are non-factorisable in $\omega\,(\sqrt{-5})$; hence $\delta = 1$. Hence the H.C.F. (if any) of $9, 3\,(1 + \sqrt{-5})$ is 3; but $2 - \sqrt{-5}$ is a factor of 9 and $3\,(1 + \sqrt{-5})$ and is not a factor of 3. Hence there is no H.C.F., and $\omega\,(\sqrt{-5})$ is not *complete*. That 3 is not factorisable in $\omega\,(\sqrt{-5})$ is shown by putting $3 = (a + b\,\sqrt{-5})\,(c + d\,\sqrt{-5})$ from which it follows that

$$9 = (a^2 + 5b^2)\,(c^2 + 5d^2)$$

and that one of $a^2 + 5b^2$, $c^2 + 5d^2$ is 9 and the other 1, since neither can be 3. Also if $a^2 + 5b^2 = 9$ the only solutions are $a = \pm 3$, $b = 0$ and $a = \pm 2$, $b = \pm 1$ of which the latter must be rejected since $\pm 2 \pm \sqrt{-5}$ does not divide 3. Similarly for $1 + \sqrt{-5}$. The numbers $3, 1 + \sqrt{-5}$ have however a common factor $(1 + \sqrt{-5})/\sqrt{2}$ or $\sqrt{-2 + \sqrt{-5}}$ not in $\omega\,(\sqrt{-5})$.

Another point requiring notice is the distinction between a non-factorisable number and a prime number. A non-factorisable number in $\omega\,(a)$ is one which has no other factors in $\omega\,(a)$ than such as are equivalent to itself or 1.   A prime number is one which cannot be a factor of a product $\beta\gamma$ without being a factor of β or of γ.   Thus 3 and $1+\sqrt{-5}$ are both non-factorisable in $\omega(\sqrt{-5})$, but neither of them is prime ; 3 is a factor of $(1+\sqrt{-5})(1-\sqrt{-5})$ but not a factor of $1+\sqrt{-5}$ or $1-\sqrt{-5}$; and $1+\sqrt{-5}$ is a factor of 6 but not a factor of 2 or 3.

In a complete holoid domain every non-factorisable element is prime and every prime element is non-factorisable (K, p. 15).

Let π be any element of the domain which is non-factorisable, and let $\alpha\beta$ be divisible by π and β not divisible by π.   Then the H.C.F. of β, $\pi \sim 1$; H.C.F. of $\alpha\beta$, $\alpha\pi \sim \alpha$; H.C.F. of $\alpha\beta$, $\pi \sim$ H.C.F. of $\alpha\beta$, $\alpha\pi$, $\pi \sim$ H.C.F. of α, π ; i.e. H.C.F. of α, $\pi \sim \pi$, or α is divisible by π ; hence π is prime.   Again if π is prime and equal to $\pi_1\pi_2$, one of π_1, π_2 is divisible by π and the other is a unit ; hence π is non-factorisable.

It is to be noticed that the proof depends only on the notions of product, quotient, and H.C.F., and is therefore applicable to any domain in which each pair of elements α, β has a product $\alpha\beta$, and an H.C.F. δ (defined as above), and may or may not have a quotient γ, defined by $\alpha=\beta\gamma$.

In a complete holoid domain any element which is not an infinite product of factors (not counting unit factors) is a unique product of prime factors if equivalent factors are regarded as the same factor.

For any element which is not prime is a product of two factors neither of which is a unit ; each of these again if not prime is a product of two factors, and so on.   Hence any element which is not an infinite product is a product of prime factors $p_1^{l_1}p_2^{l_2}\dots p_r^{l_r}$.   This resolution into factors is unique in the sense of equivalence; for if $p_1^{l_1}\dots p_r^{l_r} \sim q_1^{m_1}\dots q_s^{m_s}$, where $q_1, q_2, \dots, q_s$ are primes and none of them units, p_1 must be a factor of q_1 or $q_2 \dots$ or q_s, and if a factor of q_1, then $p_1 \sim q_1$; from which the rest follows.

The domain of all algebraic integers is a complete holoid domain (D, p. 247) but contains no prime numbers, since any number a has an infinite number of factors, e.g. $\sqrt[n]{a}$.   This property of completeness is peculiar to numbers ; it does not hold for functions, not even for relatively whole algebraic functions of a single variable.

No number in $\omega(a)$ can be an infinite product, for otherwise its norm, which is a rational integer, would be an infinite product of rational integers.   Hence if $\omega(a)$ is complete each number in it is a unique product of prime factors.

All the above remarks concerning algebraic numbers (with the exception noted) apply *mutatis mutandis* to algebraic functions.   The only difference is that there are two kinds of whole algebraic functions, relative and absolute.

An *algebraic function* is any quantity a which satisfies an algebraic equation

$$A_0 z^m + A_1 z^{m-1} + \dots + A_m = 0$$

in which the coefficients $A_0, A_1, \dots, A_m$ are whole rational functions of n variables $x_1, x_2, \dots, x_n$.

a is called a *relatively whole* (algebraic) function if A_0 does not involve the variables. In this case the numerical coefficients of $A_1, A_2, \ldots, A_m$ may be any real or complex numbers, whether algebraic or not. Moreover z is whole relatively to $x_1, x_2, \ldots, x_r$ if A_0 involves $x_{r+1}, \ldots, x_n$ only.

a is called an *absolutely whole* (algebraic) function if $A_0 = 1$ and the numerical coefficients of $A_1, A_2, \ldots, A_m$ are rational integers.

In the case of functions $\Omega(1)$ is the corpus of rational functions, and $\omega(1)$ the aggregate of whole rational functions.

In still continuing to speak of algebraic numbers it will be understood that what is said applies equally to algebraic functions. In considering the properties of algebraic numbers we naturally regard the numbers of a corpus $\Omega(a)$ and the domain $\omega(a)$ included in it as the principal subject of investigation, since these answer the most nearly to the numbers of $\Omega(1)$ and $\omega(1)$.

$\Omega(a)$ and more especially $\omega(a)$ are further subdivided. Dedekind defines a *module* in $\Omega(a)$ to be the aggregate of all numbers (or functions)

$$a_1 a_1 + a_2 a_2 + a_3 a_3 + \ldots,$$

where $a_1, a_2, \ldots$ are fixed elements of $\Omega(a)$ and $a_1, a_2, \ldots$ any elements of $\omega(1)$, that is, rational integers in the case of number modules and whole rational functions (relative or absolute) in the case of function modules. If $a_1, a_2, \ldots$ are whole numbers, that is, elements of $\omega(a)$ instead of $\Omega(a)$, the module is a module of whole numbers. Any module of whole numbers (or functions) has a finite basis $(\mu_1, \mu_2, \ldots, \mu_k)$; and any module of fractions with a finite basis $(a_1, a_2, \ldots, a_k)$ is practically the same thing as a module of whole numbers, since $a_1, a_2, \ldots, a_k$ can be multiplied by a rational integer a so as to become whole numbers $\mu_1, \mu_2, \ldots, \mu_k$, and then any element of the module $(a_1, a_2, \ldots, a_k)$ is equal to the corresponding element of the module $(\mu_1, \mu_2, \ldots, \mu_k)$ divided by a. There are modules of fractions with infinite bases; but they seem to be unimportant, and it would be simpler to restrict the meaning of the term module to a module of whole numbers or functions. A *module* would then be defined as any aggregate of elements of $\omega(a)$ such that if a_1, a_2 are any two elements of the module, $a_1 + a_2$ and $a a_1$ are also elements of the module, where a is any element of $\omega(1)$.

An *involution* of whole functions is any aggregate of elements of $\omega(a)$ such that if a_1, a_2 are any two elements of the involution, $a_1 + a_2$ and $c a_1$ are also elements of the involution, where c is any constant. In the absolute theory the elements of $\omega(a)$ are absolutely whole functions and c a rational integer.

Dedekind's definition of an *ideal* is similar but still more fundamental. An ideal is any aggregate of elements of $\omega(a)$ such that if a_1, a_2 are any two elements of the ideal, $a_1 + a_2$ and μa_1 are also elements of the ideal, where μ is any element of $\omega(a)$. Every ideal has a finite basis $(a_1, a_2, \ldots, a_k)$ and is a finite module $(a_1, a_2, \ldots, a_l)$; but not every module of whole numbers or functions is an ideal. In the domain of whole rational functions an ideal and a module are identical.

Kummer had found that the integers of a corpus did not necessarily satisfy all the simple laws of rational integers, or in other words they need not form a complete holoid domain. It occurred to Dedekind (and apparently independently to Kronecker) to consider in this case not the individual integers of a corpus only but sets of integers. For this purpose Dedekind made use of the ideals already defined. We shall in the first place consider ideals from a rather abstract point of view. The remarks apply also to some extent to modules and involutions.

The aggregate of elements of an ideal $(a_1, a_2, ..., a_k)$ constitutes an image of the properties possessed in common by all the elements of the aggregate, and especially of properties of divisibility (if any) common to $a_1, a_2, ..., a_k$. The term *ideal* should strictly be applied to these properties common to all the elements, whatever they may be ; but it is more convenient and concise to define the ideal as the aggregate of elements itself. This point of view, viz. that the ideal is a set of properties rather than a set of numbers or functions, is the justification for saying that each element of the ideal contains or is divisible by the ideal, since it possesses all the properties in question. Kronecker makes use of another image, in some respects simpler, viz., $a_1u_1 + a_2u_2 + ... + a_ku_k$ or $a_1 + a_2u + ... + a_ku^{k-1}$, where $u, u_1, u_2, ..., u_k$ are indeterminates. This is not called an *ideal* because the term had already been appropriated by Dedekind with a different meaning, but it takes the place of Dedekind's ideal.

Thus at the outset we can form a natural conception of what should be meant by saying that an ideal $(a_1, a_2, ..., a_k)$ contains or is divisible by another $(\beta_1, \beta_2, ..., \beta_l)$. The conditions should be that each of $a_1, a_2, ..., a_k$ is an element of $(\beta_1, \beta_2, ..., \beta_l)$; for all elements of $(a_1, a_2, ..., a_k)$ will then possess all the properties possessed in common by all the elements of $(\beta_1, \beta_2, ..., \beta_l)$, and this apart from the fact that we may be unable to state explicitly what these properties are.

Again we can give a natural meaning to the G.C.M. and the L.C.M. of two ideals. The G.C.M. or H.C.F. of $(a_1, a_2, ..., a_k)$ and $(\beta_1, \beta_2, ..., \beta_l)$ should be an ideal $(\gamma_1, \gamma_2, ...)$ contained in both such that every ideal contained in both is contained in $(\gamma_1, \gamma_2, ...)$. There is one and only one such ideal, viz. the ideal $(a_1, a_2, ..., a_k, \beta_1, \beta_2, ..., \beta_l)$, cf. § 23. The L.C.M. should be an ideal $(\gamma_1, \gamma_2, ...)$ which contains both and such that every ideal which contains both contains $(\gamma_1, \gamma_2, ...)$. Again there is one and only one such ideal, viz. the ideal whose elements consist of all elements of $\omega(a)$ containing both $(a_1, a_2, ..., a_k)$ and $(\beta_1, \beta_2, ..., \beta_l)$. These elements constitute an ideal by definition.

But the crux lies in the difficulty of attaching a natural meaning to the term *product*. The product of two ideals should be an ideal whose properties consist of the product of the properties of the two ideals, and to this *product of properties* we cannot attach a meaning a priori from the definition of an ideal. Moreover the aggregate of the products of any element of $(a_1, a_2, ..., a_k)$ and any element of $(\beta_1, \beta_2, ..., \beta_l)$ does not constitute an ideal. The best that can be done is therefore to define the product of these two ideals to be the ideal $(..., a_i\beta_j, ...)$, $i=1, 2, ..., k$, $j=1, 2, ..., l$. This ideal includes all products $a\beta$ of elements of the two ideals, and in addition all sums of such products. It could not be told beforehand to what a theory based on so tentative a definition might lead.

We may say that the fact of an ideal containing another is a case of true divisibility if it always follows as a necessary consequence that the first is the product of the second and a third ideal (the converse being true by definition).   This is exactly what Dedekind proved to be the case for all ideals of algebraic numbers and relatively whole algebraic functions of one variable, but only by means of a long series of subsidiary theorems.   It followed that any such ideal could be uniquely expressed as a product of prime ideals.   We know however that this is not true for ideals of functions of more than one variable, since it is not true for modules of rational functions.   Also it is not true for ideals of absolutely whole algebraic functions of one variable ; e.g. (x) contains $(x, 2)^*$ but is not the product of $(x, 2)$ and a third ideal ; for the residual $(x)/(x, 2)$ is (x), and (x) is not the product of $(x, 2)$ and (x).

Kronecker's theory (Kr) concerns whole algebraic functions in general, and one of its remarkable features is that it applies to absolutely whole as well as to relatively whole functions.   The absolute theory is based on the following fundamental theorem, which is proved by König (K, p. 78) :

If $f_1, f_2, ..., f_k$ are any k polynomials in $u_1, u_2, ...$, Π any product of coefficients of $f_1, f_2, ..., f_k$ taken one from each, and $\Pi_1, \Pi_2, ...$ the coefficients of the polynomial $f_1 f_2 ... f_k$; then Π satisfies identically an equation of the type

$$\Pi^\rho + \Pi^{(1)} \Pi^{\rho-1} + \Pi^{(2)} \Pi^{\rho-2} + ... + \Pi^{(\rho)} = 0,$$

where $\Pi^{(i)}$ is a homogeneous polynomial of degree i $(i=1, 2, ..., \rho)$ in $\Pi_1, \Pi_2, ...$ with rational integral coefficients.

Kronecker gives the theorem in the second of the two memoirs referred to in (Kr), having discovered it after the first memoir was written.   He states it for two polynomials f_1, f_2 in a single letter u or x.   König gives the theorem in the more general form above.   It is not generally necessary to introduce more than one letter or indeterminate u.   If we suppose $f_1, f_2, ..., f_k$ to be polynomials of degrees $l_1, l_2, ..., l_k$ in a single letter u the number of the quantities Π is $(l_1+1)(l_2+1) ... (l_k+1)$, while the number of the quantities $\Pi_1, \Pi_2, ...$ (which are sums of the quantities Π) is only $l_1+l_2+...+l_k+1$; and†

$$\rho = \frac{(l_1+l_2+...+l_k)!}{l_1! \, l_2! \, ... \, l_k!}.$$

---

* In the relative theory $(x, 2)=(1)$, but not in the absolute theory.   In the absolute theory a module in n variables can be of rank $n+1$ (cf. § 47); such in fact is any module which has some rational integer (but not unity) as a member, or any module which has no spread and is not (1).   In both the absolute and relative theories the non-proper module (1) is without rank.

† The value found for ρ by König for the case $k=2$ is $(l_1+l_2+1)!/l_1!(l_2+1)!$, which is not symmetrical in l_1, l_2.   It can be proved that ρ need not be greater

Let the coefficients of $f_1, f_2, ..., f_k$ be absolutely or relatively whole algebraic functions of n variables $x_1, x_2, ..., x_n$. These all belong to and determine a corpus of functions. Let $M_1, M_2, ..., M_k$ be the ideals determined by the coefficients of $f_1, f_2, ..., f_k$ respectively, and M the ideal $(\Pi_1, \Pi_2, ...)$ determined by the coefficients of $f_1 f_2 ... f_k$. Then Π is any element of the basis of the ideal $M_1 M_2 ... M_k$, and $\Pi^{(i)}$ is an element of the ideal M^i (and of the involution M^i).

Kronecker says that a quantity Π which identically satisfies an equation of the above type (where $\Pi^{(i)}$ is any element of the ith power of a given ideal M) *contains M in the wider sense* of the word. Π contains M *in the strict sense* if it is an element of M, i.e. if it satisfies a *linear* identity of the above type. One ideal contains another (in the wider sense) if each element of (the basis of) the first contains the second (in the wider sense) ; and if each of two ideals M, M' contains the other (in the wider sense) M, M' are said to be equivalent in the wider sense. We denote such equivalence by $M \sim M'$, having already denoted strict equivalence by $M = M'$. Kronecker also remarks that (in the wider sense) if M contains M' and M' contains M'' then M contains M''. Consequently if $M \sim M'$ and $M \sim M''$ then $M' \sim M''$. *If $M, M_1, M_2, ..., M_k$ have the meanings given to them above we have* $M \sim M_1 M_2 ... M_k$.

This conception of wider equivalence is of considerable importance, and is specially applicable to Kronecker's theory. To any ideal M of a given corpus of functions there corresponds a unique *closed* equivalent ideal M_0 within the corpus. The elements of M_0 consist of all whole functions Π of the corpus which satisfy identically an equation of the type

$$\Pi^\rho + \Pi^{(1)} \Pi^{\rho-1} + \Pi^{(2)} \Pi^{\rho-2} + ... + \Pi^{(\rho)} = 0,$$

where $\Pi^{(i)}$ is an element of M^i. Any Π which satisfies identically an equation

$$\Pi^\sigma + \Pi_0^{(1)} \Pi^{\sigma-1} + \Pi_0^{(2)} \Pi^{\sigma-2} + ... + \Pi_0^{(\sigma)} = 0,$$

where $\Pi_0^{(i)}$ is an element of M_0^i, satisfies a linear identity of the same type and is an element of M_0. All ideals in the corpus equivalent to M are equivalent to M_0. A closed ideal may have relevant imbedded spreads; the closed module $(x_1^2, x_1 x_2)$ is an example.

If (speaking in the wider sense) M' contains M'' then MM' contains MM'', and conversely if MM' contains MM'' then M' contains M''; consequently if $MM' \sim MM''$ then $M' \sim M''$.

This theorem is not true for strict (or linear) equivalence, i.e. if $MM' = MM''$ it does not follow that $M' = M''$ (see § 24, Ex. i) unless M is an unmixed ideal of rank 1 (defined below).

than the smaller value given above, while for some of the products Π the value of ρ is less. In the cases of the first and last product Π it is evident that $\rho = 1$. If $l_1 = l_2 = 2$, ρ is 3 for the middle product Π, and 6 for the others, except the first and last.

Let $M=(a_1, a_2, ..., a_k)$, $M'=(a_1', a_2', ..., a'_{k'})$, $M''=(a_1'', a_2'', ..., a''_{k''})$.

Then if M' contains M'' each element a' of the basis of M' satisfies an identity

$$a'^\rho + a^{(1)} a'^{\rho-1} + a^{(2)} a'^{\rho-2} + ... + a^{(\rho)} = 0,$$

where $a^{(i)}$ is an element of M''^i, i.e. a homogeneous polynomial in $a_1'', a_2'', ..., a''_{k''}$ of degree i with whole functions of the corpus for coefficients. Putting $a'a_j = a$ we have

$$a^\rho + a^{(1)} a_j{}^{\rho-1} + a^{(2)} a_j{}^2 a^{\rho-2} + ... + a^{(\rho)} a_j{}^\rho = 0,$$

where $a^{(i)} a_j{}^i$ is an element of $(MM'')^i$; hence a contains MM'', i.e. MM' contains MM''. Conversely, given that MM' contains MM'', $a'a_j$ contains MM'' where a' is any element of M', i.e. we have an identity

$$(a'a_j)^{\rho_j} + \beta_j{}^{(1)} (a'a_j)^{\rho_j-1} + \beta_j{}^{(2)} (a'a_j)^{\rho_j-2} + ... + \beta_j{}^{(\rho_j)} = 0,$$

where $\beta_j{}^{(i)}$ is an element of $(MM'')^i = (a_1, a_2, ..., a_k)^i (a_1'', a_2'', ..., a''_{k''})^i$. Hence this identity is homogeneous and of degree ρ_j in $a_1, a_2, ..., a_k$, and arranging it in power products of these, each coefficient is homogeneous and of degree ρ_j in $a', a_1'', a_2'', ..., a''_{k''}$. There are k such equations for the same a', viz. when $j = 1, 2, ..., k$. The resultant of the k equations with respect to $a_1, a_2, ..., a_k$ is a homogeneous equation in $a', a_1'', a_2'', ..., a''_{k''}$ of degree $k\rho_1\rho_2...\rho_k$, since it is homogeneous and of degree $\rho_1\rho_2...\rho_k/\rho_j$ in the coefficients of the jth equation. Also since the resultant is homogeneous in $a', a_1'', a_2'', ..., a''_{k''}$, and is found by a purely algebraical process, we can find the coefficient of $a'^{k\rho_1\rho_2...\rho_k}$ in it by supposing all of $a_1'', a_2'', ..., a''_{k''}$ to be zeros. The resultant then becomes the resultant of $(a'a_1)^{\rho_1}, (a'a_2)^{\rho_2}, ..., (a'a_k)^{\rho_k}$, viz. $a'^{k\rho_1\rho_2...\rho_k}$. The coefficient of this term is therefore 1. Hence a' contains M'', i.e. M' contains M''.

The above properties are true not only for ideals but also for modules and for involutions whether of absolutely whole or relatively whole algebraic functions.

Kronecker's way of considering a set of whole algebraic quantities $a_0, a_1, ..., a_l$ (numbers or functions) is more direct than Dedekind's. He sets them in a frame or form*

$$a_u = a_0 + a_1 u + a_2 u^2 + ... + a_l u^l,$$

where u is an indeterminate. Instead of power products of one indeterminate u we could use l indeterminates $u_1, u_2, ..., u_l$ or power products of any less

---

* We use the term *form* here and later as meaning a *representation* which is not a function but is subject to algebraic laws and operations. The form becomes a function of u if u is regarded as a variable or parameter.

The notation a_u for a form is copied from König; and the notation for an ideal $M = (a_0, a_1, ..., a_l)$ is the same as that used in the text for a module. Kronecker's notation is quite different; e.g. he uses M for an element which is denoted above by a, and the term modular system as equivalent to divisor system or basis.

number.   The indeterminates serve merely to separate the quantities $a_0, a_1, ..., a_l$.   Kronecker then expands norm a_u in powers of u, viz.

$$\text{norm } a_u = (a_0 + a_1 u + ... + a_l u^l)(a_0' + a_1' u + ... + a_l' u^l)...$$
$$...(a_0{}^{(m-1)} + a_1{}^{(m-1)} u + ... + a_l{}^{(m-1)} u^l)$$
$$= F_0 + F_1 u + F_2 u^2 + ... + F_k u^k   \qquad (k = lm),$$

where $F_0, F_1, ..., F_k$ are whole rational functions of $x_1, x_2, ..., x_n$.

If $F_0, F_1, ..., F_k$ have an H.C.F. D, which may be a rational integer only, or a whole rational function of $x_1, x_2, ..., x_n$, then, having regard to the fact that norm a_u is the product of the above factors, we may say that $a_0, a_1, ..., a_l$ have something in common of the nature of a factor, which may be called their ideal common factor, and may be represented by the form a_u.   So long as this factor D, which is the complete partial resolvent of rank 1 of the module $(F_0, F_1, ..., F_k)$, is only taken into account, while the partial resolvents of higher rank are neglected, Kronecker's theory is a theory of factorisation only.

Dedekind had established a theory of factorisation of whole algebraic numbers, which he subsequently extended to relatively whole algebraic functions of one variable.   Considering that the factorisation of whole rational functions is exactly parallel to that of whole rational numbers the question naturally arises whether the factorisation of whole algebraic functions is parallel to that of whole algebraic numbers.   Kronecker proved that it was absolutely parallel.

Kronecker says that a_u and norm a_u are *primitive* or *unit* forms if $D = 1$. This is legitimate in a theory of factorisation.   Later he says that they are properly primitive only if the module* $(F_0, F_1, ..., F_k) = (1)$.   If $D \neq 1$ then norm a_u/D is a unit form.   Kronecker names $a_u/(\text{norm } a_u/D)$ an "algebraic modulus or divisor," which may be interpreted, an "equivalent of a_u" in respect to divisibility and factorisation.   König names a_u/ϵ_u, where ϵ_u is any unit form in $\omega(a)$, an *ideal whole quantity* of $\omega(a)$; and accepts the rather absurd paradox that the sum of two such quantities is their H.C.F.   It would be preferable to name a_u/ϵ_u an *ideal whole form*.   He proves that such ideal forms can be uniquely resolved (in the sense of equivalence) into products of prime ideal forms, and shows how for a given form the prime factors can be actually found.

To compare two forms a_u and a_u' Kronecker considers the fraction a_u'/a_u and rationalizes the denominator by multiplying numerator and denominator by norm a_u/a_u, which is a (strictly) whole form in $\omega(a)$.   If the new numerator a_u' norm a_u/a_u is divisible by the D of the new denominator norm a_u then the form a_u' is said to be divisible by the form a_u.   If further the quotient of

---

* The module $(F_0, F_1, ..., F_k)$ is the aggregate of all whole rational functions $A_0 F_0 + A_1 F_1 + ... + A_k F_k$, and the ideal $(F_0, F_1, ..., F_k)$ in the domain $\omega(a)$ is the aggregate of all functions $\beta_0 F_0 + \beta_1 F_1 + ... + \beta_k F_k$, where $\beta_0, \beta_1, ..., \beta_k$ are elements of $\omega(a)$.

a_u' norm a_u/a_u by D is a unit form, then $a_u'/a_u = \epsilon_u'/\epsilon_u$, where ϵ_u, ϵ_u' are both unit forms, and the ideal forms a_u, a_u' are equivalent as regards divisibility. The divisibility of a_u' by a_u is the same thing as the divisibility of the ideal $(a_0', a_1', ..., a_{l'}')$ by the ideal $(a_0, a_1, ..., a_l)$ in the case of algebraic numbers and relatively whole algebraic functions of one variable; but not in other cases. This, as we show below, is a consequence of the fact that in these two cases $(F_0, F_1, ..., F_k) = (D)$.

Let M be the ideal $(a_0, a_1, ..., a_l)$, and, as before, let

$$\text{norm } a_u = F_0 + F_1 u + ... + F_k u^k \qquad (k = lm).$$

Then, in the Galoisian domain $\Omega(a, a', ..., a^{(m-1)})$, the ideal $(F_0, F_1, ..., F_k)$ is equivalent to the product of M and its conjugates M', M'', ..., $M^{(m-1)}$, by the fundamental theorem; and another ideal $(F_0', F_1', ..., F''_{k'})$ obtained in a similar way from any other basis of M is equivalent to $(F_0, F_1, ..., F_k)$, i.e. a homogeneous equation of degree ρ exists between F_i', $F_0, F_1, ..., F_k$, in which the coefficient of $F_i'^\rho$ is 1, and the other coefficients are whole elements of the Galoisian domain. By rationalizing the equation it follows that the *modules* $(F_0, F_1, ..., F_k)$, $(F_0', F_1', ..., F''_{k'})$ are equivalent. Hence we may define the rank of the ideal M and of the form a_u to be the rank of the module $(F_0, F_1, ..., F_k)$. We may also say that the ideal M is unmixed in the wider sense if the closed module equivalent to $(F_0, F_1, ..., F_k)$ is unmixed.

A *principal ideal* is an ideal (β) having a basis consisting of a single element β.

It can be proved without difficulty that *the only ideal in a given corpus $\Omega(a)$ equivalent to a principal ideal (β) is the ideal (β) itself.*

The ideal M above is called an *unmixed ideal of rank* 1 if $(F_0, F_1, ..., F_k)$ is a principal ideal, i.e. if $(F_0, F_1, ..., F_k) = (D) \neq (1)$.

Suppose now that $M = (a_0, a_1, ..., a_l)$ is an unmixed ideal of rank 1, and that the form a_u' is divisible by a_u in the sense defined above. Then, putting

$$\frac{\text{norm } a_u}{a_u} = \beta_0 + \beta_1 u + ... + \beta_{k-l} u^{k-l},$$

we are given that $(a_0' + a_1' u + ... + a_{l'}' u^{l'})(\beta_0 + \beta_1 u + ... + \beta_{k-l} u^{k-l})$ is divisible by D. Hence $a_i' \beta_j$ is divisible by D, i.e. $a_i' \beta_j = D \beta_{ij}$. Hence

$$a_i'(\beta_0 + \beta_1 u + ... + \beta_{k-l} u^{k-l}) = D(\beta_{i0} + \beta_{i1} u + ... + \beta_{i, k-l} u^{k-l}).$$

Multiplying by a_u, and putting $F_i = D\phi_i$, we have

$$a_i'(\phi_0 + \phi_1 u + ... + \phi_k u^k) = (\beta_{i0} + \beta_{i1} u + ... + \beta_{i, k-l} u^{k-l})(a_0 + a_1 u + ... + a_l u^l).$$

Hence $\quad (\beta_{i0}, \beta_{i1}, ..., \beta_{i, k-l})(a_0, a_1, ..., a_l) \sim (a_i')(\phi_0, \phi_1, ..., \phi_k) = (a_i')$, since $(\phi_0, \phi_1, ..., \phi_k) = (1)$, and (a_i') is a principal ideal. Hence

$$(a_0', a_1', ..., a_{l'}') = (..., \beta_{ij}, ...)(a_0, a_1, ..., a_l) \quad (i = 0, 1, ..., l', j = 0, 1, ..., k-l).$$

Conversely, if an ideal $(a_0', a_1', ..., a_{l'}')$ contains an ideal $(a_0, a_1, ..., a_l)$ the form a_u' is divisible by the form a_u, since a_i norm a_u/a_u, and therefore also a_j' norm a_u/a_u, is divisible by D.

Hence an ideal $(a_0', a_1', ..., a'_{l'})$ *which contains an unmixed ideal* $(a_0, a_1, ..., a_l)$ *of rank* 1 *is the product of* $(a_0, a_1, ..., a_l)$ *and a third ideal* $(..., \beta_{ij}, ...)$, *i.e. it has* $(a_0, a_1, ..., a_l)$ *as a true factor.* This includes Dedekind's principal result, since all ideals considered by him are unmixed ideals of rank 1. If the ideal $(a_0', a_1', ..., a'_{l'})$ is also unmixed the quotient $(..., \beta_{ij}, ...)$ is also unmixed. Hence there exists a theory of factorisation for the whole aggregate of unmixed ideals of rank 1 in a corpus $\Omega(a)$.

It follows that an unmixed ideal $(a_0, a_1, ..., a_l)$ *of rank* 1 *can be multiplied by a second unmixed ideal of rank* 1 *so as to become the principal ideal* (β), *where* β *is any element of* $(a_0, a_1, ..., a_l)$.

If it be true that any ideal of rank 1 must contain an unmixed ideal of rank 1, which is obvious in the two cases considered by Dedekind, but has not been proved in general so far as I know, then *any unmixed ideal of rank* 1 *is a unique product of unmixed prime ideals of rank* 1. For, assuming the truth of the hypothesis, it can be shown that any two given unmixed ideals M, M' of rank 1 which have a common factor must have an H.C.F., viz. the unmixed ideal M'' of rank 1 such that $(M, M') = M''M'''$, where M''' is either (1) or of rank > 1. It can be easily proved that the ideals M'', M'''' thus defined are unique, and that any unmixed ideal of rank 1 which is a factor of M and of M' is a factor of M''; hence M'' is the H.C.F. of M and M'. In the cases considered by Dedekind (M, M') is itself an unmixed ideal of rank 1, and $M'' = (M, M')$. I cannot say whether this resolution into prime factors is exactly what is meant by Kronecker in his statement XIII, p. 89; and I cannot attach any true meaning to the parallel statement XIII°, p. 92, regarded as an extension of XIII.

Kronecker also considers another kind of divisibility of a form a_u' by a form a_u, which is more adaptable to the *general* theory of ideals. A form a_u' might be defined as divisible by a_u if the ideal $M' = (a_0', a_1', ..., a'_{l'})$ contains the ideal $M = (a_0, a_1, ..., a_l)$ in the strict sense. This definition is open to the objection that $a_u'\beta_u$ could be divisible by $a_u\beta_u$ without a_u' being divisible by a_u. The objection disappears when a wider definition is taken, viz. that a_u' is divisible by a_u if M' contains M in the wider sense.

The necessary and sufficient condition that any given ideal

$$M' = (a_0', a_1', ..., a'_{l'})$$

may contain any other given ideal $M = (a_0, a_1, ..., a_l)$ in the wider sense is that the ideal corresponding to a_u' norm a_u/a_u contains the ideal $(F_0, F_1, ..., F_k)$ corresponding to norm a_u in the wider sense, *which is the same thing* as containing the module $(F_0, F_1, ..., F_k)$ in the wider sense. In other words, it is necessary and sufficient that each of the $k - l + l' + 1$ coefficients a'' of the form a_u' norm a_u/a_u should satisfy identically an equation of some degree ρ which is homogeneous in a'', $F_0, F_1, ..., F_k$, the coefficient of a''^ρ being 1, and the other coefficients whole rational functions.

Date Due

Ag 7 '67 Je 9 69T			

Demco 293-5

SAMUEL BECKETT
A Critical Study

SAMUEL
BECKETT

A Critical Study

By Hugh Kenner

GROVE PRESS, INC.   NEW YORK

This book is for
VIVIAN MERCIER,
polymath.

1193092

Contents

Preface

> But you must know something, said Mr. Hackett.
> One does not part with five shillings to a shadow.
> Nationality, family, birthplace, confession, occupation, means of existence, distinctive signs, you cannot be in ignorance of all this.
> Utter ignorance, said Mr. Nixon.
>
> — *Watt*

This book, meant not to explain Samuel Beckett's work but to help the reader think about it, bears such evidence of Mr. Beckett's courtesy that I must caution the reader against mistaking it for an authorized exposition. That sort of misunderstanding will proliferate for decades, as anyone knows who has traced the course of the Joyce legend. Let me therefore, though the book could not have been written without its subject's assistance, put on record the exact extent of his contribution to it. He placed at my disposal three jettisoned typescripts: *Mercier et Camier, Eleutheria,* and "Premier Amour"; he answered such questions of fact and date as I thought it worth while to trouble him with; and during a conversation in the spring of 1958 he made various remarks which sometimes confirmed my hunches, sometimes corrected them, and sometimes suggested lines of thought on which I should not otherwise have stumbled.

He denied, for instance, the presence in his work of some hidden plan or key like the parallels in *Ulysses.* Joyce, he recalled, used to claim that every syllable in the Joycean canon could be justified, but while that was one way to write it was not the only way. He then suggested that overinterpretation, which appeared to trouble him more than erroneous interpretation, arose from two main assumptions: that the writer is necessarily presenting some experience which he has had, and that he necessarily writes in order to affirm some general truth (this knocks out most of the theories about *Godot*). He stated that he knew very little about the race of literary beings he called "my people"; no more, in fact, than appears in the books; this led to an anecdote about an actor who in despair threw over the part of Pozzo when the author was unable to enlighten him on a dozen points concerning the character's age, race, occupation, social status, education, philosophy of life. It was clear from the drift of his talk that if Godot, for instance, really crosses the stage under a pseudonym, or if Moran actually becomes Molloy, these events (to say the least) happen without the author's knowledge; nor is Miss Fitt, as has been conjectured, in the author's private mind the Dark Lady of the Sonnets.

We are not, in short, like dogs excited by the scent of invisible meat, to snap after some item of information which the author grasps very well and is holding just behind the curtain. So to proceed is to misapprehend the quality of the Beckett universe, which is permeated by mystery and bounded by a darkness; to assail those qualities because they embarrass the critic's professional knowingness is cheap, reductive, and perverse. Like primitive astronomers, we are free to note recurrences, cherish symmetries, and seek if we can means of placating the hidden powers: more for our comfort than for theirs.

I hope the reader finds these revelations too elementary to require stating; but since they are endorsed by a man who has been familiar with the Beckett universe longer than the reader has, or than I have, it seems worth while to write them out.

I ask him to believe, then, that Mr. Beckett exists, that he is capable of discussing what he has written, and that he said on a certain occasion approximately the things I have just set down, or things very like them. I also ask him to believe (for there were no human witnesses) that on leaving Mr. Beckett's apartment I became confused in the courtyard, and applying myself to the wrong door, instead of the street I blundered into a cul-de-sac which contained two ash cans and a bicycle.

The Man in the Room

Who knows what the ostrich sees in the sand?
— Murphy

1

Mr. Beckett's patient concern with bicycles, amputees, battered hats, and the letter M; his connoisseurship of the immobilized hero; his preoccupation with footling questions which there isn't sufficient evidence to resolve; his humor of the short sentence; his Houdini-like virtuosity (by preference chained hand and foot, deprived of story, dialogue, locale) : these constitute a unique comic repertoire, like a European clown's. The antecedents of his plays are not in literature but—to take a rare American example—in Emmett Kelly's solemn determination to sweep a circle of light into a dustpan: a haunted man whose fidelity to an impossible task—quite as if someone he desires to oblige had exacted it of him—illuminates the dynamics of a tragic sense of duty. ("We are waiting for Godot to come—Or for night to fall. We have kept our appointment and that's an end to that. We are not saints, but we have kept our appointment. How many people can boast as much?") The milieu of his novels bears a moral resemblance to that of the circus, where virtuosity —to no end—is the principle of life, where a thousand variations on three simple movements fill up the time between train and train, and the animals have merely to pace their cages to draw cries of admiring sympathy that are withheld, whatever his risks, from the high-wire

13

acrobat: the spectators settled numbly in their ritual of waiting, the normal emotions of human solidarity not perverted but anesthetized.

Anesthetized, as at a rite: an execution, for instance. The clown's routine is a pantomime dialogue with his executioners, who paid for their tickets in that universe to which he has no access, outside the tent. So Mr. Beckett's Unnamable, in a place

> which is merely perhaps the inside of my distant skull where once I wandered, now am fixed, lost for tininess, or straining against the walls, with my head, my hands, my feet, my back, and ever murmuring my old stories, my old story, as if it were the first time,

cringes from unspecified Others:

> Perhaps they are watching me from afar, I have no objection, as long as I don't see them, watching me like a face in the embers which they know is doomed to crumble, but it takes too long, it's getting late, eyes are heavy and tomorrow they must rise betimes. So it is I who speak, all alone, since I can't do otherwise.

This clown, a sort of 4 A.M. Pagliacci, is an extreme case, his language an anxious audible dumb show, in a work from which Beckett has succeeded in abolishing all content save the gestures of the intellect: immaculate solipsism compelled (this is the comic twist) to talk, talk, talk, and fertile in despairing explanations of its own garrulity ("It is all very well to keep silence, but one has also to consider the kind of silence one keeps."). Another of his personae, a tattered outcast in the classic clown's outfit—clothes too long and too tight, bowler hat, pants supported by a necktie—manifests a finer self-sufficiency. He is leaning against a wall plying his trade ("I shifted my weight from one foot to the other, and my hands clutched the lapels of my greatcoat. To beg with your hands in your pockets makes a bad impression.") when an orator assails him:

> Look at this down and out, he vociferated, this leftover. If he doesn't go down on all fours, it's for fear of being impounded. . . . Every day you pass them by, resumed the orator, and when you have backed a winner you fling them a farthing. Do you ever think? The voice, Certainly not. A penny, resumed the orator, tuppence—. The voice, Thruppence. It nevers enters your head, resumed the orator, that your charity is a crime, an incentive to slavery, stultification and organized murder. Take a good look at this living corpse. . . . Then he bent forward and took me to task. I had perfected my board. It now consisted of two boards hinged together, which enabled me, when my work was done, to fold it and carry it under my arm. I like to do little odd jobs. So I took off the rag, pocketed the few coins I had earned, untied the board, folded it and put it under my arm. Do you hear me you crucified bastard! cried the orator. Then I went away, although it was still light.

Impervious to the most perfervid artillery of social protest, this man's fine rhetoric of indifference (preoccupied with the technology of begging) illustrates Beckett's invincibly comic method, which locates comedy in the very movements of the human mind. The human mind, viewed from his specialized angle, can even find a use for the *Times Literary Supplement*:

> And in winter, under my greatcoat, I wrapped myself in swathes of newspaper, and did not shed them until the earth awoke, for good, in April. The Times Literary Supplement was admirably adapted to this purpose, of neverfailing toughness and impermeability. Even farts made no impression on it.

And the bum who is determined to exact nourishment

from a stray cow ("She dragged me across the floor, stopping from time to time only to kick me. . . . Clutching the dug with one hand, I kept my hat under it with the other.") is funnier in his determination than in his posture. ("I reproached myself," he continues, "I could no longer count on this cow and she would warn the others. More master of myself I might have made a friend of her. She would have come every day, perhaps accompanied by other cows. I might have learned to make butter, even cheese. But I said to myself, No, all is for the best.")

The central Beckett situations are outrageously simple: a man named Malone, for instance, is in bed, presumably in a sort of poorhouse, dying. And the Beckett comedy lies so far from word play that it can pass intact from language to language: the trilogy of novels, *Molloy, Malone Meurt, L'Innommable,* was written in French about 1948, and the English translations, mostly the author's own, are very close. The comedy he has made his province brings something new to the resources of literature. It is prior to action and more fundamental than language: the process of the brain struggling with ideas ("It's human, a lobster couldn't do it.") : precisely the process (he will no doubt not mind us noting) that has landed western civilization in its present fix.

Malone, for instance, cannot simply lie still and die. He must make up stories, and the hero of his story must roll over on the ground and lose his hat (for these are realistic stories: a careless yarn spinner would have forgotten the hat), and Malone must speculate on the way of this: "For when, lying on your stomach in a wild and practically illimitable part of the country, you turn over on your back, then there is a sideways movement of the whole body, including the head, unless you make a point of avoiding it, and the head comes to rest x inches approximately from where it was before, x being the width of the shoulders in inches, for the head is right in the middle of the shoulders." Not otherwise did Newton take stock of falling apples. A moment later he is noting that one tends less to clutch the ground when on one's back than when on one's stomach: "There is a curious remark which might be worth following up."

Malone in bed bears curious analogies with Descartes, whose speculations, notoriously detached from the immediate inspection of visible and audible things, were by preference pursued in the same place. Descartes has at some time fixed a good deal of Mr. Beckett's attention. The marks of this are perfectly clear in *The Unnamable,* the protagonist of which knows that he thinks but would like to feel certain that he exists, as well as in *Molloy,* where the body (at first hardly distinguishable from a bicycle) is as clearly a machine as Descartes established it was, though here a machine subject to loss and decay. This Cartesian focus is something more than a pedantic coincidence. The philosophy which has stood behind all subsequent philosophies, and which makes the whole of intelligible reality depend on the mental processes of a solitary man, came into being at about the same time as the curious literary form called the novel, which has since infected all other literary genres. The novel, for all its look of objectivity, is the product of an arduous solitary ordeal: you can sing your poems and arrange to have your plays acted, but all you can do with your novels is write them, alone in a room, assembling what memories you can of experiences you had before your siege in the room commenced, all the time secretly perhaps a little ashamed of the genre you are practicing. How can all these lies be taken seriously, and all this local color? Joyce sought to put in everything, once and for all, and be done with it.

2

An answer, or one part of one answer, is that Malone making up stories is free within his own mind, and enjoying the only freedom toward which Beckett's clowns aspire. The outward sign of this freedom is apt to be confused by hasty readers, not to mention the police, with total collapse. Have we not the obligation to set an example of industry? Yet every Beckett tramp is convinced in his heart that inner peace is ideally timeless, enclosed in a parenthesis ideally as long as life.

Early in his career, when he was reading Italian at Trinity College, Beckett discovered in the fourth Canto of the *Purgatorio* one of his most persistent prototypes, the Florentine Belacqua who has a whole lifetime to recline in the shade of a rock. This is not the official way of putting it. The books of Heaven regard this long indolence on the low slopes of Purgatory as a sentence Belacqua is serving because he repented late. He must stay there until the heavens have revolved as often as they did in his life. But waiting, clearly, has always been to his taste, for Dante smiles recalling the legendary torpitude of his old friend back in Florence. "Sedendo et quiescendo anima efficitur sapiens," he used to quote when Dante upbraided him, and now his "Brother, what avails it to ascend?" falls on the ears of the purposeful Dante with a double meaning. By the terms of his sentence it would indeed be useless for him to challenge the angelic majordomo just yet, unless someone's prayer should shorten his term; but it is doubtful if he would welcome a prayer's interference with this opportunity of dreaming over, at his ease, a whole life spent in dreaming.

(*Sedendo et quiescendo* . . . this is a gloss on the turbulent grotesques, Cooper in *Murphy* and Clov in *Endgame*, whom a physical abnormality—we are given its scientific name, acathisia—prevents from sitting.)

Belacqua dreaming of Belacqua dreaming—the life in the mind repeating the life "from the spermarium to the crematorium"—holds such powerful appeal for Murphy that he actually hopes he may live to be old, the longer to serve so blissful a post-mortem sentence. "God grant no godly chandler would shorten his time with a good prayer." The image has great appeal for Murphy's author also, containing neatly as it does the situation of an author who spends working time among remembered landscapes. The Beckett country, name it or leave it nameless as he will, lies always south of Dublin, around his home suburb of Foxrock (which above the train time melee in *All That Fall* we can barely hear the stationmaster announcing as "Boghill.") It is to the station near the Leopardstown racecourse that Mrs. Rooney toils, encountering on her way the Clerk of the Course; here, too, we may locate Watt's descent from the train out of Dublin to commence his sojourn with the remotely paternal Mr. Knott. Two miles away is the institution conducted by the Hospitaller Brothers of St. John of God, where Macmann takes refuge ("You are now in the House of Saint John of God, with the number one hundred and sixty-six. Fear nothing.") . Bally, hub of the Molloy country, is undoubtedly Baile atha Cliath itself, and Malone in bed reliving the nights when he lay in bed as a boy listening to the barking of dogs from the hovels up in the hills where the stonecutters lived, is himself a reliving of a boy who lay listening at night to such sounds from the hills west of Carrickmines, the Belacqua dream within a dream here carried to three terms, and yielding Beckett one of his most hauntingly evocative passages:

> Then in my bed, in the dark, on stormy nights, I could tell from one another, in the outcry without, the leaves, the boughs, the groaning trunks, even the grasses and the house that sheltered me. Each tree had its own cry, just as no two whispered alike, when the air was still. . . .

A page later Malone returns to his fiction about Sapo/ Macmann, and notes with some surprise, "And yet I write about myself with the same pencil, and in the same exercise-book as about him." And for that sentence too, on Malone's behalf, Beckett held the pen (or pencil).

It is a kind of memory, yet not memory, this shadowy portentous landscape where identities are so in question, like the ball Dan Rooney dropped which looks like a kind of ball and yet is not a ball.

> MR. ROONEY: Give it to me.
> MRS. ROONEY: (*giving it*) What *is* it, Dan?
> MR. ROONEY: It is a thing I carry about with me.
> MRS. ROONEY: Yes, but what—
> MR. ROONEY: (*violently*) It is a thing I carry about with me!

3

In the novelist's workroom, as he watches the hand with the pen scribble its way free from the shadow of his head and then leap back, these things he carries about absorb his attention.

Beckett's principal siege in the room commenced about 1945, in ravaged France, and lasted until 1950. On that prolonged séance his fame rests: *Godot* and the trilogy were its issue. The bleak stare in the photographs which determine the public image of Samuel Beckett suggests the assault of our daylight, after six years, on a countenance long immured. That face is not strained by the ordeal of conception, but haunted by the memory of having conceived. No other writing so steeps us in total aversion from whatever the present immediacy may be: absorption, possession, by a time and place cloudily remembered, elsewhere, nowhere. The achievement dignifies Peggy Guggenheim's account of the diffident young man of about thirty whom she called Oblomov because he spent most of his days in bed: that was, it now appears, apprenticeship or Cartesian preparation for the creative ordeal that commenced in 1945, in the author's fortieth year.

He was then just back from a first gloomy inspection of postwar Ireland, where his mother lived. Postwar Ireland he found no more fit to sustain consciousness than the Ireland he had been visiting the month the war broke out. ("I immediately returned to France. I preferred France in war to Ireland in peace. I just made it in time.") On that earlier occasion, while the enemy was dividing Gaul into two parts, Beckett had holed up in his flat in the fifteenth *arrondissement* of Paris and undertaken a heroic feat of pedantry, filling sheets of paper with a French translation of the novel he had gotten published, amid total public indifference, in 1938. This was a more unlikely project than it sounds. The English *Murphy*, portions of which James Joyce knew by heart, consists of some 70,000 words tessellated into a sort of learned language, with glazed austerity and a conjuror's resourcefulness:

> "Another semitone," said Neary, "and we had ceased to hear."
> "Who knows but what we have?" said Wylie. "Who knows what dirty story, what even better dirty story, it may be even one we have not heard before, told at some

colossal pitch of pure smut, beats at this moment in vain against our eardrums?"

"For me," said Neary, with the same sigh as before, "the air is always full of such, soughing with the bawdy innuendo of eternity."

Devising an equivalent for that in the tongue of Racine—"bruissant des vieilles équivoques où s'ennuie l'éternité"—occupied the dark half of Beckett's mind between 1940 and 1942, while the German occupation set up its machinery. A similar temperament, given a slightly different distribution of talents, might have engaged in a piece of prolonged mathematical research, as exact and disinterested, say, as Molloy's statistical treatment of eructation. ("I am ashamed to tell to how many places of figures I carried these computations," wrote Newton recalling a summer of plague, "having no other business at the time.") His daylight mind, meanwhile—that is to say, the portion of his being attested to by *cartes d'identité*—was active in the affairs of the Resistance, in collaboration with his friend Alfred Péron.[1] Péron was arrested, and vanished, as it proved, forever; the Gestapo interested itself in Samuel Beckett; he left Paris "because of the Germans" ("peu avant l'arrivée chez lui de la Gestapo," says a French journalist) and "from pillar to post" in the unoccupied zone composed a second novel in English, *Watt*: Dublin and environs, larger, vaguer, dimmer, and more portentous than life, remembered from makeshift quarters at Rousillon in the Vaucluse, and filled by the diligent remembering mind with a fantastic clockwork of circumstantiality. Pages of *Watt* exceed, with increased tension, the virtuosity of *Murphy*:

---

[1] Péron and Beckett met at the École Normale Supérieure, where Beckett was Lecteur d'Anglais for two years after his 1927 graduation from Trinity College. Péron subsequently spent a year at Trinity when Beckett returned there in 1931 to take his M.A.

That, replied Louit, is the bold claim I make for my friend, in whose mind, save for the pale music of innocence you mention, and, in some corner of the cerebellum, where all agricultural ideation has its seat, dumbly flickering, the knowledge of how to extract, from the ancestral half-acre of moraine, the maximum of nourishment, for himself and his pig, with the minimum of labour, all, I am convinced, is an ecstasy of darkness, and of silence.

Other pages of *Watt* seem to have been written out in a trance of obligation, like some schoolroom imposition—

Here he stood. Here he sat. Here he knelt. Here he lay. Here he moved, to and fro, from the door to the window, from the window to the door; from the window to the door, from the door to the window; from the fire to the bed, from the bed to the fire; . . .

—and so on for some 400 words, until each possible route between bed, window, door and fire has been traced in each direction. Years later The Unnamable is to speculate concerning a task some master has imposed, a pensum to perform "as a punishment for having been born perhaps," which entails the writing out of some thousands of words before he will perhaps be allowed to conjure with words no more. If *Watt* is in part such a pensum, it is also in part the subsumption of distant memories into a style, the withdrawal of candlestickmaker's reality from a place and time now unattainable: Ireland, where old men sit on benches and strange men in lonely houses employ servants, and words are incessantly agitated and the mind is never still. This Ireland, at Roussillon between 1942 and 1944, Beckett delivered over from the remembered realm of irreducible being to the mental world where logic mimes the possibility of order and sentences linked less certainly to fact than to one another move unimpeded through the dark. As with the French translation of *Murphy,*

Beckett set aside the unpublished manuscript of *Watt,* for ten years as it proved.

These things he had done in France during the war, estranged from the home. In the first postwar silence of 1945 he spent a month in Ireland with his mother. Then, homeless still, he made his way through Normandy back to Paris, reclaimed his old flat, and commenced the siege in the room that was to last until 1950.

It was during this six-year siege that he wrote nearly everything that has made his name celebrated, and much else, all of it in French. ("I just felt like it. It was a different experience from writing in English.") Each year he made his way out of Paris to Ireland for a month. Then in 1950 his mother died and the intermittent séance suddenly ended. Since the war he had published one book, the French *Murphy* in 1947, with its dedication to Alfred Péron. His drawer was filled with manuscripts: the English *Watt,* souvenir of the Occupation, and in French four novels, two plays, four tales, and a sequence of thirteen "textes pour rien." The first novel, *Mercier et Camier,* the first play, *Eleutheria,* and one of the stories, "Premier Amour," were jettisoned. The rest, after detailed revision, the minuteness of which can be gauged from earlier versions in magazines, were published, more or less in the order of composition, at yearly intervals from 1951 to 1955: *Molloy, Malone Meurt, En Attendant Godot, L'Innommable, Watt* (out of sequence), *Nouvelles et Textes Pour Rien.*

En Attendant Godot made him very famous. Since then he has dodged the commitments of fame and the Literary Life as successfully as he dodged the Occupation, and from not dissimilar motives. Oscillating between the flat and an outpost "in the Marne mud," he wrote in 1956 his most remarkable single work, *Fin de Partie,* and for three more years busied himself dividing the universe of the novels into radio plays, for voices, and mimes, for no voice. Each time the circle tightens, the equation grows more compact. The first radio play carries us to and fro along miles of road, and employs a cast of eleven. The second confines us within the echoing skull of a single man sitting half an hour in a spot from which he barely stirs. Yet we move at the bidding of this man's imagination along the strand, around the bay, to bus stops and riding lessons, from a bleak afternoon to a crystalline winter's night, from Henry and Ada's problems to the cruel impasse of two perhaps imagined old men in a perhaps remembered great house, back years in time and forward to an interminable future. Henry, in *Embers*, murmuring on the strand, is as much the cheated king of infinite space as the man who sat in a Paris room writing the thousands upon thousands of words of a three-volume novel: for this space is curved, and returns upon itself. And that same man in turn has written the words Henry murmurs, driving headlong, by successively minuter increments, to wedge his art in a cleft where it need never stir more: the Comedian of the Impasse, genial to the last, the ever-receding last.

His one certain principle is that every work is wrested from the domain of the impossible. Let him by his previous operations have thoroughly salted some trampled patch of ground, and it is there that in time of frost he will plant his next seed. If one thing was clear to him in April 1958, it was that *The Unnamable* and the *Textes Pour Rien* had placed him in an impasse where he could not possibly write another novel. Accordingly in January 1961 he published a sort of novel, *Comment C'est*. There is neither preversity here, nor inadvertence, but stubborn policy. But let him explain it.

Chronology

Biographical Data

1906	Samuel Beckett born in Dublin
1927	B.A. in French and Italian, Trinity College, Dublin.
1928-30	Lecteur d'Anglais, École Normale Supérieure, Paris.
1931	M.A., Trinity College
1931-32	Lecturer in French, Trinity College.
1932-36	Wanderings in London, France, Germany.
1937	Settled in Paris.

Work

	Date of Writing	*Date of Publication*
1930		*Whoroscope* (poem)
1931		*Proust*
1934		*More Pricks than Kicks* (stories)
1936		*Echo's Bones* (poems)
1938		*Murphy* (in English)
1940-42	Translated *Murphy* into French.	
1942-44	*Watt* (in English)	
1945	*Mercier et Camier* (Novel—in French)	
1945-46	*Nouvelles*— ("La Fin," "L'Expulsé," Le Calmant," "Premier Amour"—in French)	

1947	*Eleutheria* (play—in French)	*Murphy* (in French)
1947-49	*Molloy* (in French) *Malone Meurt* (in French) *En Attendant Godot* (in French) *L'Innommable* (in French)	
1949-50	*Mexican Poetry* (translations)	
1950	*Textes Pour Rien* (in French)	*Molloy* (in French)
1951		*Malone Meurt*
1952		*En Attendant Godot* *L'Innommable*
1953		*Watt* (in English) *Waiting for Godot*
1954		*Nouvelles et Textes Pour Rien*
1955		*Molloy* (in English)
1956	*Fin de Partie* (in French) *All That Fall* (in English)	*Malone Dies*
1957	Translated *Endgame* into English	*Fin de Partie* *All That Fall*
1958	*Krapp's Last Tape* (in English)	*Endgame* *The Unnamable* *Mexican Poems* *Krapp's Last Tape*
1959	*Embers* (in English)	"Texts for Nothing I" *Gedichte* (including *Echo's Bones,* twelve French poems written 1937-39, and six written 1947-49).

1960	*Comment C'est* (in French)
	Embers *Krapp's Last Tape and Other Dramatic Pieces* (also includes *Embers, All That Fall*, and two *Mimes*).
1961	*Happy Days* (play—in English)
	Comment C'est *Happy Days*

He has made just one public appearance to discuss the theory of these operations. Economically disguised as an Irish pawn who quails before a Frenchman's dialectic, he played in 1949 the straightman's role in three dialogues with Georges Duthuit, on three modern painters. At the end of each dialogue he is browbeaten into silence; at one point a peroration by Duthuit concerning "desire and affirmation, . . . that which is tolerable and radiant in the world" expends its force against a *nolo contendere* denoted by the stage direction: "B.— (*Exit weeping*)." It is B. who leads the dialogues, nevertheless. Sacrificing with exquisite pertinacity piece after piece, he achieves the bare board of the classic endgame, executes two or three futile maneuvers, and then concedes by prearrangement, with the air of one satisfying Necessity.

The opening (B. to play) establishes painter #1[2] as a man who deserves the best attention of the avant-garde, having extended, as the phrase goes, the boundaries of his art.

---

[2] Tal Coat. The other two are Masson and van Velde. This exchange was printed in *Transition 49*, #5.

B.—Total object, complete with missing parts, instead of partial object. Question of degree.

D.—More. The tyranny of the discreet overthrown. The world a flux of movements, partaking of living time, that of effort, creation, liberation, the painting, the painter. The fleeting instant of sensation given back, given forth, with the context of the continuum it nourished.

Already D. sounds like a pamphlet by Sir Herbert Read, and B. with a few more moves is able to expand his own opening remark, "Question of degree," into a claim that the revolution in question is insufficiently bleak, is in fact the sort of revolution that the critical bureaucracy (ably imitated by D.) can always be counted on to back. It is simply painting adapted to a changed environment, its goal still the "expression of experience" (whatever these terms may mean), its "tendency and accomplishment" still "fundamentally those of previous painting, straining to enlarge the statement of a compromise."

In so belittling enlargement B. plays the clown. The clown enlarges no statement. He is appalled by competence in all its forms; the whip does not frighten him so much as the ringmaster's infallible skill at cracking it. In his alarm at the human ability to specialize itself, he attempts no rejoinder. Besieged by crashing eloquences, he shrugs, walks off, and leaves their advocates to foam and menace, arrange props, collect gate receipts, cite chapter and verse, confer at the summit, see to the plumbing, and otherwise engorge the world. Leonardo too did all that. "What we have to consider in the case of the Italian painters is not that they surveyed the world with the eyes of building contractors, a mere means like any other, but that they never stirred from the field of the possible, however much they may have enlarged it." And today's revolutionary art simply continues their endeavors:

B.—The only thing disturbed by the revolutionaries Matisse and Tal Coat is a certain order on the plane of the feasible.

D.—What other plane can there be for the maker?

B.—Logically none. Yet I speak of an art turning from it in disgust, weary of its puny exploits, weary of pretending to be able, of being able, of doing a little better the same old thing, of going a little further along a dreary road.

D.—And preferring what?

B.—The expression that there is nothing to express, nothing with which to express, nothing from which to express, no power to express, no desire to express, together with the obligation to express.

Shakespeare's powers of expression, it is safe to remark, were infallibly equal to his needs, chiefly since what was needed to write *Hamlet* was power of expression. But set Shakespeare the problem of writing a play about the non-appearance of his hero (for whom two tramps are waiting) , or restrict him to four characters, two legless, the third immobilized, the fourth dim, and Shakespeare in the course of attuning himself to this assignment would of necessity allow his vast abilities to wither, cease desiring this man's art and that man's scope, and relinquish the satisfactions (such as he found them) of Promethean competence.

So D. in the second dialogue produces a painter who has assigned himself the void in some such way, one concerned with "inner emptiness, the prime condition, according to Chinese aesthetics, of the act of painting." But B. will not so easily be appeased. He discerns, in this man's hunger after a stripped art, two familiar maladies, "the malady of wanting to know what to do and the malady of wanting to be able to do it." Even absence, emptiness, becomes something to be possessed: "So forgive me if I relapse . . . into my dream of an art unresentful of its superb indigence and too proud for the farce of giving and receiving."

With the third dialogue (on Bram van Velde, whom Beckett has championed since the mid-1930's) the clown takes an offensive of sorts. He defines the Beckett/van Velde situation and act:

> The situation is that of him who is helpless, cannot act, in the end cannot paint, since he is obliged to paint. The act is of him who, helpless, unable to act, acts, in the event paints, since he is obliged to paint.
> D.—Why is he obliged to paint?
> B. I don't know.
> D.—Why is he helpless to paint?
> B.—Because there is nothing to paint and nothing to paint with.

(What this can mean we see at last ten years later in *Comment C'est*.) Thus the painting of B's predilection is "bereft of occasion in every shape and form, ideal as well as material": is pure act, we may say, by pure inaction. As negative and positive numbers are equally infinite, it approaches through sheer incapacity the Cartesian angelism, devoid of occasions, subjects, objects, relations, evading the elaborate mysteries of cognition and of the interaction between mind and hand. (Descartes evaded them, speculatively.) This is easy for common sense to refute; D. refutes it: "But might it not be suggested, even by one tolerant of this fantastic theory, that the occasion of his painting is his predicament, and that it is expressive of the impossibility to express?"

By now the form D. would impose on this discourse grows clear. It resembles an endless algebraic fraction, the denominator splintering itself an infinite number of times. Discard qualities for art to seek after, and the fact that you discard them becomes itself a quality to be sought after. B. assails this very principle. For such an artist, obsessed with possessiveness, obsessed with his expressive vocation, "anything and everything is doomed to become occasion, including . . . the pursuit of occasion. . . . No painting is more replete than Mondrian's." For such an artist, consequently, art always fails; his wooing of the occasion, however sophisticated, is "shadowed more and more darkly by a sense of invalidity, of inadequacy, of existence at the expense of all that it includes, all that it blinds to." And so "the history of painting, here we go again, is the history of its attempts to escape from this sense of failure, by means of more authentic, more ample, less exclusive relations between representer and representee, in a kind of tropism towards a light of which the best opinions continue to vary, and with a kind of Pythagorean terror, as though the irrationality of pi were an offense against the deity, not to mention his creature."

The terrified Pythagorean blocked number science for a long time. Starting from the faith that the system of rational numbers and the system of the visible world can be made to express one another, they had happily complicated their computations to accord with more complicated data, until it suddenly became evident that the diagonal of a square, let the computer twist and turn as he please, is simply incommensurate with its side. Immediately such incommensurables as $\sqrt{2}$ became the subject of a cult of secrecy. Initiates were sworn not to divulge their existence to outsiders; and they were named *Alogon*, the Unnamable, a fact which links Beckett's most forbidding novel with his first and most inviting, the protagonist of which, Murphy, is freely called "a surd." (Early in *Murphy* we are advised of the retribution visited on one Hippasos "for having divulged the incommensurability of side and diagonal." Eleven years and a war separate this remark from the dialogues with Duthuit; Beckett's preoccupations are surprisingly stable.)

The implication, advanced with Hibernian insouciance, is that prose fiction has hitherto been operated like a Pythagorean cult, in a conspiracy of silence concerning its own incapacity. Beckett's people meanwhile, not through some freak of maladjustment, not on account of their superior endowments (they have none), are radically and metaphysically unassimilable, a fact corresponding to their role as tramp-philosophers. They will not fit into some vast social or fictional machine, as Joyce (who carried traditional procedures to their ultimate) fitted Leopold Bloom. Nor, in the late phases of the enterprise, will they fit into any known world. It is by program a fiction of outcasts.

At the close of the three dialogues B. makes no such ringing assertion, either about Samuel Beckett's fictions or about his friend van Velde's paintings. True to the clown's role, he simply recants, by prearrangement ("Yes, yes, I am mistaken, I am mistaken.") and slips away. Beckett's work, however, incorporates such an assertion, if it incorporates anything or asserts anything; and the parallel with Joyce, Beckett developed on another occasion, noting that whereas "the more Joyce knew the more he could," this tendency towards omniscience and omnipotence need not exhaust art. "I'm working with impotence, ignorance. I don't think impotence has been exploited in the past."

The clown exploits impotence, to be sure, when he allows to bubble up into sustained mimetic coherence his own inability to walk a tightrope, missing his footing, misplacing but never dropping his bowler hat (which catches on a button behind his collar and, obeying immutable mechanical laws, is carried round out of reach as he turns to clutch at the space where it was), collapsing in an arc which carried his hands exactly to a graspable stanchion, retarding his pace to zero for long reflection, crowding six desperate acrobatic movements into a split second. He does not *imitate* the acrobat; it is plain that he could not; he offers us, directly, his personal incapacity, an intricate art form. The man who imitates is the acrobat himself (all ropewalkers are alike), adding to what we have seen before in other circuses some new minuscule difficulty overcome, moving on felt-shod feet a little further along the dreary road of the possible.

4

Let us look at this analogy a while longer.

There is something mechanical about ropewalker's skill. Perpetually improving his technique, he moves step by step toward what Wyndham Lewis called "the sleep of the machine." A perfect, a gyroscopic, cessation of consciousness and suppression of personality could do his work perfectly, as the camera depicts or the computer figures. Alas, being conscious, being a human person, he writes things like *The Odyssey* or *The Divine Comedy*, to tease a successor into emulation. Or, succeeding himself, he writes out the pages of *Watt* that postulate, for example, a man, a door, a fire, and a window and, exhausting by system every possible relation between them, leaves nothing for a successor to do.

Clown on the contrary knows that ideal ropewalking is impossible, certainly for him; his theme, his material, is its impossibility, his incapacity; if being conscious stands in his way, he will focus on that; he will be comically, superabundantly conscious, supernally resourceful, frantically methodical, the more so as he settles his features more and more into the lineaments of the ideal mechanical sleep: the immobility of The Unnamable, or of blind Hamm in his great castered chair.

Ropewalker too becomes absorbed with consciousness. The novelist (again!) lives in the act of writing, so ropewalker discerns bitterly, as consciousness in the act of thinking. If he proposes to stop writing of himself, thinking of himself, himself entertaining such a proposition becomes in turn a theme for writing or an object of thought. (This is the scenario of the *Textes Pour Rien*.) Just in this manner the three dialogues with D. disclosed to B. an infinite perspective of checkmates. If you play chess against yourself you will always lose, though you may conceivably postpone the end of the game forever.

Ropewalker, though he keeps on, despairs, and for ample reasons. Clown mimes despair, transforming it into an exquisite ceremony. Beckett, in various books, has played both roles, gradually working, by rigorous maneuvers, toward the clown's poise and amplitude. There are books—*Proust, More Pricks Than Kicks,* and various collections of poems—in which he is not clear whether he is a comic writer or simply a bitter one, and his first comic book, *Murphy,* achieves its daft freedom in a kind of air pocket, while simultaneously poems written in French precipitate into three or four hundred words his mounting nausea with the human state. 1193092

He has had a difficult development, for he has taken on himself the burden of one conscious that he is conscious, since the seventeenth century a peculiarly Western burden. That is the meaning of his stories within stories, his plays within plays, his characters within characters. It is also, with its eerie fidelity to the movements of a mind that has noted itself in motion, the point where his highly specialized, self-immolating art impinges on our sense of the familiar. When we find Molloy momentarily forgetting who he is and strutting before himself (his phrase) like a stranger, or reflecting on the exact sense of such an expression as "I said to myself," we may be startled as by a violation of our own privacy: we recall not so much doing such things as catching ourselves doing them. From such arabesques it is but a step, in principle, to the spectacle of Malone in bed proposing to be present at his own death (we all await death), and distracting himself meanwhile by telling himself stories, notably the biography of Macmann, whose death he hopes to synchronize with his own. Beckett protagonists characteristically tell themselves stories, and the boundary between fiction and experience is impossible to fix. The whole, in turn, is enclosed in Beckett's fiction; and from the unsettling intimacy of these works with what you find when you think about yourself, their magnetic power emanates. By the end of the trilogy our attention is being held by nothing succulent, no narrative, nothing but the turning wheels of rigorous precision. It has spiraled inward—

> Where now? Who now? When now? Unquestioning. I, say I. Unbelieving. Questions, hypotheses, call them that. Keep going, going on, call that going, call that on.

—to the center of the solitary world, the world in which every man lives nine-tenths of his life alone. It offers for our inspection, even as we read fascinated, the fascination with sequence, logic, association, with the permutation of our small private stock of ideas, that enables us to keep ourselves company for many, many years.

The fallacy of most introspective fiction, which Beckett's performance has rendered largely supererogatory, lies in its too ready assumption that the inherent interest of human beings is self-evident. But it is not immediately evident, as satirists have been reminding us since Juvenal, that human charm is all-sufficient. The reader of Beckett will understand Wyndham Lewis's claim that the greatest satire is nonmoral, and constitutes an attempt to understand how man bears his own company. For that he does bear his own company, and often gladly, is a fact to be understood, not a proposition to be established. It is with great difficulty that Shakespeare's dying giants maintain their own good opinion of themselves. "And say besides that in Aleppo once. . ."

To purify such vertigo by logic has been the historic work of the great Irish writers, who have always been able to regard a human dilemma as essentially an epistemological, not an ethical, comedy. Swift trapped the reader midway between Gulliver's perception of the Lilliputians and the Lilliputians' perception of Gulliver; Yeats, in "The Phases of the Moon," presents Aherne and Robartes discussing the ignorance of a man in a tower who is meanwhile writing the poem which provides them with the knowledge they are scheming to withhold from him; Joyce placed the dreamer inside his own dream, simultaneously generating and being generated by the voices of all the world. The one certainty from which a reader may start is a mischievously self-sufficient piece of writing, the fuller, perhaps, the emptier. *Ulysses* and *A Tale of a Tub* alike urge on us the existence in our hands of the physical book, a typographical artifact which is somehow "about" its own existence. *Ulysses* even contains, as its principal characters, a writer who could not have written it and a reader who would be unequipped to read it, each of them versions, moreover, of the actual writer and the ideal reader. Such works rotate before us a narcissism which entoils our own faculties, and is somehow related to the writer's involvement in his writer's job, and the reader's awareness of this involvement.

They have also all of them what Stephen Dedalus' classmate called "the true scholastic stink": logic, marginalia and cross-references, transposing a tradition of learned manuscripts into that of Gutenberg technology. The Irish, who go constantly into exile, have supplied the Age of Reason and its successors with several reincarnations of the vagrant scholar: Swift, rewarded with the Deanship of St. Patrick's like a twelfth-century clerk with a canonry, or Joyce, after much wandering, the schoolmaster of Paris, with Samuel Beckett, Master of Arts of Trinity College, Dublin, for a time a clerk in his entourage. We are never far, in Beckett's world, from the academic *flâneur*. Mr. Rooney notes that the Gaelic "Fir" on the door of the men's room is "from Vir Viris, I suppose, the V becoming F, in accordance with Grimm's Law," and with still more surprising accuracy derives "buff" from "buffalo." Moran in decline lists sixteen theological questions that have preoccupied him, notably "What value is to be attached to the theory that Eve sprang not from Adam's rib but from a tumour in the fat of his leg (arse?)?" The great casuistical speech of the vagrant Lucky is staged like a Master's Oral before three examiners—

> POZZO: Think, pig! . . .
> LUCKY: Given the existence as uttered forth in the published works of Puncher and Wattmann of a personal God quaquaquaqua. . . .

And the most sustained set piece in the canon details the performance, before an examining committee, of a certain Louit who has expended a fifty-pound grant, allegedly on research concerning *The Mathematical Intuitions of the Visicelts*, and is now to report on "the impetus imparted to his studies by his short stay in the country," during which, *inter alia*, the boots, "for the purchase of which fifteen shillings had been allotted to him from the slender College funds . . . had unfortunately been sucked off his feet by a bog, which in the fading light, and the confusion of his senses consequent on prolonged inanition, he had mistaken for a field of late onions." On these twenty-eight pages of *Watt* time stands still, and we barely notice the expenditure of six of them on a mathematical analysis of how the random mutual glances of a five-man or n-man committee could, in an ideal world not much different from the one in hand, be systematized so that no looks are duplicated or go astray. Endless leisurely academic procedure ("Sivinty-thray? said Mr de Baker. Perhaps he means seventy-three, said Mr O'Meldon. Does he mean seventy-three? said Mr Fitzwein. He said seventy-three, said Louit. Did he indeed, said Mr de Baker. My God, said Mr MacStern. His What? said Mr O'Meldon. His God, said Mr Magershon.") —this is one mode of an earthly paradise, *in terra Samuelis.*

He remains, until nearly forty, himself the wandering scholar, chiefly in Paris but sometimes elsewhere in Europe. *Whoroscope* (which won a prize for poems about Time) has 98 lines and 17 footnotes, a higher average than *The Waste Land.* Attached to no academy (though he was two years Lecteur d'Anglais at the École Normale Supérieure, and a year back in Trinity as lecturer in French), he published his monograph on Proust, emitted at irregular intervals his landscape poems of an intellectual vagrant (*Echo's Bones,* and others uncollected), and amassed short stories, with mutual cross-references like a set of learned texts, about a Trinity man—solipsist, jongleur, lecher, pedant, poet—named Belacqua Shuah, the improbable pronomen compounded from Dante and gutter-Irish ("Bollocky"): a notably Goliardic assortment of juvenilia.

Uncollected pieces mirror the décor of the international 30's: a "Text" in the manner of Joyce ("Come come and cull me bonny bony doublebed cony swiftly my springal"), poems in the manner of Stephen Dedalus—

> (Fool! do you hope to untangle
> the knot of God's pain?
> Melancholy Christ that was a soft one!
> Oh yes I think that was perhaps just a very little inclined to be rather too self-conscious)

—and stories in the manner of an erudite youth fondling

private jokes. These have all slipped into decent oblivion in the files of *Transition* and the *New Review*, detritus of the mind of an academic bohemian (Dublin, Paris, Frankfort) preoccupied with its own cleverness and inclined toward macaronic effects because (Joyce aside) it is interested mainly in exteriorizing its own processes, which include dexterity with the languages it happens to know: English, French, German, Italian, Latin. Like the uncollected poems (of which one title should be salvaged: "Casket of Pralinen for a Daughter of a Dissipated Mandarin"), the ones in *Echo's Bones and Other Precipitates* (1936) flaunt a Goliardic swing, a macaronic texture, and an insouciant impenetrability, all these qualities numbed by a barely controlled violence of objurgation:

> this clonic earth
> all these phantoms shuddering out of focus
> it is useless to close the eyes
> all the chords of the earth broken like a woman pianist's
> the toads abroad again on their rounds
> sidling up to their snares
> the fairy-tales of Meath ended
> so say your prayers now and go to bed
> your prayers before the lamps start to sing behind the
> larches
> here at these knees of stone
> then to bye-bye on the bones

Creation has the bad taste to be unsatisfactory.

The Belacqua stories squander comparable ingenuities of expression, ravelling out into (unsupplied) footnotes. We are told, for instance, that Belacqua and Winnie had not been long on the hilltop "before he began to feel a very sad animal indeed"; and the fit reader's pleasure is divided between the impropriety of the information here secreted, and the aplomb with which he has fielded an allusion to Galen's "omne animal post coitum triste est."

Amid sardonic verbal moraines, contrivances of willed absurdity, and bouts of forced laughter, Belacqua ricochets from affair to affair, leaving girl after girl standing in tableau bewilderment, marries thrice, and dies into the immobility toward which all his rampages have been obliquely oriented. None of this needs to be revived, though it is enlightening to know it exists.

These writings turn on a discrepancy between the mind's operations and what the world presents; so it is with no surprise that we discover the protagonist of Beckett's first published book, the 1930 *Whoroscope*, to be René Descartes soliloquizing in a Dublin accent.

This Descartes shares three attributes with the protagonists of the future trilogy: a recurrent obsession (here, about eggs) ; an incapacity for brushing the wing of his mind against persons or things without nausea; and a singular absence of what can only be called identity. He addresses his breakfast:

> Are you ripe at last,
> my slim pale double-breasted turd!
> How rich she smells,
> this abortion of a fledgling![3]
>
> I will eat it with a fishfork.
> White and yoke with feathers.
> Then I will rise and move moving
> toward Rahab of the snows,
> the murdering matinal pope-confessed amazon,
> Christina the ripper. . . .

The "abortion of a fledgling" he castigates in an ecstasy of disgust; Queen Christina of Sweden incurs his wrath because ("matinal amazon") she required his presence

---

[3]A footnote informs us that Descartes "liked his omelette made of eggs hatched eight to ten days; shorter or longer under the hen and the result, he says, is disgusting."

at five o'clock in the morning; as for himself, he is simply the spot where these two and twenty other particular distastes intersect. A year after printing this witty eructation, Beckett (Descartes temporarily slumbering somewhere in his soul) produced his study of Proust, in the foreword of which he announces that the page references are to "the abominable edition of the *Nouvelle Revue Française*, in sixteen volumes."

5

As this exasperation indicates, the Cartesian clown is dormant in *Proust; Proust* is the bitter academic soliloquy of one condemned on this earth to walk ropes. With insinuating candor it tears down the world. Its author (age 25) displays a colubrine suddenness of invective and an odd intense tranquillity of appreciation, the former for the human condition, the latter for Proust, an ideal Proust. A style that oscillates between Pater and neurasthenia delivers the elements of the Proust-Beckett universe, in which "we are not merely more weary because of yesterday, we are other, no longer what we were before the calamity of yesterday"; in which therefore, since he who attains is no longer he who desired, "the wisdom of all the sages, from Brahma to Leopardi, . . . consists not in the satisfaction but in the ablation of desire"; the failure of all human relationships is preordained; and "the immediate joys and sorrows of the body and the intelligence are so many superfoetations," because "the only world that has reality and significance" is "the world of our own latent consciousness." Clearly, Proust writing in bed brings up to date Belacqua dreaming in the shadow of his rock; clearly too, Molloy or Malone writing in bed is a hobo Proust.

Thus all that does and suffers is unreal, harvesting only in its moments of inattention the ingredients of the peace involuntary memory may later recover and illuminate; hence the accessible is without exception disagreeable ("And if there were two things that Watt loathed, one was the earth, and the other was the sky."); and any willed relationship of person to person, here and now, "the attempt to communicate where no communication is possible, is merely a simian vulgarity, or horribly comic." (Molloy has such an experience, with a Mrs. Lousse.)

From this not very arresting disenchantment, reminiscent of the rotting apple Auden at a similar age kept on his mantel at Oxford to remind him of the state of Europe, there depends a further argument both facile and subtle. Since the conscious life is an ignoble traffic with the practical world, what is usually called "memory," the faculty that reproduces those impressions of the past that were consciously formed, can recall nothing but the soiled shirts and half-eaten sandwiches of earlier practical trafficking. To augment the banalities of today, the man with a good memory can summon the banalities of yesterday. But in some inner *"gouffre interdit à nos sondes"* is stored what was never corrupted by practical attention, "the essence of our selves, the best of our many selves, . . .the best because accumulated shyly and painfully under the nose of our vulgarity." But this is inaccessible. We cannot be happy in the present because we must be conscious of it; nor can we normally recall that of which we were never conscious. We can only wait, for death, for Godot, or for the Proustian miracle. For, says Proust—and this is the nub of Beckett's fascination with him—what memory cannot locate, nor the most successful evocative experiment do more than echo, will once in a while flood us by accident, when "by some miracle of analogy the central impression of a past sensation recurs as an immediate stimulus," and opens the inner gulfs.

> The most trivial experience—he says in effect—is encrusted with elements that logically are not related to it and have consequently been rejected by our intelligence: it is imprisoned in a vase filled with a certain perfume and a certain colour and raised to a certain temperature. These vases are suspended along the height of our years, and, not being accessible to memory, are in a sense immune, the purity of their climatic content is guaranteed to forgetfulness, each one is kept at a distance, at its date. So that when the imprisoned microcosm is besieged in the manner described, we are flooded by a new air and a new perfume (new precisely because already experienced), and we breathe the true air of Paradise, of the only Paradise that is not the dream of a madman, the Paradise that has been lost.

One may be suffused for instance by "a sour and distinguished prose, shaped and stated by his mother's voice, muted and sweetened almost to a lullaby, unwinding all night long its reassuring foil of sound before a child's insomnia."

Beckett images have a way of recurring. A quarter century later in *Endgame*, where Hamm's active lifelong denial of love—translating the Proustian apathy into a rhetoric of revulsion—has made everything go wrong, those perfumed jars where the past is sealed away are transmogrified into two ash cans, which dominate the left side of the stage in metallic obduracy and contain his legless parents. His mother, in one of them, is rapt back by a chance remark to Lake Como, and for a few minutes enjoys before our eyes the Proustian bliss ("It was deep, deep. And you could see down to the bottom. So white. So clean."). And emanating from the other ash can the father's rebuke recalls the child's insomnia:

Whom did you call when you were a tiny boy and were frightened of the dark? Your mother? No. Me. We let you cry. Then we moved you out of earshot, so that we might sleep in peace.

Now it is their conversations that trouble his sleep:

> HAMM (*wearily*): Quiet, quiet, you're keeping me awake. (*Pause.*) Talk softer. (*Pause.*) If I could sleep I might make love. I'd go into the woods. My eyes would see . . . the sky, the earth. I'd run, run, they wouldn't catch me. (*Pause.*) Nature! (*Pause.*) There's something dripping in my head. (*Pause.*) A heart, a heart in my head.

Blind, in his rigid chair, he gropes in dreams toward "the only Paradise that is not the dream of a madman, the Paradise that has been lost," or contrives fictions in which he figures as the heartless voice of Necessity striking postures before cringing tenants, rapping out harsh rodomontades in a Paradise that never was.

6

We may call what is set forth in *Proust* the ropewalker's view of life. It exudes such a person's dreary dignity, surveying human experience from that great height which anyone can attain with a ladder, and suggesting that there is nothing much to do but plant one foot before the other, in circumstances where this procedure entails great technical difficulty. It is not a doctrine one would expect to nourish a great comic writer, and indeed it does not. The great comic writer pays it little heed, except when he allows Nell her memory of Lake Como, or the speaker of *Comment C'est* a few images of his past life "up there in the light."[4] The mind that chose to publish this exposition retains its stain, however. To the last his people expect nothing of the practical world, and seek equilibrium in entropy.

Thus Murphy regards the mental patients he is paid to attend "not as banished from a system of benefits" by their disorder, "but as escaped from a colossal fiasco," and is greatly soothed by "the absolute impassiveness of the higher schizoids, in the face of the most pitiless therapeutic bombardment." Thus Watt, the most engaging of Beckett's creations, has the utmost difficulty in accommodating his mind to the most utile objects:

> For Watt now found himself in the midst of things which, if they consented to be named, did so as it were with reluctance. . . . Looking at a pot, for example, or thinking of a pot, one of Mr Knott's pots, it was in vain that Watt said, Pot, pot. Well, perhaps not quite in vain, but very nearly. For it was not a pot, the more he looked, the more he reflected, the more he felt sure of that, that it was not a pot at all. It resembled a pot, it was almost a pot, but it was not a pot of which one could say, Pot, pot and be comforted.

In the trilogy this fluid bewilderment deposits jagged crystals. Thus Molloy rehearses the sensations of dissolution:

> This time, then once more I think, then perhaps a last time, then I think it'll be over, with that world too. Premonition of the last but one but one. All grows dim. A little more and you'll go blind. It's in the head. It doesn't work any more, it says, I don't work any more. You go

---

4 "and yet a dream I am given a dream as if I had tasted of love of a little woman within my reach and dreaming too it's in the dream too of a little man within hers I have that in my life this time on and off as I journey." We meet the indomitable comedian in the next words: "or failing kindred flesh emergency dream a ewe sheep she would not come to me I would go to her huddle in her fleece."

dumb as well and sounds fade. The threshold scarcely crossed that's how it is.

Thus Malone, exacerbated by padded-cell amenities:

. . . And indeed the silence at times is such that the earth seems uninhabited. That is what comes of the taste for generalization. You have only to hear nothing for a few days, in your hole, nothing but the sounds of things, and you begin to fancy yourself the last of human kind. What if I started to scream?

Thus the Unnamable:

In a word, no change apparently since I have been here, disorder of the lights perhaps an illusion, all change to be feared, incomprehensible uneasiness.

Last, capping this increasingly bitter series, the equally anonymous protagonist of *Comment C'est*:

life then without visitors present version no visitors no stories but mine no sounds but mine no silence but the silence I must break when I can bear it no more it's with that I must endure.

This one at least is capable of finding the Belacqua bliss intolerably lonely. Murphy had no such qualms when, more than twenty years before *Comment C'est*, he first inspected the padded cells:

The pads surpassed by far all he had ever been able to imagine in the way of indoor bowers of bliss. The three dimensions, slightly concave, were so exquisitely proportioned that the absence of the fourth was scarcely felt. The tender luminous oyster-grey of the pneumatic upholstery, cushioning every square inch of ceiling, walls, floor and door, lent colour to the truth, that one was a prisoner of air. The temperature was such that only total nudity could do it justice. No system of ventilation appeared to dispel the illusion of respirable vacuum. . . .

Though *Murphy* is a genial book, and *Watt* a work whose understanding with the reader is suffused with deliquescent lyricism, the tone of the next three novels promises nothing except that the writer will be released from exacerbation only when he has died, and the reader perhaps when he reads no more. *The Unnamable* ends without even the satisfaction of Malone's expiring "Never anything/ there/ any more"; it ends, ". . . I don't know, I'll never know, in the silence you don't know, you must go on, I can't go on, I'll go on."

This disillusion with solipsist joys is already latent in *Proust*, which is a bitter book, aboil beneath its elegant prose with the violence that contorts the poems of the same period. It is forecast also in "Dante and the Lobster," the opening story of the 1934 *More Pricks than Kicks*. At the climax of this tale the commonplace to which Belacqua Shuah has succeeded in reducing all relations with living creatures crumbles upward to engulf him in panic: he has never before realized that lobsters are boiled alive. One gets used to these things, as Belacqua is used to every other happening, and what you are used to you can then at your pleasure invest with fangless drama, as Belacqua eats his bread with saturnine savagery. ("This meal that he was at such pains to make ready, he would devour it with a sense of rapture and victory, it would be like smiting the sledded Polacks on the ice. He would snap at it with closed eyes, he would gnash it into a pulp, he would vanquish it utterly with his fangs.") But the boiling of the lobster, raping his consciousness, is excruciating like all the facts habit has not yet empearled.

> "Have sense," she said sharply. "Lobsters are always boiled alive. They must be." She caught up the lobster and laid it on its back. It trembled. "They feel nothing," she said.

In the depths of the sea it had crept into the cruel pot. For hours, in the midst of its enemies, it had breathed secretly. It had survived the Frenchwoman's cat and his witless clutch. Now it was going alive into the scalding water. It had to. Take into the air my quiet breath.

Belacqua looked at the old parchment of her face, grey in the dim kitchen.

"You make a fuss," she said angrily, "and upset me and then lash into it for your dinner."

She lifted the lobster clear of the table. It had about thirty seconds to live.

Well, thought Belacqua, it's a quick death, God help us all.

It is not.

There have been few inventions in fiction to compare with the voice from universal space that speaks those three words. It is later, soured and personified, the prevailing voice of the trilogy. The genial décor of *Murphy* comes to epiphany as Murphy, in his garret room, tied to his rocking chair ("slowly he felt better, astir in his mind, in the freedom of that light and dark that did not clash, nor alternate, nor fade nor lighten except to their communion. . . . Soon his body would be quiet, soon he would be free."), lightens his incandescent mind by a gentle rocking dissolution; when someone, mistaking one chain for another in the water closet, turns on the unlit gas, and Murphy is set free as he had not foreseen. Well, the tone of the narrative seems to say, it's a quick death, God help us all; and Molloy, Malone and the Nameless One stir in their hopeless beds to reiterate, "It is not."

7

That the tone of *Murphy* makes the claim later so rebuked, is a fact related to its narcissism of style. Though the novel is a vastly smoother performance, the author's mind is no more engaged with human fact than it was in the galvanically disrupted short stories of *More Pricks than Kicks*. Nor is it any more constrained than before or later to assent to the chief assumption of the European novel, that something valuable draws people together. On the contrary, a gaggle of grotesques needs Murphy, or needs to find him, but Murphy, the author's favorite, needs no one and nothing.

Our affection, not merely our admiration, is nonetheless evoked, but by the writing. The book is meant to be reread lovingly, sentence by sentence. The coroner wishes he were on the golf course: "He closed his eyes and struck a long putt. The ball left the club with the sweet sound of a flute, flowed across the green, struck the back of the tin, spouted a foot into the air, fell plump into the hole, bubbled and was still." With two details, the flute and the bubbling, this sentence makes easy jest of its own virtuosity. So does the deft procatalepsis which acknowledges how Miss Counihan's endowments are distributed: "I fear you would not pass through the door of my cupboard, not even sideways, not even frontways rather." So does the dialogue of Wylie and Neary, whose effortless amplitude of diction is neither wholly theirs nor wholly the author's:

> "But betray me," said Neary, "and you go the way of Hippasos."
> "The Akousmatic, I presume," said Wylie. "His retribution slips my mind."
> "Drowned in a puddle," said Neary, "for having divulged the incommensurability of side and diagonal."
> "So perish all babblers," said Wylie.

In this exact, pellucid brilliance of language, each sentence strained and filtered, we discern Murphy, the "seedy solipsist," drifting grotesquely, mutely to annihilation while an assortment of minor characters, each in solemn pursuit of some goal for the achievement of which Murphy is preposterously indispensable, dart after him like minnows toward a piece of bread. For Murphy, who is unaware of the pursuers, the central situation is that his body loves Celia, who wants him to go to work and support the two of them—thereby taking her off the streets—while his mind abhors the complications she introduces into his quest for anonymity, for a state of being "not free, but a mote in the dark of absolute freedom," a state most readily approximated by rocking naked in a dark room in a rocking chair "of undressed teak, guaranteed not to crack, warp, shrink, corrode, or creak at night," to which he binds himself with seven scarves. When he dies, Celia returns sadly to her old profession, and we realize with surprise that she has moved through this highly stylized novel wholly untouched by either satire or sentimentality. In the final chapter she gazes at a kite-spangled sky "simply to have that unction of soft sunless light on her eyes that was all she remembered of Ireland."

> The ludicrous fever of toys struggling skyward, the sky itself more and more remote, the wind tearing the awning of cloud to tatters, pale limitless blue and green recessions laced with strands of scud, the light failing —once she would have noticed these things. She watched the tandem coming shakily down from the turmoil, the child running forward to break its fall, his trouble when he failed, his absorbed kneeling over the damage. He did not sing as he departed, nor did she hail him.

The exquisite poise of this writing, its breath timelessly caught between Celia, the sky, and its own eggshell comeliness, concentrates with rare ease the best of Beckett's first novel. Though frequently he indulges in japes and epigrams, it is the aloof compassion with which Celia is presented that secures the book's flutelike purity. The characters—she is the test case—move unimpeded; they are not dolls, no joke is "on" them, they and the author share a pedantically austere estimate of the vanity of human wishes as they circulate through the plot's extravagant minuet. They don't, of course, exist; Celia is a transparent phantasm, the rest are points to which are tied the balloon strings to their characteristic jests. So there is no rictus, neither a point scored by the author nor a fist shaken in the face of eternity, in what an angrier writer would have contrived for the climax of the book, the reading of Murphy's will:

> With regard to the disposal of these my body, mind and soul, I desire that they be burnt and placed in a paper bag and brought to the Abbey Theatre, Lr. Abbey Street, Dublin, and without pause into what the great and good Lord Chesterfield calls the necessary house, where their happiest hours have been spent, on the right as one goes down into the pit, and I desire that the chain be there pulled upon them, if possible during the performance of a piece, the whole to be executed without ceremony or show of grief.

That his ashes are instead scattered by inadvertence on the floor of a pub isn't a last cruel joke (there is no cruelty in this world of bubbles) nor even an auctorial belch, merely a Quixote-like misadventure which doesn't matter. Murphy wouldn't have minded. One retains great affection for Murphy.

8

Yet *Murphy* is not a typical Beckett book. No reader of his earlier writings would have expected him to be able to deal with a character like Celia, and in no obvious way does the more celebrated later work derive from it.

To write it he simply evaded the madness in himself. To write the later books he confronted this madness. The madness in himself, the emetic hysteria of *Echo's Bones*—

> And the stillborn evening turning a filthy green manuring the night fungus

—went into abeyance with the first sentence of *Murphy*, as Beckett gave himself for the first time to his own vein of rich pedantic resignation: "The sun shone, having no alternative, on the nothing new." This retains, it is true, a juvescent smartness; the bleakness of the trilogy is more casual. But it leads without pyrotechnics into another tranquil absurdity: "Murphy sat out of it, as though he were free, in a mew in West Brompton," and that sentence to a third, and within five pages dialogue has subvened and reached without effort a plane of splendid grotesqueness:

> "The love that lifts up its eyes," said Neary, "being in torments; that craves for the tip of her little finger, dipped in lacquer, to cool its tongue—is foreign to you, Murphy, I take it."
> "Greek," said Murphy.

Yet what went into abeyance as this was written, and 70,000 words as good as these, arranged with a discipline that foreshadows the ferocious discipline of *Watt*, was not exorcised but simply metamorphosed. While the clown's mind gambolled in English, the ropewalker slipped into French; and we find, dating from about the time of *Murphy*, such poems as the one entitled "La Mouche," in which a fly is contemplated with Dedalian morbidity:

> entre la scène et moi
> la vitre
> vide sauf elle

ventre à terre
sanglée dans ses boyaux noirs
antennes affolées ailes liées
pattes crochues bouche suçant à vide
sabrant l'azur s'écrasant contre l'invisible
sous mon pouce impuissant elle fait chavirer
la mer et le ciel serein[5]

Having delineated the beast with precise repulsion, he squashes it, and the heavens, for no clear reason, are reversed in their courses. He is playing God, perhaps, and the fly (sucking the void, sabring the azure) is being made to play man. One cannot tell where the gratuitous apocalypse comes from, nor why the precisions of such special-purpose words as *crochues* and *chavirer* are thought relevant. The fly on the window conjures up a headlong violence which its presence does not suffice to explain, a violence merely latent in the poet; the poem testifies to this latency.

Ten years later, about the time he was writing the trilogy, we find him asking in another poem what he should do without this world, without a face, without questions,

où être ne dure qu'un instant où chaque instant
verse dans le vide dans l'oubli d'avoir été;

what would he do, he goes on, without this silence, abyss of murmurs, without this sky, which uplifts itself on the dust of its ballast? And we have barely time to reflect that the sky is rendered visible thanks to dust, and to wonder again at a seeming irrelevance of specification (why ballast?) before he is answering that as to what he would do without

---

[5] Between the scene and me/the pane/void save for it/flat on its belly /girt in its black guts/antennae quivering wings tied/legs clawing mouth sucking the void/sabring the air crushing itself against the invisible/under my impotent thumb it whelms/sea and serene sky.

all these dull things, why he would do as he does anyhow, peering through his porthole, shut up within himself:

> que ferais-je je ferais comme hier comme aujourd'hui
> regardant par mon hublot si je ne suis pas seul
> à errer et à virer loin de toute vie
> dans un espace pantin
> sans voix parmi les voix
> enfermées avec moi[6]

These are intense but facile despairs. It is when the clown imitates them that they leap into elegance:

> Unfortunately I do not know quite what floor I am on, perhaps I am only on the mezzanine. The doors banging, the steps on the stairs, the noises in the street, have not enlightened me, on this subject. All I know is that the living are there, above me and beneath me. It follows at least that I am not in the basement. . . . Perhaps there are other vaults even deeper than mine, why not? In which case the question arises again as to which floor I am on, there is nothing to be gained by saying I am in a basement if there are tiers of basements one on top of another. . . . There is naturally another possibility that does not escape me, though it would be a great disappointment to have it confirmed, and that is that I am dead already and that all continues more or less as when I was not. Perhaps I expired in the forest, or even earlier. In which case all the trouble I have been taking for some time past, for what purpose I do not clearly recall except that it was in some way connected with the feeling that my troubles were nearly over, has been to no purpose whatsoever. . . .

---

6 what would I do what I did yesterday and the day before
peering out of my deadlight looking for another
wandering like me eddying far from all the living
in a convulsive space
among the voices voiceless
that throng my hiddenness

Between this gallant logical pertinacity and the naked statement that I walk voiceless amid the voices shut up in me; between the clown's endlessly resourceful ritual of incapacity, of which short quotation can impart only a vestigial idea, and the ropewalker's grim insistence that he is moving very carefully with little joy; between the books that mime and the poems that merely state, and state little except their author's want of élan; between these pairs of thing there is all the difference art can make.

The passage just cited (it is from *Malone Dies*) was first written and published in French. Art chose for its battleground the French language, into which, by the time *Murphy* was being written, the author's endemic morbidity had transferred itself. The strange instinct that, about 1937, divided the two halves of his temperament, the gentle comedian and the morbid solipsist, between two languages, was obeying a psychic principle not difficult to reconstruct. Between a native language and a language of adoption is a difference not merely of tools but of selves. The words in which I carry on that unending dialogue that accompanies my conscious existence, these words cluster, ramify, and so color the unique person that I am as to precipitate within it what introspection knows as a *self*. ("It's a question of words, of voices," thinks the Unnamable; "the words are everywhere, inside me, outside me . . . I'm in words, made of words.") New words then will seek to precipitate a modified self, though the person is the same. And a system of new words learned later in life with the assistance of the disciplined understanding will attract, if they are allowed to invest the consciousness, whatever potential selfhood floats closest to the ratiocinative. (And we may note in passing how Beckett's French keeps recalling the systematic drill of the classrooms in which it was learned: "Elles n'ont pas germé. . . . Si elles devaient

germer elles auraient germé. Elles ne germeront jamais.")
It is perhaps not impertinent to speculate that a precocious
morbidity in our author did not mature or assimilate but
hung in the pit of his psyche, indigestible; that so long as
he was a monolingual writer it infected his words with
frenzy; that he was freed to pursue in English the gentle
career of Murphy when this clot of despairs had begun
speaking French; and that in writing the trilogy in French
a decade later he was facing it down on what had become its
home ground, as Moran in the first division of the trilogy
hunts down Molloy.

Molloy and Moran are more or less the author's Irish
and French selves respectively. The former, wild and er-
ratic, moves on "the island" in the vicinity of Bally, a
town whose name is half Irish cliché, half English obscenity. The latter, prim and constrained, with his chickens
and his parish priest, hails from a Turdy which suggests
not only a second Anglo-Saxon obscenity but the Tour
Eiffel. The hunt ruins Moran forever (there are to be
no more books like *Murphy* and *Watt*), but the writer
has thenceforward the freedom, in whatever he does, of
his whole personality.

Not that his "ideas" enlarge, only his powers. About
our situation Beckett has as little that is interesting or
useful to tell an interviewer as, probably, Shakespeare
would have had to say had the question been put to him.
And what little he seems to say is especially unwelcome
because we sense that it has been arrived at with exces-
sive facility, by giving temperament rein. "Les absents
sont morts," says one of the poems for instance, "les présents
puent," so "bouffe brûle fornique crève seul comme devant."
But the author of the plays and novels does not offer us
a statement. He offers rather to set before us a leaping mind
encased in ignorances very like our own, and to let that

mind, Molloy's or Malone's or Didi's or Gogo's or Hamm's, pantomime its own (our own) incapacity for reposing in stable conclusions. The ropewalker we admire with some distaste, unless he spice his performance with danger (a very high rope, for instance, which makes no real difference to what he *does*.) But to the clown, whatever his despairs, our hearts go out in what one reviewer well called "profound and sombre and paradoxical joy."

9

Before this decisive confrontation with the specter, he achieved one last tour de force in Anglo-Irish. This is *Watt*, where the inhabitants of the daylight world are banished at the outset to a farcical distance, exchanging conversation like this:

> These northwestern skies are really extraordinary, said Goff, are they not.
> So voluptuous, said Tetty. You think it is all over and then pop! up they flare, with augmented radiance.

Watt makes his appearance in this slapstick setting. "Tetty was not sure whether it was a man or a woman. Mr Hackett was not sure that it was not a parcel, a carpet for example, or a roll of tarpaulin, wrapped up in dark paper and tied about the middle with a cord." They are asking in fact the sort of question Watt is later to ask with more mournful tenacity: what? And if, as seems probable, the tireless explicitness of the book is indebted to certain premises of Ludwig Wittgenstein,[7] then the protagonist's name seem a compromise between What and Witt.

---

[7] The father of Logical Positivism, for whom, as for Watt, "to distinguish between what can be said about an event and what the event *really* means is sheer nonsense." See Jacqueline Hoefer's article on *Watt* in *Perspective*, Autumn 1959.

Having established the fact that the external Watt stumbles like an animated parcel through the world of policemen, love verses, hunchbacks, trams, births, and other vaudeville paraphernalia, the narrative settles down lovingly amid the shifting landscapes of the internal Watt, where all is a vagueness, a questioning, a cascade of deliquescent hypotheses. Watt enters, there is no knowing why, the employ of a Mr. Knott. His duties are rudimentary. He stays an indefinite length of time. He is then replaced, as appears to be the custom, and leaves. That is the entire plot, and whoever chooses to see in it a metaphor for human life is welcome to do so.

Mr. Knott is almost as elusive as the deity, and Watt in the Knott-world spends most of his time puzzling over the enigmatic arrangements of the establishment. The remains of Mr. Knott's dinner, when he has not eaten the whole of it, are invariably set outside to be eaten by a hungry dog; and how it can always be insured that a hungry dog will present itself on these occasions torments Watt through four solutions and fourteen objections, until he is compelled to postulate a retinue of at least six famished dogs, "suitably maintained at Mr. Knott's expense in a suitable place in a famished condition," plus five generations of a family named Lynch, maintained on annuities to look after the dogs. After twenty-six pages of detailed speculations, "once Watt had grasped, in its complexity, the mechanism of the arrangement, how the food came to be left, and the dog to be available, and the two to be united, then it interested him no more, and he enjoyed a comparative peace of mind, in this connexion."

For Watt is tormented by a faculty Beckett omitted from the more facile synthesis of *Murphy*. He bears the Cartesian cross, the discursive intellect, with its irremediable itch to think explicable worlds into existence, stumbling through corridors of exquisite absurdity toward some talismanic formula with which it can be temporarily at rest.

> Not that for a moment Watt supposed that he had penetrated the forces at play, in this particular instance, or even perceived the forms that they upheaved, or obtained the least useful information concerning himself, or Mr Knott, for he did not. But he had turned, little by little, a disturbance into words, he had made a pillow of old words, for a head.

Composing *Molloy* in French three years later, Beckett admits no such gentle cadences. What gains for Watt a pillow brings Molloy only protracted irritation, different only in quality from the irritation of keeping silence. He is entranced by some of the details he recalls, his bicycle horn for example ("If I were obliged to recall, in a roll of honour, those activities which in the course of my interminable existence have given me only a mild pain in the balls, the blowing of a rubber horn—toot!—would figure among the first."). But his characteristic tone is the one that dominates his account of his one love affair: "A mug's game in my opinion, and tiring on top of that, in the long run. . . . We met in a rubbish dump, unlike any other, and yet they are all alike, rubbish dumps, I don't know what she was doing there. I was limply poking about in the garbage, saying probably, for at that stage I must still have been capable of general ideas, This is life. . . . Our commerce was not without tenderness, with trembling hands she cut my toe-nails and I rubbed her rump with winter cream. This idyll was of short duration."

If Molloy, unlike Watt, pursues no questions, it is because the phenomena of the visible world simply do not interest him. He tired of them, he gives us to understand, long ago.

10

The late novels turn their surfaces, then, from the light, which falls on bodies in repetitive, cyclic, violent motion. (That is all that an orthodox Cartesian is likely to make of bodily activities, and Beckett from the first has found some variety of Cartesianism much to his taste.) One day just before the war he visited a tramp in prison. This tramp some weeks previously in a Paris street had suddenly stabbed him, and left him to be carried to a hospital with a perforated lung, James Joyce in the background placing anxious calls to specialists. Confronting the prisoner, Beckett now gently requested to know why. "Je ne sais pas, monsieur." The Occupation, from certain points of view, was not less senseless.

Revolving such things, the 1948 trilogy draws down suddenly into a spiraling void the wit, geniality, and relatively engaging sadness of *Murphy* and *Watt*. Molloy expends 300 words on a technical account of how a man on crutches, by applying the principle of the pendulum, can severely kick another man whom he has knocked down. ("I carefully chose the most favorable position, a few paces from the body, with my back of course turned to it. Then, nicely balanced on my crutches, I began to swing . . . in an ever-widening arc, until I decided the moment had come and launched myself forward with all my strength and consequently, a moment later, backward, which gave the desired result.") So is the physical world dismissed as mechanism, and cruelty as an incidental feature. "I rested, then got up, picked up my crutches, took up my position on the other side of the body and applied myself with method to the same exercise. I always had a mania for symmetry."

And the trilogy leaves its fastidious stench on the subsequent plays. Though the author resumes his grasp on the handles of practical affairs, and even generates, in the 1957 *All That Fall*, a bleached poetry of mundane fatigue, the memory of that secular dark night is not to be exorcised. There is no literary parallel for the three books in which Samuel Beckett, releasing a certain violence of temperament evident in his earliest works and suppressed in *Murphy* and *Watt*, turned his face away from every accessible satisfaction, even from the familiar contours of his own language, and jettisoning the very matrices of fiction—narrator, setting, characters, theme, plot—devoted his scrutiny (under the sign of Belacqua) to the very heart of novel writing: a man in a room writing things out of his head while every breath he draws brings death nearer.

From that everything flows, including the bedridden Malone's frequent proposal to enumerate his possessions, like a senescent Crusoe. Reminiscence, fantasy, description, reflection, all the paraphernalia of fiction pass through these books with the disarming obviousness of the unexpected. The narrator constantly shifts his focus of attention in order to keep himself interested. That is what the professional fictionist does too, though he would claim if pressed that he did it in order to keep the reader interested. Yet from no one is a reader more remote than from a novelist; the sheer labor of covering pages fills up his working days.

"There's this man who comes every week. Perhaps I got here thanks to him. He says not. He gives me money and takes away the pages. So many pages, so much money. . . . Yet I don't work for money. For what then? I don't know." Thus Molloy on the problems of authorship.

"I have always been sitting here, at this selfsame spot, my hands on my knees, gazing before me like a great horned owl in an aviary." Thus The Unnamable on the mode of fictitious existence. There are lights, there are sounds, but there is no place and he is no one exactly, like a character in fiction, which is what he is, and somehow a projection of the sedentary author's, which is what he is also.

As for events, we have for instance this:

> I have lost my stick. That is the oustanding event of the day, for it is day again. . . . It would of course have been better for me to relinquish my bed than to lose my stick. But I had not time to think. The fear of falling is the source of many a folly. It is a disaster. I suppose the wisest thing now is to live it over again, meditate upon it and be edified. It is thus that man distinguishes himself from the apes and rises, from discovery to discovery, ever higher, towards the light. Now that I have lost my stick I realize what it is I have lost and all it meant to me. And thence ascend, painfully, to an understanding of the Stick, shorn of all its accidents, such as I had never dreamt of. What a broadening of the mind. So that I half discern, in the veritable catastrophe that has be-fallen me, a blessing in disguise. How comforting that is.

This is no more pessimistic than *King Lear*, and considerably funnier. If Swift's "Meditation Upon a Broomstick" lies behind it, so do acres of fictional moralizing, reams of gnomic self-praise, and bundles of romances chronicling the acquisition and dispersal of portable property, from *Robinson Crusoe* to *The Spoils of Poynton*. The trilogy is, among other things, a compendious abstract of all the novels that have ever been written, reduced to their most general terms.

11

And not only novels; for the trilogy also manages a sardonic counterpoint to the epic tradition of the West, which proved to be mortal, and indeed came to an end (unless we are going to take *Paradise Lost* for a new beginning) at about the time the novel was invented. That tradition started with Homer, who if he had been a twentieth-century Irishman living in Paris, might well have written the first half of *Molloy* instead of what he did write, if it was he who wrote it at all.

What Molloy is writing, sitting up in bed, is perhaps a faithful narrative, or perhaps he is making it up. At any rate, it purports to deal with his journey to that room. He set out, it seems, on a bicycle, intending to visit his mother (also bed-ridden) ; and he has executed a huge sweep, more or less circular, through the to him known world, in the course of which he has lost the bicycle, the use of his legs, the toes on one foot, everything indeed but his crutches and the will to proceed. There has been a Calypso, named Lousse, in whose house he stayed some months after an acquaintance founded on running his bicycle over her dog. There has been a Cyclopean police sergeant, who threatened him with a cylindrical ruler, and before whom our wanderer altered his fortunes by proclaiming his own name. ("My name is Molloy, I cried, all of a sudden, now I remember.") There have been ramparts, and seaboard privations. He had just reached the point when it was impractical to drag himself further on his stomach, and was considering rolling, when help mysteriously arrived.

The narrative is now assumed by a certain Moran. He also is writing, and his story follows Molloy's about as faithfully as Virgil's followed Homer's. Like Virgil, he also imparts a notably administrative tone, being (unlike Molloy, or Homer) a citizen of a substantial community. ("I have a huge bunch of keys, it weighs over a pound. Not a door, not a drawer in my house but the key to it goes with me, wherever I go.") He is writing the narrative of a journey, by bicycle and on foot, accompanied by his son, which was meant to be a search for Molloy, but which in fact brought him back to his own house, minus son and bicycle, crippled, stripped, discredited, and barely distinguishable from his quarry.

So much for the *Odyssey* and *Aeneid* of this new graph of civilization. We next encounter its *Divine Comedy*, which revolves about another man in bed. He is called Malone, at least that is what he is called now, though there are signs that he is a new phase of Molloy, or perhaps of Molloy and Moran together (unless a Molloy is simply what a Moran turns into when he goes looking for a Molloy). Malone too is writing, with a stub of a pencil in an exercise book. What he is writing is an account of his final weeks on earth, and also, by fits and starts, a piece of fiction, to distract himself from speculation about his mysterious surroundings. His narrative concerns a certain Sapo, who midway changes his name to Macmann, ends up in an institution not unlike that in which Malone appears to be confined, and expires at the same moment as his creator.

If The Unnamable, in turn, were Malone dead it would not be surprising. He is seated in a gray space, menaced by mysterious lights, and frantically writing, he is not clear how or with what. He can hardly be Malone, however, since Malone periodically executes an orbit about him. Indeed, he is convinced that all the previous characters are in this place with him, in fact that he invented them and the whole "ponderous chronicle of moribunds in their courses, moving, clashing, writhing or fallen in short-lived swoons." (Were Molloy and Moran, for that matter, fictions of Malone's? Ulysses, it is true, appears in the *Divine Comedy*, and so do Virgil and Homer.) His problem, at the end of this counter-epic series, is to disappear, to cease from being and from troubling, a problem he will be powerless to resolve until he has given satisfactory evidence that he exists in the first place. This is difficult, since he is neither a kind of Virgil, nor of Homer, nor of Dante, but more or less a kind of Descartes (who Boileau asserted had cut the throat of poetry). Nevertheless he too tells sketchy stories, for instance about a certain Mahood who on one leg and crutches executed a world-wide spiraling Odyssey, and on another occasion was confined night and day outside a restaurant in a jar to which the menu was affixed, but despite his efforts to attract attention stayed apparently invisible to everyone but the proprietress. There is an important difference between these stories and Malone's, however, for it is not at all clear whether The Unnamable is inventing Mahood, or whether Mahood is partly responsible for inventing The Unnamable, having told the latter these stories about himself as part of the conspiracy to make him believe he exists. He is locked up with his fictions, at the mercy of an inchoate "they" who have supplied him with the very language he struggles with (yet which of us has made his own language?) , and "they" are still perhaps fictions of his, or he of theirs.

Homer, Virgil, Dante, Descartes: these are not continents on a map Beckett has been following; Rorschach configurations, rather, which his groupings of tension and emphasis encourage us to see. They appear because his concentric narratives and serial narrators, each in turn more densely conscious of having had the experience of all the previous ones, succeed one another in the same manner as the major efforts of the Western imagination, each master in turn more burdened by responsibility for the preceding ones, as in Mr. Eliot's vision of The Mind of

Europe. That is why outlines seem to grow clearer and purposes firmer as we work backward: Chaucer was not troubled by reading *Hamlet*, nor Homer by the cosmology of Mount Purgatory. It was the mind of Europe before the mind of Beckett that turned literature toward a more and more intricate self-consciousness, confronting a Joyce or a Proust with an intellectual landscape whose most mysterious feature is himself performing the act of writing. Beckett may be absolved of responsibility for turning even the novel in upon itself. Flaubert's first achieved fiction was a serious and powerful novel about a woman who has become what she is by reading novels.

The plays deal more openly with the past. *Waiting for Godot* reflects in its dusty but accurate mirror the Noh drama (tree, journey, concatenated rituals), Greek theater (two actors, messengers, expectation of a *deus ex machina*), and *commedia dell'arte* (unflagging improvisation round a theme), while *Endgame* beats its bleak light on Shakespeare's stage, dominated by a prince of players named Hamm. Novels and plays alike recapitulate the past of their art, so sparely that if we stare at a parallel it vanishes, so casually that if we ask Beckett the meaning of all this incumbent tradition he can cry with Dan Rooney, "It is a thing I carry about with me!" Yet its presence contributes to the powerful sense—irradiating his inert material—that he has gotten at the form's central sources of energy, and looks into a long tradition with X-ray eyes.

So he propels the trilogy's extraordinary *reductio* for some 180,000 words, incorporating as he goes by the *roman policier*, the picaresque chronicle, the *Bildungsroman*, the universes of Proust and Defoe (these two superimposed), the fiction of self-interrogation. Our attention is held without a plot (a broom that sweeps everything in the same direction), without an undertow of ideas, with a minimum of incident, with no incubus of profundity. What holds us is in part the unquenchable lust to know what will happen in the next ten words, in part the hypnotic fascination of the nearly motionless (flies on a windowpane). Yet he has so distilled these appeals that they operate with uncomfortable immediacy; we are not allowed to suppose that we are reading "for the story," or for some improving purpose. His transparent syntax establishes a tone, a tone of genial resignation, within which the events of the trilogy declare themselves; and these events are small items become momentous, a minute shift of attention, the toot of a bicycle horn, the whereabouts of a boot. For Beckett, manipulating a form that has always indulged itself in copious triviality, has invented for it a convention that can accommodate any amount of detail while rendering nothing too trivial to be interesting.

12

Let us concede that "the novel" is a bore. Wyndham Lewis, the last Titan, caused one of his characters to throw *Middlemarch* into the sea, in default of some appropriate archive. " 'The historic illusion, the scenes depicted, and the hand depicting them . . . should not be handed down as a living document. It is a part of history'—with this he dismissed it." This summary judgment on the trivialities of systematized humanism should jar us into noticing how large an assumption traditional fiction makes about the inherent interest of human beings: people who walk upstairs, walk downstairs, eat eggs, quarrel, marry, converse with clergymen, and ride in trains.

The place of such detail in a work of art has never been satisfactorily explained; Aristotle was not confronted with the problem. Its place in a work of entertainment, however, is a by-product of social history. Defoe filled *Robinson Crusoe* with inventories and iterative chronicles to delight a new mercantile class, who were entranced with the material rewards of self-reliance, and generations of children, who like to tell over possessions. ("Quick quick my possessions," cries Malone, sensing that his time is running out. "A needle stuck into two corks . . . the bowl of my pipe . . .") Subsequently nineteenth-century aesthetics—of the period of Landseer and Rosa Bonheur —certified an art of middle-distance detail as "verisimilitude" (thus defining *veritas*), and nineteenth-century liberalism certified the novel's preoccupation with people preoccupied by trivia as art's truest note, a proper human compassion.

The crucial place of Ireland in the recent history of Western literary art is accounted for by the historical fact that Ireland escaped the humanist dogma. Consequently the great Irish nihilists (for so they appear in a humanist perspective) have been the persistent reformers of the fictional imagination. Swift, a bare seven years after *Robinson Crusoe*, ascribed an overriding concern for footling verisimilitude to a mind so biased toward positivism and so devoid of moral resources that it could be permanently imposed on by talking horses. *Gulliver's Travels* is crammed with inventories and numerical estimates; the narrator's cousin informs us that he edited as much more of the same kind out of the manuscript. The point of so drowning sense in number is to characterize the narrator as a barbarian. The point of the similar exhaustiveness of *Ulysses*, the next great Irish book, is to characterize Mr. Leopold Bloom as a lost mind immersed to the eyes in quantifiable matter. The number of *things* to the square inch of Joyce's text defies computation.

They are the kind of things which are lightly distributed through standard works of fiction to make us feel at home (" . . . a pink ribbon which had festooned an Easter egg in the year 1899 . . ."), and in *Ulysses* they comprise not a background for human identity but a densely compacted substitute. Two chairs, one squat and stuffed, one slender, splayfoot, of glossy cane curves, set mutely before us the tryst of Marion Bloom and Blazes Boylan, and two pages compiled from a furniture wholesaler's catalogue epitomize the imagined fruition of a human life. Insofar as Joyce had designs on the bourgeois novel, his design was to run it to the ground. And in the great catechism of the seventeenth chapter, from which Beckett likely derived the style of *Watt*, Joyce makes it clear that within the bourgeois novel's vaulted recesses nothing human, unless it be the analytic faculty, can survive.

Watt confirms this discovery; and Beckett's next novel after *Watt*, the jettisoned *Mercier et Camier* is his farewell to the bourgeois novel.

> Why do we not throw away the waterproof? said Camier. What use is it to us?
> It retards the action of the rain, said Mercier.
> It is a shroud, said Camier.
> Do not exaggerate, said Mercier.
> Shall I tell you what I think? said Camier. Whichever one of us is wearing it is as much incommoded, both physically and morally, as the one who is not.
> There is something in what you say, said Mercier.
> They looked at the waterproof. Spread out at the foot of the ridge, it looked flayed. The shreds of a flecked lining, pleasingly faded, adhered to the shoulders. A clearer yellow marked the areas which the dampness had not yet penetrated.
> Could I apostrophise it? said Mercier.
> There is time, said Camier.
> Mercier reflected. Farewell, old gabardine, he said.

The silence lengthened. Camier said, That is all of your apostrophe?

Yes, said Mercier.

Let us be off, said Camier.

When they have walked a little away from it, the question arises, whether anything has been left in the pockets.

Punched tickets of all kinds, said Camier, burnt matches, on the edges of bits of newspaper obliterated notes of irrevocable appointments, the classic final tenth of a pointless pencil, several creased sheets of toilet paper, some condoms of doubtful impermeability, and dust. A whole life.

Nothing we need? said Mercier.

As I say, a whole life, said Camier.

How many thousand affecting incidents does this scene not epitomize and write off? As a few pages of Wordsworth's absorb and supersede a century of meditative Miltonic nature musing, so does Mercier's timeless farewell to the gabardine, and the finely pointless inventory of its contents, subsume three hundred novels preoccupied with bourgeois man's chief good, portable property. A few narrative touches, a little epithetic color, would have shaped us one grotesque incident (*in-cidere*, to befall). But this tableau of Virgilian gravity is not to be dismissed as an incident. Beckett's disarmingly effortless presentation has yielded instead what is virtually a myth, like e $=$ mc^2, transparent, static, wholly general. By means no different Dante made Neptune's quizzical glance at the Argo, which any merely vivid writer might have thought to exploit, into a timeless gaze: *che fe' Nettuno ammirar l'ombra d'Argo.*

Into this effortless book there vanish, indeed, the practiced storyteller's repertoire of gestures, never more to exert tension on Beckett's pages: two characters, a journey, a goal, mystery, fulfillment, dialogue and setting, meditation, local color, and major structure. It is a third-person narrative (Beckett's last), and it derives a peculiarly engaging astringency from the fact that the narrator seems not to hear our habitual curiosities, so entranced is he by his protagonists. They meet by appointment and set forth on a journey, we do not know why; before leaving the city they are parted from bicycle, haversack, and umbrella, we do not know how; they return from the country in order to recover these objects, it is not clear under what necessity. That is half the action: hear them discourse on it:

> . . . The things (I say things, for want of a better word), whatever they are, which we believe we need, in order to pursue our journey—
> Our journey, said Mercier, what journey?
> Our journey, said Camier, with the maximum chance of success, these things we had and we have them no longer. Now we placed them in the haversack, as being something to contain them. But on further reflection we have no proof that they are not in the umbrella, or attached to some part of the bicycle, with twine, perhaps. All that we know is that we had them once and have them no longer. And even of that we are not certain.
> As premises go, these are premises, said Mercier.

Back in the city they find the remains of the bicycle, they find the umbrella and lose it again for good, and the sack they do not find. They undertake a new journey, it is not clear where, and are separated, we cannot tell why. They meet briefly a last time, and talk by the canal:

> You remember the parrot? said Mercier.
> I especially remember the hare, said Camier.
> I think it is dead, said Mercier.
> We didn't encounter many animals, said Camier.
> I believe it was already dead the day she told us she had sent it to the country, said Mercier.
> He went a second time to the water's edge. He gazed a

while at the water, then returned to the bench.
Well, I am going, he said. Good-bye, Mercier.
Good night, said Mercier.

Rain falls steadily throughout the book. The locale is plainly Ireland, the city Dublin.

These last pages are steeped in a pathos the origins of which are obscure until we notice how the book works. It works by insisting on the utter reasonableness of everything in the immediate vicinity of the passage we are reading at the moment. The reasoning behind the ritualistic dialogue, as in that of Gogo and Didi in *Waiting for Godot,* is of nearly idiotic transparency, very appealing. And no minor contretemps goes unexplained; when on the second page Mercier and Camier play out for forty-five minutes an elaborate mime of repeatedly missing one another at the rendezvous, their timetables are charted with finicky care. This hallucinatory plausibility, as in dreams, is abetted by the casualness with which, amid our ignorance of many things, small certainties are dispensed: the bicycle, for instance, was a ladies' model, without a free wheel, braked by pedaling backwards. Nor has the narrator shirked formal unity; every third chapter of the book's twelve consists of a convenient résumé of the two preceding, whether to facilitate review, or to emphasize the fuguelike interplay of incident, or simply to make it quite clear that he has not been woolgathering but knows very well what he has just finished writing. Close up, then, we are attended by Reason, Farce (which springs from the forehead of Reason) , and Structure, the handmaiden of Farce. But as the book proceeds, the mere fact that we are familiar with more and more of it prompts longer and longer views: and these long views disclose local coherence to be enveloped by the absurd. Two men, for instance, engaged on unformulable business (like ourselves here and now), and surrounded by enigma and darkness (not to mention incessant rain), are squandering their every atom of moral resource on a missing bicycle (ladies' model). So incidents no less trivial than the opening peekaboo become, in the later stages of the book, formidable and ominous. Man's fate, it seems, is to inscribe the figures of plane geometry on a spherical surface. From over his shoulder, we may be heartened by his sureness and finesse. It is when we get a sufficient distant view of the sphere that we can discern pathos in his illusion that he is accomplishing straight lines and right angles, drawing an accurate map or plotting a reliable course.

These increasingly long perspectives are a function simply of the book's duration. They unfold from the simple fact that narrative takes time. It is usual, in Beckett's work, for the very nature of the form he is employing to effect in this way his most elusive declarations. Late in the second act of *Godot*, for instance, the revelation that Pozzo's satchels are full of sand sets up solemn human resonances, whereas a comparable disclosure early in the play would have been no more than a normal vaudeville detail. So in *Mercier et Camier* our persistent sense that we are on familiar novel-reader's ground, familiar signposts of fiction (dialogue, setting, motivation) always in sight, is constantly menaced by our growing conviction that the book's world isn't contained in fiction's crystal box where all is trimmed and at hand and sensible. The certainties of a form rooted in documentation are slowly eroded by a pervasive aimlessness; and *that*, instead of fiction's familiar positivisms, comes to justify the volitional climate in which the two friends do not abandon their enterprise but simply run down.

On page 266 of *Murphy* Celia is able to identify her

lover's body by a large birthmark on the right buttock, of which she became cognizant on page 29 as a result of the nude Murphy having been turned upside down by a rocking chair mishap early on page 28. But *Murphy* is Beckett's sole exercise, and an anomalous one, in the workman-like linkages of Flaubertian fiction. Such fiction explores a locked world; the world of *Mercier et Camier* is open for miles around, clear into the sunless void, in every direction. In Flaubertian fiction, of which *Ulysses* and *Finnegans Wake* are supreme examples, a myriad of unimportant matters are not scattered like sand over the text but nestle into it perfectly. (They differ in this way from the touches of verisimilitude in less crafty books, which mean to give the impression that everyday untidiness surrounds the action.) James Joyce, who had studied the third chapter in the sixth book of the *Metaphysics*, was aware that if the quotidian is pointless it is far from untidy. He was the only writer of prose fiction to face and examine the fact that all, literally *all,* the details and incidents of everyday experience do in fact dovetail together, in the manner of a Thomas Hardy plot, and that this neatness of fit not only does not have to be imported into "life" by the novelist, but of itself signifies nothing whatever. To any natural happening a cause can be assigned, and to that in turn a remoter cause or causes. These little inevitabilities litter fiction: Crusoe's tool chest contains just what he requires, because he was trained by the civilization that selected those tools. The ropewalker's road of accomplishment leads past *Ulysses* to, if possible, yet denser and more authoritative manipulation of such congruences. And the clown's instinct ("I don't think impotence has been exploited in the past.") is to rid himself of the whole problem.

In *Mercier et Camier* he does this by placing the narrative at the mercy of a craftsman sufficiently bored by idiot consistency to suppress its linkages. This man's relationship to the content of the book is artlessly disposed of in the first sentence: "The journey of Mercier and Camier I can recount in full, if I choose, for I was with them, all the time." His continual invisible presence, he does not mind divulging here and there, was that of creator and puppet master; on the third page of the typescript he reduces the mechanics of an elaborately botched rendezvous to a timetable of unsynchronized arrivals and departures, stares at it, and comments, "What a stink of artifice." In the last chapter, where there are signs that Beckett is tiring of the book, we are surprised by a sudden encounter with none other than Watt, whose only connection with Mercier and Camier is a common authorship. Watt smilingly assures Camier that he knew him from the cradle, whereupon Mercier vaguely recalls a certain Murphy, now ten years dead. "They never recovered his body, imagine." In these intramural pleasantries, which contain the germ of *The Unnamable* ("I am neither, I needn't say, Murphy, nor Watt, nor Mercier, nor—no, I can't even bring myself to name them . . ."), we discern Beckett's sudden realization of the way to lay the present book to rest. If he simply stops writing it he will not violate its decorum, since it has all the time existed, in an essentially lyric mode, as an amusement of its creator, an amusement fiercely pursued. The intensely formal dialogue gratifies his pursuit of form, the descriptive vignettes his taste for silken cadence and abrasive evocation, the arbitrary disposition of incident his somber faith in human orderliness amid perpetual assaults from the irrational. The world of the novel (constantly raining) is the narrator's mental landscape: hence its elusive geography. It grows suddenly clear that we are on the brink of the trilogy; that Mercier and Camier, the narrator, and Beckett who holds the pen, constitute a converging series whose terms are difficult to distinguish; and that this fiction is less close to any other reality than to the mental world of a man sitting in a room before a sheaf of papers.

The Rational Domain

Ah the old questions, the old answers, there's nothing like them!

—*Endgame*

Not count! One of the few satisfactions in life?

—*All That Fall*

1

Let the serpent commence swallowing his tail, and let this process continue to some ideal limit: then ultimately the tip of his tail (who doubts it?) must end up stuffed as far back inside the serpent as it is possible to reach: i.e., inside the tip of his tail. In the same way, Molloy's narrative, composed in bed, of the events which brought him to this bed, must one day be brought down in time to the moment when it was itself commenced; and then discuss the writing of its own first paragraph; and so at last traverse itself to that limit where the writing of the word now being written becomes its own subject. This is what in fact happens in *Malone Dies*, the man in bed writing about himself in bed writing, and proposing to track himself to his own death, so that his last word may be about his last word—better, may *be* his last word; as a spring with no thickness, wound sufficiently tight, will become a point. Malone even introduces a new train of terms to converge on this limit, the sequence of fantasies about Macmann, who if all goes well (and it seems to) will die when he does. The Unnamable, finally, for whom all is always now, need coax no past to catch up with him, nor manage no present *durée* toward a terminus. In that domain where division by zero yields any answer you like, the narrative and its substance grow absolutely identical, and that in which they fuse is pure activity, the ape of pure Act: a going on ("I can't go on, I'll go on.")

A bodily career, then (2) an immobility, then (3) a writing, then (4) a writing about the writing, along with (4a) a fiction arising from and paralleling the writing, then (5) a writing become a writing: this is not only the shape of the trilogy, and by inference Mr. Beckett's Pocket History of Western Thought from Homer to The Unnamable, it has also become an archetypal intellectual career: James Joyce's, for example, driving heroically toward a huge echoing impasse, the introduction into which of any amount of extraneous material will never avail (since I it was who chose it) to transcend the echoes of me. So cartloads of learning, some of it commissioned from disciples like S. Beckett, M.A., will not efface from *Finnegans Wake* the lineaments of the Joyce family, and Mr. Pound's Emperors intimately resemble Mr. Pound.

Descartes himself carried the process as far as 4a, the generated fiction, like the tale of Macmann. For what he does, having brought the narrative of the *Discourse* through wars and wanderings down to the point where he discovers himself thinking, is commence to generate a mental world: for, granted my own existence, then God exists if I conceive Him, and I do; and given the First Cause, I can work out a set of causes; and "examining what were the first and most ordinary effects that could be deduced from these causes . . . I have found heavens, stars, an earth, and even on the earth, water, air, fire, minerals, and some other things of this kind"—minerals, look you, and perhaps even cows, if we can live long enough to work out the details, with the help, alas, of "many particular experiments."[1] Nor will these cows be common cows, but cows begotten by necessary reason, otherwise indistinguishable from the common cows our bodily senses shadow.

This is exquisite comedy, the more so when we look round that century and behold so many homemade worlds, each hung from a simple principle. Give Leibnitz a monad, or Crusoe a chest of tools, and in a little while you will behold yet another simulacrum of the familiar places. So in the final hours of this world's Endgame the blind reasoner and his artisan are creating a hygienic dog. One leg is still to be affixed, and the sex goes on last.

> HAMM (*his hand on the dog's head*) : Is he gazing at me?
> CLOV: Yes.
> HAMM (*proudly*) : As if he were asking me to take him for a walk?
> CLOV: If you like.
> HAMM (*as before*) : Or as if he were begging me for a bone. (*He withdraws his hand.*) Leave him like that, standing there imploring me. (*Clov straightens up. The dog falls on its side.*)

It is Descartes who leads the Western mind to the place where realistic fiction, its accuracy checked by "many particular experiments," becomes a focal mode of art. His journey to the famous room with the stove foreshadows the novelist's journey to the room where one writes day after day, alone. Beckett would seem to be the first to have read the *Discours de la Méthode* as what it is, a work of fiction. In his own memoir Descartes passes more quickly than Molloy over nine years' wandering, "a spectator rather than an actor in the plays exhibited on the

---

[1] *Discourse on Method,* Part VI.

theater of the world," but the correspondence remains. He even alludes to Molloy's forest, where travelers, he notes, "ought not to wander from side to side, far less remain in one place, but proceed constantly towards the same side in as straight a line as possible . . . ; for in this way, if they do not exactly reach the point they desire, they will come at least in the end to some place that will probably be preferable to the middle of a forest." He was guided, he tells us, by three or four maxims, the third of which confirms the author of *Proust* in his view of human desire. "My *third* maxim was to endeavour always to conquer myself rather than fortune, and change my desires rather than the order of the world; . . . and this single principle seemed to me sufficient to prevent me from desiring for the future anything which I could not obtain, and thus render me contented."[2] For nothing, he says, was at the disposal of the most fortunate sages of antiquity except their own thoughts, and it is wise therefore to abdicate from the ambitions of the great world. It is all the more wise to so abdicate, when one reflects on the satisfactions to which thought can attain: the child who knows that 2 plus 2 equals 4 "may be assured that he has found, with respect to the sum of the numbers before him, all that in this instance is within the reach of human genius." Descartes' restless mind does not often pause to savor such plenitudes. Murphy, less a conquistador asks for nothing more.

His vote was cast. "I am not of the big world, I am of the little world," was an old refrain with Murphy, and a conviction, two convictions, the negative first. How should he tolerate, let alone cultivate, the occasions of fiasco, having once beheld the beatific idols of his cave?

[2] *Discourse on Method*, Part III.

In the beautiful Belgo-Latin of Arnold Geulincx: *Ubi nihil vales, ibi nihil velis.*

The beauty of this Latin is highly relevant. Geulincx (1624-1669) was a second-generation Cartesian of whom it is not unfair to say that he moves entranced for 1,500 pages through the balance and ceremony of his own iterations, which uncoil gently like smoke. *Partes Humilitatis sunt duae: Inspectio sui et Despectio sui.* "Vales, velis; inspectio, despectio": it is usless to resist alliances that have lain prepared in the Latin language so many ages, now with such gravity to be decanted. The divisions of Humility are two: to inspect oneself, to despise oneself. What Beckett character has omitted these operations, or omits continually to report on the results? "The fact is, it seems, that the most you can hope is to be a little less, in the end, the creature you were in the beginning, and the middle": so runs a portion of Molloy's *despectio sui.*

What especially characterized Geulincx however, and qualifies him for repeated mention in the Beckett canon, is not simply the ceremonious resignation of his prose, but the curious doctrine it serves. It is the doctrine of a "bodytight" mental world, around which, or perhaps attached to which, the body performs its gyrations according to laws the mind need not attempt to fathom. Though he holds it true that we know from our minds outward, we need entertain no Berkeleian doubts about the body; it is real. Nor are body and mind united in the pineal gland, as Descartes supposed; they are not united at all. They are, in the language of *Murphy*, partially congruent, no more. Murphy, we are told, "neither thought a kick because he felt one nor felt a kick because he thought one"; and he was "content to accept this partial congruence of the world of his mind with the world of his body as due to some process of supernatural determination."

All this follows, for Geulincx, from the fact that I do not know how I lift my hand: and *Quod nescis quomodo fiat, id non facis*: because you do not know how it was done, you did not do it. My willing to lift my hand was the occasion for some supernatural agency to re-create it in a lifted posture. Geulincx for this reason receives a footnote in the larger histories of philosophy as the first of the Occasionalists, a school of post-Cartesians of whom Malebranche is the least forgotten. The sun, in the same way, is unlikely to know how it warms me; therefore it does not, though it is true to say that I am warmed in its presence. I move, then, through the courses of my mental life, with which alone I am conversant, bounded by a darkness and surrounded by the corporeal irrelevancies The Unnamable characterized as "moribunds in their courses, moving, clashing, writhing or fallen in short-lived swoons."

Here we have the entree to that strange detachment with which Beckett's people regard the things their hands and feet do: their tendency to analyze their own motions like a man working out why a bicycle does not topple, and their reluctance to live through the senses without scrupulous interrogation of all that the senses report. "I know I am seated," writes The Unnamable, "my hands on my knees, because of the pressure against my rump, against the soles of my feet, against the palms of my hands, against my knees. Against my palms the pressure is of my knees, against my knees of my palms, but what is it that presses against my rump, against the soles of my feet? I don't know. My spine is not supported. I mention these details to make sure I am not lying on my back, my legs raised and bent, my eyes closed." These are strangely contemporary preoccupations; he is like an astronaut in his capsule, referring to gravitation (when there is any) some meaning for "up" and "down." We are all growing used to a world in which long chains of analysis have invaded the most commonplace experiences: motion study, communications theory, motivational research, astro-navigation, these specialisms begin to preempt the plane of behavior on which one makes the bed, talks to one's neighbor, desires a hat, or moves from place to place. The motion study expert can instruct as how best to make the bed in our minds before we make it with our hands, the better to spare the lumbar vertebrae and the metatarsals. By emptying our statements of all content whatsoever, we can build with perfect precision the most general chains of inference, and reproduce them in a computer's switching systems. The very learning process can be programed into branching chains of question and answer, leading the student, like Huxley's young man playing chess with Nature, to an exacting dialogue with an infinitely patient machine. Beckett is the first writer to explore the resources of pity and terror that lurk in a wholesale abstraction now so familiar; he is profoundly right in finding the seventeenth-century Occasionalists aesthetically relevant to an age that has no difficulty in diagnosing their speculative shortcomings.

And science, by no accident, begat science fiction. Since my mental life (Geulincx says) is my own, fiction is its freedom; and fiction, John Locke's anomalous aberration, grows easier to account for than its coincidence with fact. We have seen how Hamm, Malone, and the others continually solace themselves with stories. "Perhaps," thinks The Unnamable, "I shall be obliged, in order not to peter out, to invent another fairy-tale, yet another, with heads, trunks, arms, legs and all that follows, let loose in the changeless round of imperfect shadows and dubious light." These stories draw on what the doctrine of body tightness forbids us to call experience, but only research; in *Murphy* the feminine lead is introduced with a column of measurements, Forearm 9½″, Wrist 6″, Bust 34″, Waist 27″, Hips 35″, etc. That the stories always run parallel to or converge on empirical fact, as Malone's chronicle of Macmann is asymptotic to Malone's experience of being Malone, is a special case of the Occasionalist principle that mental and physical events are somehow congruent. Physical events in the same way do not interact but coincide. So Watt hears, as in an early score by John Cage, three frogs croaking Krak! Krek! and Kirk! at nine-beat, six-beat and four-beat intervals respectively; and one sees from the page on which this is written out how, after a simultaneous start, 79 croaks, 120 beats, 360 occasions taken or not taken, must intervene before the sequence recurs; and how the combination Krek! Krik! occurs seven times, Krak! Krik! four, and Krak! Krek! two, while the unbroken sequence Krak! Krek! Krik! is heard once only. We owe this symmetry to no Ranarian design; each frog attends only to its private schedule of croaks. Similarly we read in *Comment C'est* of a futile ballet on the heath, executed by a man, a woman, and a dog:

> suddenly yip left right off we go chins up arms swinging the dog follows head down tail on his balls nothing to do with us he had the same idea at the same instant Malebranche less the rosy hue . . .

> . . . right about inward turn fleeting meeting face to face transfers and hand in hand again arms swinging silent relishing of sea and isles heads pivoting as one towards the city fumes silent distinguishing of monuments heads back front as though on an axle

> suddenly we are eating sandwiches in alternate mouthfuls I mine she hers and exchanging endearments my

sweet girl I bite she swallows my sweet boy she bites
I swallow we don't yet coo with our bills full

darling girl I bite she swallows darling boy she bites
I swallow brief blackout and there we are again off
through the fields hand in hand arms swinging . . .

This Occasionalist courtship is the type of many Beckett
descriptions—Watt walking, for instance:

> Watt's way of advancing due east, for example, was to
> turn his bust as far as possible towards the north and at
> the same time to fling out his right leg as far as possible
> towards the south, and then to turn his bust as far as
> possible towards the south and at the same time to fling
> out his left leg as far as possible towards the north. . . .
> The knees, on these occasions, did not bend. . . . The
> arms were content to dangle, in perfect equipendency.

Here we have a congeries of gestures owning no intelligible interrelationship, united apparently by happen-
stance like the croaks of the three frogs and only conven-
tionally to be abridged under the concept "locomotion."
By allowing no flow of intention from mind to body, by
positing a succession of supernatural interventions to
bring my hand through millions of ever so slightly altered
interim positions to a place where it can scratch my ear,
Geulincx and his school are driven to a treatment of motion as grotesquely analytic as the work sheets of a Disney
animator.[3] Watt's walking is less something he does than
something we can observe his body doing. "Sicut in omni
corpore sunt tres dimensiones," writes Geulincx, "as in
all bodies there are three dimensions, so in all motion

---

[3] By depriving Mickey Mouse of his tail as a measure of wartime economy, the studio is said to have saved many thousands of dollars: not in
ink, but in time required to keep track of the tail's movements. The
animated cartoon, in which everything must be preprogramed, is
the type of all up-to-date technology.

three tendencies, *abitus, transitus, aditus;* for in all movement there is a parting from somewhere, a passage somewhere, a going to somewhere. . . . . But there is no departure without transit and arrival, no transit without departure and arrival, etc." Or again, "Divisio et motus re ipsa nihil differunt," movement and analysis are inseparable; and the 24 frames into which the movie camera analyzes each second of action correspond to an infinite process of subdivision performed by the moving body itself.[4] And since nothing, in the midst of movements however complex, is acting to the slightest degree on anything else, the parts of the closest description are immersed in a fine irrelevance: "my sweet girl I bite she swallows my sweet boy she bites I swallow."

Other things in the Beckett cosmos, in addition to the pervasive self-abnegation and the analytic treatment of process, seem sponsored by Geulincx. The most important of these is the voice that injects postulates into the otherwise closed system of discourse. "I quote," says the protagonist of *Comment C'est* time and again: *je cite . . . je cite . . . je cite . . .*; and The Unnamable, who can experience with his eyes nothing but the void directly ahead of him, ascribes his general knowledge to a shadowy and doubtless unreliable committee by which he half recalls being instructed. These authorities derive perhaps from a supposition of Geulincx, that what he does not know of his own account he is somehow taught. "There are certain modes of knowing in me, which are independent of me and which I myself do not excite in myself. They are, therefore, excited in me by something other than myself (for it is impossible that they come to me from nothing).

---

[4] These come respectively from the *Physica Vera,* II-12, and the *Annotata ad Metaphysicam,* ad II-10.

And this other, whoever he be, must be conscious of this business; for he is the agent and it is impossible that he be doing whatever he does without knowing how."[5] This power of course Geulincx means to call God, transmitting thoughts to me through my body (for what I call sensory experience, since I experience it in my mind, must be called a mode of thought). To this conclusion, however, no Beckett character warms. They find that the body reports chiefly news of its own decomposition, and furthermore they distruct whatever they are not working out for themselves. So everything the mysterious authority has to say is disquieting.

What you work out for yourself, moreover, is fiction: fiction, man's comfort. "I am too nervous this evening to listen to myself decay," muses one of these outcasts from life at the opening of the story called "Le Calmant," too nervous "to wait for the red torrents of the heart's falls, the caecum blindly writhing, and for there to be accomplished in my head the long assassinations, the assaults on unshakeable pillars, the love with corpses." So, "I am going to tell myself a story, I am going to try and tell myself yet another story, to try and calm myself." This man's successor, Malone, takes infectious joy in the processes of fiction. Macmann's coat he describes for a page, luxuriating in the detail of the buttons. The hat next, "marred by a wide crack or rent extending in front from the crown down and intended probably to facilitate the introduction of the skull. For coat and hat have this much in common, that whereas the coat is too big, the hat is too small." Then fiction debouches on fiction, as a consideration of how well coat and hat are assorted leads to the speculation that before they came to Mac-

---

[5] *Metaphysica Vera.* I-5.

mann they might have been bought "one at the hatter's, the other at the tailor's, perhaps the same day and by the same toff, for such men exist, I mean fine handsome men six foot tall and over and all in keeping but the head, small from over-breeding. And it is a pleasure to find oneself again in the presence of one of those immutable relations between harmoniously perishing terms. . . ." And lo, we have drifted without noticing, so great is fiction's narcotic power, to the very nirvana of all Beckett lucubrations, where effortlessly the mathematic powers cascade. Geulincx, the imperturable Geulincx, austere as Watt, plays in this way mathematician to Descartes' romancer, not telling us of journeys through woods and evenings spent by a stove, but pouring from hand to hand his graceful abstract sentences forever, their pairs and trios of homonymous terms permuted like the three notes of Watt's frogs. Or he will invest a didactic catalogue with his own pleasure in supple fulgent words: "Video nubes, saepe candidas, nonnunquam atras, interdum quamplurimis coloribus sub vesperam ac auroram distinctas:"[6] Clouds he says he sees, often white, sometimes black; and storms and snow, and smoke and limpid sky, and empty space. But we are not to believe a word of it; it is all words, where we feel his warming presence in this way, words and his pleasure in handling them. As for the clouds and sky, he does not see them, they are exhibited to him. All that he himself does is link word to word, thought to thought, guess perhaps to guess, like Malone lying by the small window beyond which is whatever he fancies. He declares "omnem Actionem meam, quatenus mea est, intra me manere"; all freedom (such as it is) lies behind the eyes. The protagonist of "The End" re-

---

6 *Ethica*, I-ii-2.

ceived long ago, from one Ward, Geulincx's *Ethics* and a pair of dark glasses, the latter perhaps accessories to the practice of what the former preached. Geulincx was no idealist, and to Ward's death, "crumpled up in the water closet, his clothes in awful disorder, struck down by an infarctus," there clings none of the irony that would have attended the similar demise of a Berkeleian. Geulincx merely shut the domain of the body away, in a gesture mimed by perhaps his most pervasive legacy to the Beckett imagination, a firm, affirmative, slightly narcissistic, functionally ornate, faintly French, Latin style.

2

Let us look again. He is the principal master in our time of the formal declarative sentence, a mastery he has consolidated during his years of writing in French, where one places the subject before the verb and the object after it, and unites modifiers to their substantives with a fragile but inflexible logic. Every such sentence advances the narrative, or the argument, to an exact and measurable degree; there is no ellipsis, no *rubato,* no homely leap of the precipitate heart. The *pace* of this prose is even and indomitable, utterly unrelated to the pace of events. Like cinema it can convince us, despite cuts and flashbacks, that the real is declaring itself from moment to moment, without intervention, abridgment, or acceleration. Hence its suitability to drama, where what happens happens before us now, neither "presented" nor interfered with. Hence, in the novels, its unique identity with its subject, which is not a sequence of re-created happenings but a fondling, by the intellect, of remembered sequence.

Thus Malone, for instance, having just consolidated his belongings, discerns one or two unimportant discrepancies between estimate and tally:

I see then that I had attributed to myself certain objects no longer in my possession, so far as I can see. But might they not have rolled behind a piece of furniture? That would surprise me.

The analytic intelligence examines this hypothesis at its own speed, and with its own criteria of reasonableness. The analytic intelligence then declines to be hurried away from evidence of some complexity:

A boot, for example, can a boot roll behind a piece of furniture? And yet I see only one boot. And behind what piece of furniture? In this room, to the best of my knowledge, there is only one piece of furniture capable of intervening between me and my possessions, I refer to the cupboard. But it so cleaves to the wall, to the two walls, for it stands in the corner, that it seems part of them.

Beckett's absolute sureness of decorum, juxtaposing without a quaver sentences that might have come from the prosecutor's summing up ("I refer to the cupboard.") with scraps of the bleakest notation ("And yet I see only one boot.") presides over a highly formal elegance, into which every qualification required by a reliable formullation ("in this room, to the best of my knowledge . . .") can find its way with scientific precision. No sentence prolongs itself merely because it cannot find out where to end, or is reduced to less than full coherence by human passion however intense. Macmann and Moll make love in a context of bountiful explicitness:

And though both were completely ignorant they finally succeeded, summoning to their aid all the resources of the skin, the mucus, and the imagination, in striking from their dry and feeble clips a kind of sombre gratification. So that Moll exclaimed, being (at that stage) the more expansive of the two, Oh would we had but met sixty years ago! But on the long road to this what flutterings, alarms and bashful fumblings, of which only this, that they gave Macmann some insight into the expression, Two is company.

Macmann's exegetical insight illustrates that of the man in "Premier Amour" whose epitaph, composed long ago, gives him unfailing satisfaction: "Elle illustre un point de grammaire."

> Cî-gît qui y échappa tant
> Qu'il n'en échappe que maintenant.
> Il y a un syllabe de trop dans le second, et dernier, vers, mais cela n'a pas d'importance, à mon avis.

And nothing, it seems, can retard or advance the pace of this implacable notation, which ultimately, as one would not expect, sustains Moll and Macmann by the courtesy of so patient an attention. Within this earnest detachment Moll's exclamation loses half its absurdity, and contrives to change from the echo of some negligible novel into an appropriate expression of human passion suffused with human dignity: "Oh would we had but met sixty years ago!" "Would we had" strikes the Roman note.

The Winnie of *Happy Days* in the same way, buried to the waist and later to the neck, maintains a logician's, a grammarian's detachment from her plight.

> Then. . .now. . .what difficulties here, for the mind. (*Pause.*) To have been always what I am—and so changed from what I was.

Though the earth now turns so slowly that through the intensely hot day she feels her body menaced by spontaneous combustion (". . . oh I do not mean necessarily burst into flames . . ."), yet she considers with some agitation whether the hairs or hair one brushes and combs are properly styled "them" or "it" ("Brush and comb it? Sounds improper somehow."), and feels it outweighs the day's miseries to have learned the proper definition of "hog":

> Oh this *is* a happy day! This will have been another happy
> day! (*Pause.*) After all. (*Pause.*) So far.

At her most possessed, she achieves with two dozen words
a Calder-like syntactic equilibrium, its parts gently swaying
to the rhythm of her consternation. Thus struggling to un-
furl her umbrella she articulates in distracted snatches a
sentence as perfectly shaped as any in the canon:

> One keeps putting off—putting up—for fear of putting up—
> too soon—and the day goes by—quite by—without one's
> having put up—at all.

The mind prevising a sentence's latter part, the will
directing the sentence past all distractions, the imagination building with just so many achieved sentences as
may be needed, these faculties rise over our otherwise
benumbing affinity with the animals that cry. A sentence
reproduces in slow motion some mental gesture. For the
mind to systematize in retrospect its dartings through
chaos, and between salient points on that reconstructed
trajectory to draw unswerving syntactic lines, is to trans-
fer to graph paper movements the hares and butterflies
can only perform. Thus human dignity asserts itself in
syntax: a principle abandoned in the English written language some time after Dryden, but still active in French.
The regnant principle of English style, a connoisseurship
of incandescent phrases, lays an unusual burden on individual words; hence Joseph Conrad's complaint that no
English word is a word, that in English you cannot say
"an oaken table" without conveying perhaps more than
you meant to. You are going bail, in such a phrase, for
the table's substantiality, worth, and age. "Une table de
chêne" specifies a material and stops. This quality of the
language in which they were first composed enters into
the very sinews of Beckett's plays.

HAMM: Va me chercher deux roues de bicyclette.
CLOV: Il n'y a plus de roues de bicyclette.
HAMM: Qu'est-ce que tu as fait de ta bicyclette?
CLOV: Je n'ai jamais eu de bicyclette.
HAMM: La chose est impossible.

This strophic exchange is our first intimation that the world is crumbling away on every side of the room where Hamm sits in his chair; it determines, therefore, the rigorous stoicism with which the bleak ambience is to be regarded. This determination the French makes without assistance from the actor. "Il n'y a plus de roues de bicyclette" states merely that from the universe there has been subtracted the category "roues de bicyclette"; it does not posture, it does not declaim. "There are no more bicycle wheels" is unsustained by this philosophic sureness of negation; spoken rapidly, it is overly casual; spoken with feeling, it expends its sonorities in a rhetoric of deprivation, beating fists on an unyielding absence. Translating his dialogue into English, Beckett has had no choice at this point but to use dictionary equivalents, and *Endgame* is noticeably weaker at this point than *Fin de Partie*. Elsewhere, pursuing as always an ideal of impartial exactness, he has had to prune the English very considerably to keep sentiment out.

NAGG: (*geignard*) : Qu'est-ce que c'est?
CLOV: C'est le biscuit classique.

This becomes,

NAGG (*plaintively*): What is it?
CLOV: Spratt's medium.

—a desperate equivalent for the aloof precision of "le biscuit classique." Some minutes later Hamm ascertains from Clov that his seeds have not sprouted, that if they were going to sprout they would have sprouted by now:

CLOV: Si elles devaient germer elles auraient germé.
Elles ne germeront jamais.
Un temps.
HAMM: C'est moins gai que tantôt.

There is nothing that can be done for Hamm's comment in the course of transposing this exchange into a more sentimental idiom: spoken English cannot protect "moins gai" with the rigor of the negative comparative, as impersonal as a minus sign, nor prevent "tantôt" from expanding into a yearning after vanished yesterdays; nor can it, for that matter, supply an equivalent for "Elles ne germeront jamais" sufficiently austere to declare its meaning and stop. Determined at all costs to keep at bay a pathos that would ruin the play, Beckett having written "They'll never sprout" instructs the actor to utter this line *"violently,"* and as for "C'est moins gai que tantôt," he has contented himself with "This is not much fun."

It is clear that when he quailed before the prospect of rewriting this play in English and wrote to Alan Schneider that the English text would inevitably be a poor substitute ("the loss will be much greater than from the French to the English *Godot*"), the author spoke the simple truth. This is not the generic problem of "untranslatability," a question of values and nuances. It is a principle entoiled in the very conception of *Fin de Partie*, which carries to one extreme (there are others) the Beckett concern with style as a phenomenon of explicitness, and elucidates his prolonged immurement with the French language.

One side of explicitness is pedantry: that habit of mind which takes keen pleasure not in knowing but in retracing the process of arriving at knowledge. (Virtue, wrote Arnold Geulincx, is the Love of Reason: *Virtus est Amor Rationis*; and by reason is meant the rational process, not the contemplation of its results: *Nam Virtus solam Rationem admittit, solam illam sinu complexuque suo dignatur; omnem aliam contemplationem excludit.*) The pedant is not impelled to use the Theorem of Pythagoras for squaring off a building lot, he delights to savor each of the stages by which the theorem itself is proved: an act of pure connoisseurship, yielding nothing new, one human approximation to the pure intellection of the angels, who make no discoveries. As Molloy describes step by step the Odyssey that brought him to this bed, so the pedant rehearses the past because it is bounded, definite, mysterious yet circumscribed. He is chained to some point of origin, and fondles lovingly each of the links, with a rapture analogous to the mathematical passions. If ax^2 plus bx plus c equals zero, then without fail, exception, or doubtful case x will equal minus b, plus or minus the square root of b^2 minus $4\,ac$, the whole divided by $2a$ and this truth, if it can never expand, can never be worn out. So we are invited to refinger the smoothed formulations of Watt: "Obscure keys may open simple locks but simple keys obscure locks never"; or, "By what means then were the dog and the food to be brought together, on those days on which, Mr Knott having left all or part of his food for the day, all or part of the food was available for the dog?" Or at greater length, and with further nuances of pedantry,

Now Erskine's room was always locked, and the key in Erskine's pocket. Or rather, Erskine's room was never unlocked, nor the key out of Erskine's pocket, longer than two or three seconds at a stretch, which was the time that Erskine took to take the key from his pocket, unlock his door on the outside, glide into his room, lock his door again on the inside and slip the key back into his pocket, or take the key from his pocket, unlock his door on the inside, glide out of his room, lock the door again on the outside and slip the key back into his pocket. For if Erskine's room had been *always* locked, and the key *always* in Erskine's pocket, then Erskine himself, for all his agility, would have been hard set to glide in and out of his room, in the way he did, unless he had glided in and out by the window, or the chimney. But in and out by the window he could not have glided, nor in and out by the chimney, without being crushed to death. And this was true also of Watt.

Here, expanded into a kind of aesthetic principle, and equipped with a protagonist to correspond, we have the technical narcissism of *Murphy*, obeying the impulse of every principle in the Beckett cosmos to declare itself somewhere in full and at leisure. Watt, who inhabits the house of Mr. Knott in a kind of weak-eyed speculative daze, illustrates the principle that the pedant is the supreme aesthete (Lyly; Wilde), and so that every use of language sufficiently comprehensive and explicit tends, at the expense of brevity, to aesthetic status. Consider for instance the ten pages of *Watt* that caress the incident of the Galls, father and son. These two appear at Mr. Knott's door, and the younger, a middle-aged man, makes a brief speech of introduction:

> We are the Galls, father and son, and we are come, what is more, all the way from town, to choon the piano.

They already sound as though they have rather invented themselves on the spot than walked in from a busy world. "What is more" is delicious. After the piano is tuned the younger Gall speaks again:

> The mice have returned, he said.
> The elder said nothing. Watt wondered if he had heard.
> Nine dampers remain, said the younger, and an equal number of hammers.
> Not corresponding, I hope, said the elder.

In one case, said the younger.

The elder had nothing to say to this.

The strings are in flitters, said the younger.

The elder had nothing to say to this either.

The piano is doomed, in my opinion, said the younger.

The piano-tuner also, said the elder.

The pianist also, said the younger.

This was perhaps the principal incident of Watt's early days in Mr Knott's house.

Watt, however, cannot forbear to rehearse the incident in his head until it has "developed a purely plastic content and gradually lost, in the nice process of its light, its sound, its impacts and its rhythm, all meaning, even the most literal." It thus becomes—and this receives several pages of study—an incident "of great formal brilliance and indeterminable purport" (like all the rest of the book), so that it is plausible to ask whether whatever happened had actually no meaning in the least at the moment of its taking place: "Were there neither Galls nor piano then, but only an unintelligible series of changes, from which Watt finally extracted the Galls and the piano, in self-defense?"

That things and events are extracted in self-defense from an unintelligible continuum of changes is one of philosophy's self-cancelling propositions, assailing the very act of its own affirmation. It is thus ideally suited to Beckett's characteristic comedy of the impasse. It is first cousin to the statement, "Every statement that I make is meaningless." It hands over all discourse to the domain of Style; terms have sounds but not referents, sentences shape but not purport. Thus Watt begins to communicate "back to front":

Day of most, night of part, Knott with now. Now till up, little seen so oh, little heard so oh. Night till morning from. Heard I this, saw I this then what. Things quiet, dim. Ears, eyes, failing now also. Hush in, mist in, moved I so.

Later he inverts ("with all his usual discretion and sense of what was acceptable to the ear, and aesthetic judgement") not only the order of the words in the sentence but that of the letters in the word and that of the sentences in the period:

> Dis yb dis, nem owt. Yad la, tin fo trap. Skin, skin, skin. Od su did ned taw? On. Taw ot klat tonk? On. Tonk ot klat taw? On. Tonk ta kool taw? On. Taw to kool tonk? Nilb, mun, mud. Tin fo trap, yad la. Nem owt, dis yb dis.[7]

In rhythm, in symmetry, even often in euphony, this is as formal as anything in the book. As for coherence, it obeys the rule that the terms on either side of an equation may be arranged in any order. "I am interested in the shape of ideas," Beckett told Harold Hobson, "even if I do not believe in them. There is a wonderful sentence in Augustine. I wish I could remember the Latin. It is even finer in Latin than in English. 'Do not despair; one of the thieves was saved. Do not presume; one of the thieves was damned.' That sentence has a wonderful shape. It is the shape that matters."

We are back among the formulations of *Proust*. Daily expediency finds one ordering of the sensate tumult convenient, the mind at ease within itself may cherish quite another, and occasionally the two may intersect. No special prestige attaches to any grouping the mind may choose to impose: the odds against any combination of thirteen cards are exactly as great as the odds against thirteen spades. The rules of a game which impute special virtue to the latter (no rarer in itself than any other grouping)

---

[7] Sid by sid, two men. Al day, part of nit. Dum, num, blin. Knot look at wat? No. Wat look at knot? No. Wat talk to knot? No. Knot talk to wat? No. Wat den did us do? Niks, niks, niks. Part of nit, al day. Two men, sid by sid.

simply acknowledge that symmetry is satisfying in itself, and helpful to the memory.

So fact dissolves into symmetry; not that "fact," for Watt, is anything but a collective prejudice. *Watt* touches the unreflecting world at just four points: first, on a Dublin street, where a narrative that began in pedantry ("They sat down beside him, the lady on the one side, the gentleman on the other. As a result of this, Mr Hackett found himself between them.") passes through ceremony to fantasy; second, in the not-world of Mr. Knott, where the episodes of Erskine's key, and the scavenging dog, and the Galls, father and son, are melded in the deliquescent faculties of Watt; third, in an institution for the gently unbalanced, where Watt communicates his experiences to a certain Sam, who assumes responsibility for the narrative in its present form; and fourth, at the station, where in Part I we find Watt detraining for his sojourn with Mr. Knott, and in Part IV we find him to have somehow disappeared. (I omit, as not pertaining to any known world, the book's *Paradiso*, the twenty-eight page fantasy transacted in a college committee room.) Each of these milieux—street, house, asylum, station—undergoes, as did the Galls, father and son, an eerie disintegration into cadence, balance, and imperturbable reason. Imperturbable reason is the soul of pedantry, cadence and balance its ceremonial. They have power to dilute the importunity of things and neutralize the energetic passions. Watt considers at length in what order, if at all, he should shut the door, set down his bags, and rest; and pedantry, having rehearsed every combination of these actions, counsels him to undertake none: "For the sitting down was a standing up again, and the load laid down another load to raise, and the door shut another door to open, so hard upon the last, so soon before the next, as to prove, very likely, in the long run, more fatiguing than refreshing." Or the socks of the footsore Watt call for ceremonious attention:

> By wearing, on the foot that was too small, not one sock of his pair of socks, but both, and on the foot that was too large, not the other, but none, Watt strove in vain to correct this asymmetry. But logic was on his side, and he remained faithful, when involved in a journey of any length, to this distribution of his socks, in preference to the other three.

That there should be three other distributions of two socks, and that this, which has been chosen, can be resolved into its elements and reasons assigned thereto; that logic indeed is on the side of this one only: to linger in the presence of these truths yields to the pedantic mind enduring satisfaction, into which is appreciably subsumed the raw discomfort of wearing a boot, size twelve, and a shoe, size ten, on feet sized each eleven. So inventory yields ceremony, and ceremony anesthesia.

Quotation is a mode of ceremony. "What are those wonderful lines?" asks the buried Winnie time and again, calling to her aid scraps ne'er so well expresse'd: ". . . Go forget me why should something o'er that something shadow fling . . ." —small rituals of the sensibility, once learned, now from the ebbing memory summoned up for refingering. "One loses one's classics," she reflects with a sigh.

> Oh not all. (*Pause.*) A part. (*Pause.*) A part remains. (*Pause.*) That is what I find so wonderful, a part remains, of one's classics, to help one through the day.

By similar means as much of the given and actual as has lodged in the understanding can be decalcified. The real gives up its strangeness, the unexpected its arbitrariness, for the pedantic intellect that can perceive the unexpected event as a term in a series of events, and enumerate additional terms in that series, or that can accept the real thing as but the actualization of one potentiality among many, and consider in turn the others. So the absurdity of the arrangements by which the dog and the remains of Mr. Knott's food are brought together is alleviated, for Watt, by considering alternative arrangements as the author of these arrangements must have considered them, and discarding them as he must have discarded them. ("Not that for a moment Watt supposed that he had penetrated the forces at play, in this particular instance, or even perceived the forms that they upheaved, or obtained the least useful information concerning himself, or Mr Knott, for he did not. But he had turned, little by little, a disturbance into words, he had made a pillow of old words, for a head.")

So far are these passages, and the mental processes they enumerate, from idiosyncracy, that an Abelard would have gloried in them. They apotheosize the long labor of the West to restore the particular to its genera, and assign the genera to causes, and subsume causes in the First Cause, so pillowing many a head teased by among other things (we may speculate) the inherent ordonnance of the Latin language, which ought to be communicable to the obdurate things language handles. Scholastic philosophy could not have been carried on in, say, English prose as it stood in the thirteenth century. Modern English prose was developed in the seventeenth century to fill the need for a vernacular for such things as Latin speculation to be translated into. Beckett in the same way abandoned English after *Watt*, having carried as far as he could an English much indebted to the Ithaca episode of *Ulysses*, and conceived his trilogy with the assistance of French. He subsequently developed a new English in the course of translating what he had conceived in a different linguistic climate. He could hardly have done both jobs at once.

3

And here we encounter his concern with number. It is not that of a bookkeeper or a physicist; it sorts with the cadences of pedantry and allies itself with the Pythagorean and Augustinian pursuit of essences. The universe of number is not only one whose internal relationships are locked in place for the pedantic intellect to fondle in tranquility forever, it is also a world devoid of gritty specification. Its points have position without magnitude, its forms not only formal perfection but ideal non-existence. If they specify the mundane, it is by coincidence, as the fine six-place recurring decimal which Watt hears sung by an invisible choir—

> Fifty two point two eight five seven one four two eight five seven one four two

—happens to reduce to decimal notation a leap year expressed in weeks. The song goes on to speak of blooming, withering, drooping, and the passage of generations; but these processes can be purged away and the longest year contemplated under an ideal aspect, climate abridged, pain negated, devouring Time blunting no lion's claws, by whoever knows how to divide 7 into 366. He will empty it also of lions, suns, and love, but no procedure is unflawed. "To know nothing is nothing," Molloy reflects, "not to want to know anything likewise, but to be beyond knowing anything, to know you are beyond knowing anything,[8] that is when peace enters in, to the soul of the incurious seeker.

---

[8] The French text is sharper: "Car ne rien savoir, ce n'est rien, ne rien vouloir savoir non plus, mais ne rien pouvoir savoir, savoir ne rien pouvoir savoir. . . ."

It is then the true division begins, of 22 by 7 for example, and the pages fill with the true ciphers at last." Twenty-two by 7 is the schoolbook approximation to pi, the circle-squarer. And the "true ciphers" are 3.142857, 142857, 142857 . . . , accumulating, to no definite end, invariable patterns that grow less and less significant. As their sum gradually approximates toward the secret of the circle, their importance gradually dwindles toward zero. They are also, oddly enough, the same figures that recur in the invisible choir's reduction of the year to weeks, as though Time itself were circular. "Why, Mr. Joyce seems to say, should there be four legs to a table," wrote Beckett twenty years before he conceived Molloy, "and four to a horse, and four seasons and four Gospels and four Provinces in Ireland? . . ."

Pi recalls Pythagoras and the dialogues with Duthuit. The art which, helpless, unable to come into being, does come into being ("Why?" "I don't know.") has a taste for the extreme case on which the very logic of the artist's situation converges. Beckett invariably backs the mode he is practicing into its last corner, and is most satisfied if he can render further performance in that mode, by him, impossible. Every game is an endgame. If fiction, for instance, mirrors the minutiae of life, then there stretches before every fiction-writer an infinity of possible novels: more various even, if that be possible, than life, since after a time the novels themselves commence to interbreed. But if the series can be made not to diverge but to converge toward some limit, then very close to that limit we shall find the Beckettian writer amassing his negligible increments. Fiction, for instance, will converge if narrator M_1 and his story are inventions of narrator M_2, who in turn . . . In Beckett's particular realization of this series the increments grow negligible after three terms, the third being called, with a nod at Pythagoras, The Unnamable. Its trailing off is documented in a series of thirteen Textes Pour Rien, the limit of the series being perhaps zero and the final words being

> que tout serait silencieux et vide et noir, comme maintenant, comme bientôt, quand tout sera fini, tout dit, dit-elle, murmure-t-elle.

This procedure has, not unsurprisingly, the shape of the classic statement of the classic Pythagorean problem. That aboriginal surd, the square root of two, which threw the custodians of the rational into panic, is exactly

$$1 + \cfrac{1}{2 + \cfrac{1}{2 + \cfrac{1}{2 + \cfrac{1}{2 + \dots}}}}$$

the denominator growing steadily emptier the further we carry it, and the expression as tidy to even the untrained eye as Beckett's converging fictions, even in abstract statement, are to the mind.

The analogy grows still tidier once we realize its range and simplicity, for surds and continued fractions are not the obstreperous rarities they may seem. Begin by imagining, tidily arrayed, all the numbers there are: the *domain of the rational numbers*—all the integers, all the fractions, stretching to infinity on either side of Zero: a domain vast, orderly, and accessible to anyone who can count pennies or cut a pie. Any member of this domain can be precisely located with respect to its neighbors (seven is midway between six and eight), precisely identified in terms of them (five is three plus two), precisely ranked with reference to them (fifteen is larger than seven and one-half, and is moreover just twice as large). Each has its name, its address, its normal occupation, like Rémy de Gourmont's bourgeoisie ("animal reproducteur, animal électoral, animal contribuable"). On this plane move Micawber, Becky Sharp, Emma Bovary, Julien Sorel; also Pozzo and Moran.

But next imagine this domain shadowed and interpenetrated by the domain of the irrational numbers, infinitely more numerous, each maintaining its station in the unexpected gaps between adjacent rationals, which normally ignore its existence as the bourgeois ignores the *clochard*. These anomalies we can more or less locate, but not exactly; the best we can do is narrow down the limits between which they lurk. Thus between $1 \frac{2}{5}$ and $1 \frac{5}{12}$, or more exactly between $1 \frac{12}{29}$ and $1 \frac{29}{70}$, or more exactly still between $1 \frac{169}{408}$ and $1 \frac{70}{169}$ we may expect the root of two to exist, though we should not expect to find it. (Molloy, Moran thinks early in his quest, is somewhere "in the Molloy country," namely "that narrow region whose administrative limits he had never crossed.") Should we be able to find one, we could not, in the usual way, express it in terms of its neighbors, though without having found it we can give it a name. ("Molloy, or Mollose, was no stranger to me," recalls Moran. "Perhaps I had invented him, I mean found him ready made in my head.") Their existence, as the Pythagoreans perceived, is essentially scandalous, overturning as it does one's settled belief that the rational domain will suffice to contain all conceivable entities and all practical operations. ("If anyone else had spoken to me of Molloy I would have requested him to stop and I myself would not have confided his existence to a living soul for anything in the world.") If we are forced to name it more precisely, we can add terms to an endless decimal of which only the initial processes are accessible. ("What I heard, in my soul, I suppose, where the acoustics are so bad, was a first syllable, Mol, very clear, followed almost at once by a second, very thick, as though gobbled by the first, and which might have been oy as it might have been ose, or one, or even oc.") It exists, we know, between converging limits. "[Molloy] had very little room. His time too was limited. He hastened incessantly on, as if in despair, towards extremely close objectives. Now, a prisoner, he hurled himself at I know not what narrow confines, and now, hunted, he sought refuge near the centre.") We can also conceive of operations to be performed with such an unutterably entity, just as we can perform the standard arithmetical operations with a rational number once we have located it. ("My particular duties never terminated with the running to earth. That would have been too easy. But I had always to deal with the client in one way or another, according to instructions. Such operations took a multitude of forms, from the most vigorous to the most discreet.") Molloy, needless to say, is never found; for Moran ("so meticulous and calm in the main, so patiently turned towards the outer world as towards the lesser evil, . . . reining back his thoughts within the limits of the calculable") has been assigned a quest which to discharge he would have to forsake the rational domain where alone he can exist and try to conceive his quarry. He contemplates, composing himself for the quest, a domain "where masses move, stark as laws. Masses of what? One does not ask." Only in this atmosphere "of finality without end" can he venture to consider the work in hand. "For where Molloy could not be, nor Moran either for that matter, there Moran could bend over Molloy."

In this other domain which we can think about but not enter with our minds the irrational numbers exist, more numerous even than the infinitely numerous rationals. And it is in the analogy between these interpenetrating but incommensurable domains that Beckett discerns his central analogy for the artist's work and the human condition. ("There somewhere man is too, vast conglomerate of all of nature's kingdoms, as lonely and as bound.") As the Molloy domain is to the Moran, as that of the irrational numbers is to that of the rational, so the clown's is to the citizen's. The clown's role is a furtive enactment of all that orderly behavior will never attain to. He is sometimes wistful, more often in the Beckett landscape self-sufficient, always elusive, trapped between converging limits but never bound. The very shape of the Beckett plots, as Vivian Mercier has brilliantly noted,[9] can be prescribed by equations, Cartesian Man's inflexible oracles; Watt's career the curve of a function that approaches and turns around zero (Knott) before disappearing irretrievably off the paper, The Unnamable perhaps a spiral confined to the third quadrant where both coordinates are negative, and capable of straightening out and blending with zero if only it can protract itself to infinity.

The processes of mathematics offer themselves to the Beckett protagonists as a bridge into number's realm of the spectrally perfect, where enmired existence may be annihilated by essence utterly declared. Let a calculation get under way, let but a waft of mathematical terminology pass across the page, and the unpurged images of day recede. At least it is reasonable to expect that they will, but Beckett's is a world of anticlimax. It is a true that Arsene nearly succeeds in freezing gluttony into a formal composition with the merest touch of Euclidean symmetry:

9 "The Mathematical Limit," in *The Nation*, Feb. 14, 1959, 144.

. . . At the moment that one hand presses, with open palm, between the indefatigable jaws, a cold potato, onion, tart, or sandwich, the other darts into the pouch and there, unerringly, fastens on a sandwich, onion, tart, or cold potato, as Mary wills. And the former, on its way down to be filled, meets the latter on its way up to be emptied, at a point equidistant from their points of departure, or arrival. . . .

But Molloy is not so lucky in his attempt to deal with the frequent escapes of gas from his fundament. "It's hard not to mention it now and then, however great my distaste. One day I counted them." Struggling in vain to reduce three hundred and fifteen occasions in nineteen hours to some inconspicuous statistic, he subsides before the obduracy of "not even one fart every four minutes. It's unbelievable. Damn it, I hardly fart at all, I should never have mentioned it. Extraordinary how mathematics help you to know yourself." No consternation, however, can unseat his grammatical punctilio, and "mathematics" governs a plural verb.

Sometimes it is the transition from data to numeration that gives trouble, since the grip between these two worlds must occur in an imperfectly prehensile mind. Having been thrown down a flight of stairs, the protagonist of "L'Expulsé" would welcome a talismanic figure to sustain his contention that the flight was after all not a long one. Alas, though he had counted them a thousand times, "I have never known whether you should say one with your foot on the sidewalk, two with the following foot on the first step, and so on, or whether the sidewalk shouldn't count. At the top of the steps I met with the same dilemma. In the other direction, I mean from top to bottom, it was the same, the word is not too strong. . . . I arrived therefore at three totally different figures, without ever knowing which of them was right." Worse yet, he remembers none of the three, and all three are moreover essential; for to recall one, or two, of three adjacent numbers does not empower you to deduce the missing two, or one.

At least once a literal calculation (Lat. *calculus,* a stone used in reckoning) arouses the disinterested mania for symmetry, and proves as taxing to Molloy's limited talents as, no doubt, the half-developed calculus was to Newton's. He has sixteen stones, and four pockets; and without numbering the stones, he would insure that he can suck each one of them in turn, without risk, before the conclusion of the series, of sucking the same one twice. No more desperate assault on the randomness of things has ever been chronicled. He pounds his fists in rage, fills page after page with the narrative of strategies discarded, and settles at last for a Pyrrhic victory answering the conditions of the problem but marred by two aesthetic flaws. That is to say, the problem is only stunned, not solved at all, for it was an aesthetic problem from its inception. He has been compelled to sacrifice "the principle of trim," which would have kept the stones perpetually in uniform sets of four, and he has negotiated a short-term solution valid through any cycle of sixteen but never reliably repeatable. So the dream of commanding a method adequate to even the scanty requirements of sucking-stones is dissipated in compromise and frustration, and asceticism at length replaces system. He throws away all of the stones but one, and that one he ultimately loses.

Over the Beckett landscape, then, there hovers an inaccessible world of number and relation, to which his people fitfully try to approximate their actions. Molloy attempts circular movement, but achieves perhaps a great polygon ("perfection is not of this world."). One of The Unnamable's surrogates moves in spirals. Murphy considers with agitation that his assortment of five biscuits will not "spring to life before him, dancing the radiant measure of its total permutability, edible in a hundred and twenty ways!" until he can learn not to prefer any one to any other. His preference for the Ginger, which he saves for the last, leaves only four to permute in twenty-four ways; and his distaste for the Anonymous biscuit, which he therefore wolfs immediately, further reduces the number of ways in which he can consume the remainder to "a paltry six," his egregious selfhood diminishing the spectrum of availability twentyfold. Utter ablation of choice will confer utter freedom, which is by definition access to some plane on which all possibilities are equally available because all have been cleansed of identity and significance: and this is the world of number: "Neither elements nor states, nothing but forms becoming and crumbling into the fragments of a new becoming, without love or hate or any intelligible principle of change." Here Murphy (if he can enter this world, which he bears somewhere within him) is position without magnitude, "a point in the ceaseless unconditioned generation and passing away of line." (If Sisyphus thinks each journey is the first, thinks Moran, that "would keep hope alive would it not, hellish hope. Whereas to see yourself doing the same thing endlessly over and over again fills you with satisfaction.")

To consider, with Murphy that bliss consists of the full availability of all the elements of a set that are theoretically possible, is to encounter from a new direction the unique translucent enumerating style, which educes from whatever it handles the delights of total co-presence, nothing abridged. It works by a tireless survey of possibilities, rotating each being and situation before the mind in an arctic clarity of disclosure.

> *All three take off their hats simultaneously, press their hands to their foreheads, concentrate.*

ESTRAGON: (*triumphantly*). Ah!

VLADIMIR: He has it.

POZZO: (*impatient*). Well?

ESTRAGON: Why doesn't he put down his bags?

VLADIMIR: Rubbish!

POZZO: Are you sure?

VLADIMIR: Damn it haven't you already told us?

POZZO: I've already told you?

ESTRAGON: He's already told us?

VLADIMIR: Anyway he has put them down.

ESTRAGON: (*glance at Lucky*). So he has. And what of it?

VLADIMIR: Since he has put down his bags it is impossible we should have asked why he does not do so.

POZZO: Stoutly reasoned!

ESTRAGON: And why has he put them down?

POZZO: Answer us that.

VLADIMIR: In order to dance.

ESTRAGON: True!

POZZO: True!

Silence. They put on their hats.

"Haven't you already told us?" "I've already told you?" "He's already told us?" This is worthy of Bach. It is a dramatic extreme of the style which in its lyric extreme generates the indefatigable enumerations, in *Watt*, of every relevant qualifying circumstance.

Well, said Mr Fitzwein, it is always a pleasure for us, for me for one for my part, and for my colleagues for two for theirs, to meet a moron from a different crawl of life from our crawl, from my crawl and from their crawl. And to that extent I suppose we are obliged to you, Mr Louit. But I do not think we grasp, I do not think that I grasp and I should be greatly surprised to learn that my collaborators grasp, what this gentleman has to do with the object of your recent visit, Mr Louit, your recent brief and, if you will allow me to say so, prodigal visit to the western seaboard.

Like a circle straining to approach or recede from its center, this discourse is held between prodigality and ellipsis by opposed forces that ensure its elegant curve, ceremonious but never diffuse. Like the planets in their courses it discloses as it makes its way the laws which appear to be governing its movement, but which in fact serve only as a summary description. There is not an obscure instant; the syntax combs out and distinguishes thousands of short words, syntactic permutations keep them in motion, and repeatedly the precise individual word ("crawl," "moron," "prodigal,") reminds us that this elegance is not hypnotized by its own formulae, that its eyes are constantly open. It is an austere prose, not narcissistic nor baroque. It is not opulent. It moves with the great calm of some computation, doing a thousand things but only necessary ones. Such is the aesthetic of *Watt,* where the style declares itself fully.

In subsequent works it complicates itself. It seizes on smaller systems and permutes their elements more rapidly, producing a less ample surface, a more rapid rate of involution. But to the last syllable of *Comment C'est* it works by enumeration and permutation, longing to be threading Murphy's delicious world of darkness where all combinations are equally available. Here is Moran trying out a newly stiffened knee:

> . . . But when you sit down on the ground you must sit down tailor-wise, or like a foetus, these are so to speak the only possible positions, for a beginner. So that I was not long in letting myself fall back flat on my back. And I was not long either in making the following addition to the sum of my knowledge, that when of the innumerable attitudes adopted unthinkingly by the normal man all are precluded but two or three, then these are enhanced. . . . And it would not surprise me if the great classic paralyses were to offer analogous and perhaps

even still more unspeakable satisfactions. To be literally incapable of motion at last, that must be something! My mind swoons when I think of it. And mute into the bargain! And perhaps deaf as a post! And who knows blind as a bat! And as likely as not your memory a blank! And just enough brain intact to allow you to exult! And to dread death like a regeneration.

From savoring the sensations of a stiff knee to coveting the great classic paralyses, there is no flaw in this logic. It is not by chance that within a page Moran has begun to contemplate shoring up his decaying body with a bicycle: the machine, wrote Jack B. Yeats, that runs by the power of arithmetic.

The Cartesian Centaur

... whilst this machine is to him. . .
— *Hamlet*

Il n'y a plus de roues de bicyclette.
—*Fin de Partie*

Molloy had a bicycle, Moran was carried on the luggage rack of a bicycle, Malone recalls the cap of the bell of a bicycle, bicycles pass before Watt's eyes at the beginning and at the end of his transit through the house of Knott; Clov begged for a bicycle while bicycles still existed, and while there were still bicycles it was the wreck of a tandem that deprived Nagg and Nell of their legs. Like the bowler hat and the letter M, the bicycle makes at irregular intervals a silent transit across the Beckett *paysage intérieur,* whether to convince us that this place has after all an identity of sorts, or else like the poet's jar in Tennessee to supply for a while some point about which impressions may group themselves. If it is never a shiny new substantial bicycle, always a bicycle lost, a bicycle remembered, like Nagg's legs or Molloy's health, that is a circumstance essential to its role; like the body it disintegrates, like the body's vigor it retires into the past: *Hoc est enim corpus suum,* an ambulant frame, in Newtonian equilibrium.

Molloy is separated from his bicycle as the first stage in a disintegration which entails the stiffening of one leg, the shortening of the other leg which had previously been stiff, the loss of the toes from one foot (he forgets which), a staggering in circles, a crawling, a dragging of himself flat on his belly using his crutches like grapnels, brief thoughts of rolling, and final immobility, in a ditch. "Molloy could stay, where he happened to be." Formerly, while he possessed the bicycle, he had a less derelict posture in which to stay where he happened to be:

> Every hundred yards or so I stopped to rest my legs, the good one as well as the bad, and not only my legs, not only my legs. I didn't properly speaking get down off the machine, I remained astride it, my feet on the ground, my arms on the handle-bars, and I waited until I felt better.

In this tableau man and machine mingle in conjoint stasis, each indispensable to the other's support. At rest, the bicycle extends and stabilizes Molloy's endoskeleton. In motion, too, it complements and amends his structural deficiencies:

> I was no mean cyclist, at that period. This is how I went about it. I fastened my crutches to the cross-bar, one on either side, I propped the foot of my stiff leg (I forget which, now they're both stiff) on the projecting front axle, and I pedalled with the other. It was a chainless bicycle, with a free-wheel, if such a bicycle exists. Dear bicycle, I shall not call you bike, you were green, like so many of your generation, I don't know why. . . .

This odd machine exactly complements Molloy. It even compensates for his inability to sit down ("the sitting posture was not for me any more, because of my short stiff leg") ; and it transfers to an ideal, Newtonian plane of rotary progression and gyroscopic stability those locomotive expedients improbably complex for the intact human being, and for the crippled Molloy impossible.

In various passages of the canon, Beckett has gone into these expedients in some detail. For more than half a page he enumerates the several classes of local movement entailed by "Watt's way of advancing due east, for example";

the protagonist of "L'Expulsé" devotes some 500 words to a similar topic, noting that every attempt to modify his somewhat awkward methods "always ended in the same way, I mean by a loss of equilibrium, followed by a fall," while the characteristic progression of the protagonist of "Le Calmant" "seemed at every step to solve a statodynamic problem without precedent." The hands and knees, love, try the hands and knees," cries Winnie in *Happy Days*. "The knees! The knees! (*Pause.*) What curse, mobility." For the human body is to the Newtonian understanding an intolerably defective machine. It possesses, in the upright position, no equilibrium whatever; only by innumerable little compensatory shiftings does it sustain the illusion that it is standing motionless, and when it moves forward on its legs it does so by periodic surrender and recovery of balance, in a manner too hopelessly immersed in the *ad hoc* for analytic reconstruction. Every step is improvised, except by such dogged systematizers as Watt. And this was the kind of machine whose union with the pure intelligence puzzled Descartes, who invented the mode of speculation in which all Beckett's personages specialize.

> But there is nothing which that nature teaches me more expressly than that I have a body which is ill affected when I feel pain, and stands in need of food and drink when I experience the sensations of hunger and thirst, etc. And therefore I ought not to doubt but that there is some truth in these informations.

That last sentence, despite Descartes' proclaimed certainty, has Molloy's tone, and the whole passage—it is from the Sixth Meditation (1641)—prompts comparison with certain speculations of The Unnamable:

> . . . Equate me, without pity or scruple, with him who exists, somehow, no matter how, no finicking, with him whose story this story had the brief ambition to be. Bet-

ter, ascribe to me a body. Better still, arrogate to me a mind. Speak of a world of my own, sometimes referred to as the inner, without choking. Doubt no more. Seek no more. Take advantage of the brand-new substantiality to abandon, with the only possible abandon, deep down within. And finally, these and other decisions having been taken, carry on cheerfully as before. Something has changed nevertheless.

These fiats and revulsions come closer to the Cartesian spirit than Descartes himself; for Descartes, when he took his attention away from the immutable truths of mathematics, could resolve manifold confusions about the human estate "on the ground alone that God is no deceiver, and that consequently he has permitted no falsity in my opinions which he has not likewise given me a faculty of correcting." But this premise comes from outside the System, and a Molloy or a Malone have little confidence in it; to say nothing of The Unnamable, who assumes that the superior powers deceive continually. The Beckett protagonists would accord the classic resolutions of the Cartesian doubt a less apodictic weight than Descartes does; and notably his conclusion that the body, "a machine made by the hands of God," is "incomparably better arranged, and adequate to movements more admirable than is any machine of human invention." For unlike that of Molloy, the Cartesian body seems not subject to loss of toes or arthritis of the wrists.

So committed is Descartes to this perfect corporeal mechanism, that the question how a fine machine might be told from a man requires his most careful attention, especially in view of the circumstance that a machine can do almost anything better: "A clock composed only of wheels and weights can number the hours and measure time more exactly than we with all our skill." His answer is far from rigorous, based as it is on just that interpenetration of body and reason which he is elsewhere so hard put to explain. Molloy or Malone would have less difficulty with this question. The body, if we consider it without prejudice in the light of the seventeenth-century connoisseurship of the simple machines, is distinguished from any machine, however complex, by being clumsy, sloppy, and unintelligible; the extreme of analytic ingenuity will resolve no one of its functions, except inexactly, into lever, wedge, wheel, pulley, screw, inclined plane, or some combination of these. If we would admire a body worthy of the human reason, we shall have to create it, as the Greeks did when they united the noblest functions of rational and animal being, man with horse, and created the breed to which they assigned Chiron, tutor of Asclepius, Jason, and Achilles. For many years, however, we have had accessible to us a nobler image of bodily perfection than the horse. The Cartesian Centaur is a man riding a bicycle, *mens sana in corpore disposito.*

This being rises clear of the muddle in which Descartes leaves the mind-body relationship. The intelligence guides, the mobile wonder obeys, and there is no mysterious interpenetration of function. (The bicycle, to be sure, imposes conditions; there is no use in the intelligence attemptng to guide it up a tree. God in the same way cannot contradict His own nature.) Down a dead street, in "Le Calmant," passes at an unassignable time a phantom cyclist, all the while reading a paper which with two hands he holds unfolded before his eyes. So body and mind go each one nobly about its business, without interference or interaction. From time to time he rings his bell, without ceasing to read, until optical laws of unswervng precision have reduced him to a point on the horizon. Across the entire Beckett landscape there passes no more self-sufficient image of felicity.

It grows clear why for Molloy to describe his bicycle at length would be a pleasure, and why Moran "would gladly write four thousand words" on the bicycle his son buys, which must once have been quite a good one. Though neither of these descriptions is ever written, we do receive a sufficiently technical account of the mode of union—not to say symbiosis—between each of these bicycles and its rider. ("Here then in a few words is the solution I arrived at. First the bags, then my son's raincoat folded in four, all lashed to the carrier and the saddle with my son's bits of string. As for the umbrella, I hooked it round my neck, so as to have both hands free to hold on to my son by the waist, under the armpits rather, for by this time my seat was higher than his. Pedal, I said. He made a despairing effort. I can well believe it. We fell. I felt a sharp pain in my shin. It was all tangled up in the back wheel. Help! I cried. . . .") The world is an imperfect place; this theme deserves to be explicated on a more ideal plane. Let us try.

Consider the cyclist as he passes, the supreme specialist, transfiguring that act of moving from place to place which is itself the sentient body's supreme specialty. He is the term of locomotive evolution from slugs and creeping things. Could Gulliver have seen this phenomenon he would have turned aside from the Houyhnhnms, and Plato have reconsidered the possibility of incarnating an idea. Here all rationalist metaphysics terminates (as he pedals by, reciprocating motion steadily converted into rotary). The combination is impervious to Freud, and would have been of no evident use to Shakespeare. This glorified body is the supreme Cartesian achievement, a product of the pure intelligence, which has preceded it in time and now dominates it in function. It is neither generated nor (with reasonable care) corrupted. Here Euclid achieves mobility: circle, triangle, rhombus, the clear and distinct patterns of Cartesian knowledge. Here gyroscopic stability vies for attention with the ancient paradox of the still point and the rim. (He pedals with impenetrable dignity, the sitting posture combined with the walking, *sedendo et ambulando*, philosopher-king.) To consider the endless perfection of the chain, the links forever settling about the cogs, is a perpetual pleasure; to reflect that a specified link is alternately stationary with respect to the sprocket, then in motion with respect to the same sprocket, without hiatus between these conditions, is to entertain the sort of soothing mystery which, as Moran remarked "with rapture" in another connection, you can study all your life and never understand. The wheels are a miracle; the contraption moves on air, sustained by a network of wires in tension not against gravity but against one another. The Litany of the Simple Machines attends his progress. *Lever, Pulley, Wheel and Axle*: the cranks, the chain, the wheels. *Screw*, the coaster brake. *Wedge*, the collar that attends to the security of the handlebars. And the climax is of transparent subtlety, for owing to the inclination of the front fork, the bicycle, if its front wheel veers left or right, is returned to a straight course by the action of an invisible sixth simple machine, the *Inclined Plane*; since so long as it is not holding a true course it is troubled by the conviction that it is trying to run up hill, and this it prefers not to do. Here is the fixation of childhood dream, here is the fulfillment of young manhood. All human faculties are called into play, and all human muscles except perhaps the auricular. Thus is fulfilled the serpent's promise to Eve, *et eritis sicut dii*; and it is right that there should ride about France as these words are written, subject to Mr. Beckett's intermittent attention, a veteran racing cyclist, bald, a "stayer," recurrent placeman in town-to-town and national championships, Christian name elusive, surname Godeau, pronounced, of course, no differently from Godot.[1]

Monsieur Godeau, it is clear from our speculations, typifies Cartesian Man in excelsis, the Cartesian Centaur, body and mind in close harmony: the mind set on survival, mastery, and the contemplation of immutable relativities (*tout passe, et tout dure*), the body a reduction to uncluttered terms of the quintessential machine. From the Beckett canon it is equally clear that M. Godot, this solving and transforming paragon, does not come today, but perhaps tomorrow, and that meanwhile the Molloys, Morans, and Malones of this world must shift as they can, which is to say, badly. Cartesian man deprived of his bicycle is a mere intelligence fastened to a dying animal.

The dying animal preserves, however, stigmata of its higher estate. Molloy, after his bicycle has been abandoned, does not then resign himself to the human shuffle and forego that realm where arc, tangent, and trajectory describe the locus of ideal motion. No, even in his uncycled state he is half mechanized; he can lever himself forward, "swinging slowly through the sullen air."

> There is rapture, or there should be, in the motion crutches give. It is a series of little flights, skimming the ground. You take off, you land, through the thronging sound in wind and limb, who have to fasten one foot on the ground before they dare lift up the other. And even their most joyous hastening is less aerial than my hobble.

---

[1] It may calm the skeptical reader to know that my knowledge of this man comes from Mr. Beckett.

("But these are reasonings, based on analysis," he is careful to add, locating but not submitting to the tragic flaw in the Cartesian paradise.) After his legs give out he is able to adapt the principle of the rack and pawl: "Flat on my belly, using my crutches like grapnels, I plunged them ahead of me into the undergrowth, and when I felt they had a hold, I pulled myself forward, with an effort of the wrists." Periodically, as he crashes forward in this way, like the prototype of a moon-camion, he improves on the analogy with a bicycle of some inefficient pattern by blowing his horn ("I had taken it off my bicycle") through the cloth of his pocket. "Its hoot was fainter every time."

Reciprocating motion, it seems, is a characteristic of Molloy's, whether mounted on his bicycle or not. The unusual chainless bicycle, transmitting power apparently locomotive-fashion by the reciprocating rod,[2] accents this motif. Nor is he the only person in these books whose mode of progression is a studied and analyzed thing, distinct from human inconsequence. It is oddly relevant to say of Beckett characters, as of Newtonian bodies, that they are either at rest or in motion; and in the Beckett universe, motion, for those who are capable of setting themselves in motion, is an enterprise meriting at least a detailed description, and more likely prolonged deliberation. Malone's creature Macmann, for example, commences to roll on the ground, and finds himself "advancing with regularity, and even a certain rapidity, along the arc of a gigantic circle probably," one of his extremities being heavier than the other "but not by much." "And without reducing his speed he began to dream of a flat land where he would never have to rise again and

---

2 Mr. Beckett recalls seeing such a bicycle when he was a boy in Dublin.

hold himself erect in equilibrium, first on the right foot for example, then on the left, and where he might come and go and so survive after the fashion of a great cylinder endowed with the faculties of cognition and volition."

Malone himself, on the other hand, is at rest; and so far is the Cartesian mechanism dismantled, that it would take, he estimates, several weeks to re-establish connection between his brain and his feet, should there be any need for that. He has, needless to say, no bicycle, and nowhere speaks of a bicycle; but he includes among his possessions not only half a crutch but the cap of his bicycle bell: the least rudiment, like the knucklebone of a dinosaur. Yet to him too occurs the idea of playing at Prime Mover: "I wonder if I could not contrive, wielding my stick like a punt-pole, to move my bed. It may well be on castors, many beds are. Incredible I should never have thought of this, all the time I have been here. I might even succeed in steering it, it is so narrow, through the door, and even down the stairs, if there is a stairs that goes down." Unhappily at the first trial he loses hold of the stick instead, and meditating on this disaster claims intellectual kinship with another speculative Mover: "I must have missed my point of purchase in the dark. Sine qua non. Archimedes was right."

Let Archimedes' presence disconcert no one: the Beckett bicycle can orchestrate all the great themes of human speculation. Since the Beckett people transact their most palpable business in some universe of absence, however, it is without surprise that we discover the bicycle to have put in its most extended and paradigmatic appearance in a novel which has not been published. This is the composition of *c*. 1945 which details certain advantures of what The Unnamable is later to call "the pseudocouple Mercier-Camier." I translate from a French typescript:

You remember our bicycle? said Mercier.

Yes, said Camier.

Speak up, said Mercier. I hear nothing.

I remember our bicycle, said Camier.

There remains of it, solidly chained to a railing, said Mercier, that which can reasonably be said to remain, after more than eight days' incessant rain, of a bicycle from which have been subtracted the two wheels, the saddle, the bell, and the carrier. And the reflector, he added. I nearly forgot that. What a head I have.

And the pump, naturally, said Camier.

You may believe me or you may not, said Mercier, it is all the same to me, but they have left us our pump.

Yet it was a good one, said Camier. Where is it?

I suppose it was simply overlooked in error, said Mercier. So I left it there. It seemed the most reasonable course. What have we to pump up, at present? In fact I inverted it. I don't know why. Something compelled me.

It stays just as well inverted? said Camier.

Oh, quite as well, said Mercier.

This exchange bristles with problems. Having undergone a Molloy's dismemberment, has the bicycle at some stage rendered up its identity? Or is it identifiable only as one identifies a corpse? And in no other way? In some other way? Again, assuming that a bisected rhomboid frame of steel tubing equipped with handlebars and a sprocket is recognizably a bicycle, has this congeries of sensible appearances relinquished its essence with the removal of the wheels? From its two wheels it is named, on its two wheels it performs its essential function. To what extent ought a decisiveness of nomenclature persuade us to equate function, essence, and identity? These are matters to agitate a schoolman; they would certainly have engaged the careful attention of Watt. Mercier, *homme moyen sensuel*, is sufficiently schooled in precision to acknowledge in passing the problem, what can reasonably be said to remain of a bicycle thus reduced, but insufficiently curious to pursue this investigation. His attention lingers instead, a bit antiseptically, on two human problems, the first perhaps ethical (whether, since the anonymous autopsist has presumably only forgotten the pump, it ought not to be left for him) and the second hermeneutic (why, having chosen to leave it, he himself did not forbear to turn it upside down).

These several classes of questions, as it turns out, are of greater formal brilliance than practical import. The Mercier-Camier universe is soured by unassignable final causes, as in their astringent laconism the two of them seem half to acknowledge. They are in the presence, actually, of an archetypal event, or perhaps a portent, or perhaps a cause: there is no telling. In retrospect, anyhow, one thing is clear: from the dismemberment of their bicycle we may date the disintegration of Mercier and Camier's original lock-step unity. In the final third of this novel they gradually become nodding acquaintances, like the two wheels which were once sustained by a single frame but are now free to pursue independent careers. This separation is not willed, it simply occurs, like the dissolution of some random conjunction of planets: "pseudo-couple," indeed.

For The Unnamable there is no stick, no Archimedes, no problem whatever of the Malone order, or of the Mercier-Camier order, chiefly because there is no verifiable body; and there is no mention of a bicycle nor reflection of a bicycle nor allusion to a bicycle from beginning to end of a novel, in this respect as in others, unprecedented in the Beckett canon. Nor is this unexpected; for *The Unnamable* is the final phase of a trilogy which carries the Cartesian process backwards, beginning with a bodily *je suis* and ending with a bare *cogito*. This reduction begins with a journey (Molloy's) and a dismembering of the Cartesian Centaur; its middle term (*Malone Dies*) is a stasis, dominated by the unallayable brain; and the third phase has neither the identity of rest nor that of motion, functions under the sign neither of matter nor of mind because it evades both, and concerns itself endlessly to no end with a baffling intimacy between discourse and non-existence.

This is not to say, however, that the fundamental problems of a seventeenth-century philosopher, and notably the problems of bodies in motion, do not confront The Unnamable in their baldest form. The first body in motion is, unexpectedly, Malone, appearing and disappearing "with the punctuality of clockwork, always at the same remove, the same velocity, in the same direction, the same attitude." He may be seated, he "wheels" without a sound; the evidence in fact points to his being borne through this ideal space on some quintessential bicycle. So much for cosmology. We next confront a certain Mahood, under two aspects: Mahood in motion, Mahood at rest. In motion, on crutches but minus a leg, he executes a converging spiral; at rest, he inhabits a jar. In either aspect, he is a Descartes cursed by the dark of the moon. At rest in the jar, he pursues the *cogito* sufficiently to think of demanding proof that he exists ("How all becomes clear and simple when one opens an eye on the within, having of course previously exposed it to the without, in order to benefit by the contrast."). So pursuing "the bliss of what is clear and simple," he pauses "to make a distinction (I must be still thinking):"

> That the jar is really standing where they say, all right,
> I wouldn't dream of denying it, after all it's none of my
> business, though its presence at such a place, about the
> reality of which I do not propose to quibble either, does

not strike me as very credible. No, I merely doubt that I am in it. It is easier to raise the shrine than bring the deity down to haunt it. . . . That's what comes of distinctions.

The jar, clearly, is what the body, geometrically conceived, is reducible to by the systematizing intelligence. As for the one-legged man with the crutch, he pursues his converging spiral (the first curve to have been rectified by Descartes), complementing with his ideally incommoded motion the other's ideally perplexed cogitation, and so completing a little cosmos pervaded by the two Cartesian functions, movement and thought. He jerks, hops, swings and falls, so remote from the ancient symbiosis with a bicycle as not even to be visited by such a possibility, yet enacting as best the deficiencies of the flesh will allow his intent parody of some obsessed machine. Molloy too progressed in spirals, "through imperfect navigation," and when he was in the woods slyly resolved to outwit the deception which is reputed to draw benighted travelers into involuntary circles: "Every three or four jerks I altered course, which permitted me to describe, if not a circle, at least a great polygon, perfection is not of this world, and to hope that I was going forward in a straight line." Molloy's is plane geometry; the spiral described by the surrogate of The Unnamable is located on the surface of a sphere, and hence, if it originates from a point, can enlarge itself only until it has executed a swing equal to the globe's greatest circumference, and after that must necessarily commence to close in again. When we take up his tale, his global sweep is converging into a very small space indeed, preliminary to the moment when it will have nothing to do but reverse itself for lack of room. At the pole of convergence we are surprised to discover his family, keeping watch, cheering him on ("Stick it, lad, it's your last winter."), singing hymns, recalling that he was a fine baby.

Yet none of the enmired but recognizably human will to prevail that once animated Molloy's progress toward his mother impresses the reader of these later pages. The narrative, for one thing, is no longer impregnated by indefatigable first person energy. Mahood's progress, half something experienced by The Unnamable but half something unreliably told him, is unhitched from his empathic passions, and endeavoring to recall his (or Mahood's) thoughts and feelings he can only report absorption in the technicalities of spiral progression. "The only problem for me was how to continue, since I could not do otherwise, to the best of my declining powers, in the motion which had been imparted to me." The annihilation of his family by poison does not arrest him as he completes his rounds, "stamping under foot the unrecognizable remains of my family, here a face, there a stomach, as the case might be, and sinking into them with the ends of my crutches both coming and going."

The bicycle is long gone, the Centaur dismembered; of the exhilaration of the cyclist's progress in the days when he was lord of the things that move, nothing remains but the ineradicable habit of persisting like a machine. The serene confidence of the lordly *Cogito* . . . is similarly dissociated, in this last phase of the dream of Cartesian man, into a garrulity, vestigially logical, which is perhaps piped into him by other beings: a condition oddly prefigured by the parrot which a friend of Malone's had tried to teach to enunciate the *Nihil in intellectu quod non prius in sensu,* a doctrine it would have travestied whenever it opened its beak. It got no further than *Nihil in intellectu,* followed by a series of squawks. More profoundly than its great forerunner, *Bouvard et*

Pécuchet, the Beckett trilogy takes stock of the Enlightenment, and reduces to essential terms the three centuries during which those ambitious processes of which Descartes is the symbol and progenitor (or was he too, like The Unnamable, spoken through by a Committee of the *Zeitgeist?*) accomplished the dehumanization of man. It is plain why Godot does not come. The Cartesian Centaur was a seventeenth-century dream, the fatal dream of being, knowing, and moving like a god. In the twentieth century he and his machine are gone, and only a desperate élan remains: "I don't know, I'll never know, in the silence you don't know, you must go on, I can't go on, I'll go on."

Life In The Box

"Once a certain degree of insight has been reached," said Wylie, "all men talk, when talk they must, the same tripe."
—*Murphy*

1

The drama is a ritual enacted in an enclosed space into which fifty or more people are staring. They are all more or less patiently waiting for something: the Reversal, the Discovery, the *Deus ex Machina,* or even the final curtain. Settled numbly for the evening, they accept whatever interim diversions the stage can provide: tramps in bowler hats, for instance.

The space into which they are staring is characterized in some way: for instance, *A country road. A tree. Evening.* "Evening" means that the illumination on stage is not much brighter than in the auditorium. "A country road" means that there is no set to look at. As for the tree, an apologetic thing tentatively identified as a leafless weeping willow, it serves chiefly to denote the spot, like the intersection (coordinates O,O) of the Cartesian axes. "You're sure it was here?" "What?" "That we were to wait." "He said by the tree." If it accretes meaning of an anomalous sort in the course of the evening, reminding us, when the two tramps stand beneath it with a rope, of ampler beams which once suspended the Savior and two thieves, or again of the fatal tree in Eden (and the garden has, sure enough, vanished), or even of the flowering staff in *Tannhäuser,* it does this not by being explicated but simply by its insistent continual presence, during which, as adjacent events diffract the bleak light, we begin to entertain mild hallucinations about it. Only in a theater can we be made to look at a mock tree for that length of time. Drama is distinguished from all other forms of art by its control over the *time* spent by the spectator in the presence of its significant elements.

These events, these elements, assert only their own nagging existence. "The theatrical character," remarked Alain Robbe-Grillet in this connection, *"is on stage,* this is his primary quality—he is there." Hence, "the essential function of the theatrical performance: to show what this fact of *being there* consists of." Or as Beckett was later to write of a later play, "Hamm as stated, and Clov as stated, together as stated, *nec tecum nec sine te,* in such a place, and in such a world, that's all I can manage, more than I could."

In *Waiting for Godot,* the place with its tree is stated, together with a single actor engaged in a mime with his boot. His inability to get it off is the referent of his first words, "Nothing to be done," a sentence generally reserved for more portentous matters. To him enter the second actor, as in the medial phase of Greek Theater, and their talk commences. What they talk about first is the fact that they are both there, the one fact that is demonstrably true not only in art's agreed world but before our eyes. It is even the one certainty that survives an evening's waiting:

> BOY: What am I to tell Mr. Godot, sir?
> VLADIMIR: Tell him . . . (*he hesitates*) . . . tell him you saw us. (*Pause*) You did see us, didn't you?
> BOY: Yes Sir.

The realities stated with such insistence are disquietingly provisional. The tree is plainly a sham, and the two tramps are simply filling up time until a proper dramatic entertainment can get under way. They are helping the management fulfill, in a minimal way, its contract with the ticket holders. The resources of vaudeville are at their somewhat incompetent disposal: bashed hats, dropped pants, tight boots, the kick, the pratfall, the improper story. It will suffice if they can stave off a mass exodus until Godot comes, in whom we are all so interested. Beckett, it is clear, has cunningly doubled his play with that absence of a play which every confirmed theatergoer has at some time or other experienced, the advertized cynosure having missed a train or overslept or indulged in temperament. The tramps have plainly not learned parts; they repeatedly discuss what to do next ("What about hanging ourselves?") and observe from time to time that tedium is accumulating:

> Charming evening we're having.
> Unforgettable.
> And it's not over.
> Apparently not.
> It's only beginning.
> It's awful.
> Worse than the pantomime.
> The circus.
> The music-hall.
> The circus.

Thus a non-play comments on itself. Or the audience of the non-play is reminded that others the previous night sat in these seats witnessing the identical futility ("What did we do yesterday?" "In my opinion we were here.") and that others in turn will sit there watching on successive nights for an indeterminate period.

> We'll come back to-morrow [says tramp No. 1].
> And then the day after to-morrow.
> Possibly.
> And so on.

And so on, until the run of the production ends. It will end, presumably, when there are no longer spectators interested, though it is difficult to explain on Shakespearean premises what it is that they can be expected to be interested in. Or perhaps not so difficult. What brings the groundlings to *Macbeth*? Why, they are waiting for the severed head. And to *Hamlet*? They are waiting for Garrick (or Irving, or Olivier). And here?

> Let's go.
> We can't.
> Why not?
> We're waiting for Godot.
> (*despairingly*) Ah!

The French text manages an inclusiveness denied to English idiom: "Pourquoi?" "On attend Godot." Not *"nous"* but *"on"*: Didi, Gogo, and audience alike.

If the seeming improvisation of the tramps denies theatricality, it affirms at the same time quintessential theater, postulating nothing but what we can see on stage: a place, and men present in it, doing what they are doing. And into this quintessential theater there irrupts before long the strident unreality we crave:

> POZZO: (*terrifying voice*). I am Pozzo! (*Silence.*) Pozzo! (*Silence.*) Does that name mean nothing to you? (*Silence.*) I say does that name mean nothing to you?

This is at last the veritable stuff, that for which we paid our admissions: an actor, patently, with gestures and grimaces, who has furthermore memorized and rehearsed his part and knows how they talk in plays. He makes his entrance like Tamburlaine driving the pampered jades of Asia (represented, in this low-budget production, by one extra); he takes pains with his elocution, assisted by a vaporizer, like an effete *Heldentenor*; he recites a well-conned set speech on the twilight, with "vibrant," "lyrical," and "prosaic" phases, and contrapuntal assistance from well-schooled hands (two hands lapsing; two hands flung amply apart; one hand raised in admonition; fingers snapped at the climax, to reinforce the word "pop!"). This is theater; the evening is saved. Surely he is Godot?

But he says not; and we are disconcerted to find him fishing for applause, and from the tramps. They are his audience as we are his and theirs. The play, in familiar Beckett fashion, has gotten inside the play. So too when Lucky (who has also memorized his part) recites his set speech on the descent of human certainty into "the great cold the great dark" ("for reasons unknown but time will tell"), it is for the amusement of his master, and of the tramps, and incidentally of ourselves. The same is true of his symbolic dance, a thing of constrained ✗ gestures, as in Noh drama[1]. So the perspective continues to diminish, box within box. In this theater, the tramps. Within their futile world, the finished theatricality of Pozzo. At Pozzo's command, Lucky's speech; within this speech, scholarship, man *in posse* and *in esse*, all that which, officially endorsed, we think we know, notably the labors of the Acacacacademy of Anthropopopometry; within these in turn, caca (Fr. colloq., excrement) and popo, a chamberpot: a diminution, a delirium.

Such metaphysics as the Beckett theater will permit is entailed in this hierarchy of watchers and watched. Throughout, and notably during Lucky's holocaust of phrases, we clutch at straws of meaning, persuaded at

---

[1] "Do you know what he calls it? . . . The Net. He thinks he is entangled in a net." Compare the words Miscio Ito spoke, "with perfect precision," to Ezra Pound: "Japanese dance all time overcoat." The one stable item of Noh décor is painted on the back of the stage: "a pine tree, symbol of the unchanging."

bottom only of one thing, that all four men exist, embodied, gravid, speaking; moving before us, their shadows cast on the wall, their voices echoing in the auditorium, their feet heavy on the boards.

The second act opens with the song about the dog's epitaph, another infinitely converging series of acts and agents. The Unnamable also meditates on this jingle, and discovers its principle: "third verse, as the first, fourth, as the second, fifth, as the third, give us time, give us time and we'll be a multitude"; for it generates an infinite series of unreal beings, epitaph within epitaph within epitaph. Correspondingly, near the end of the act Didi muses over the sleeping Gogo:

> At me too someone is looking, of me too someone is saying, He is sleeping, he knows nothing, let him sleep on.

So we watch Didi move through his part, as he watches Gogo, and meanwhile Lucky's God with the white beard, outside time, without extension, is loving us dearly "with some exceptions for reasons unknown but time will tell."

It remains to recall that the Beckett universe, wherever we encounter it, consists of a shambles of phenomena within which certain symmetries and recurrences are observable, like the physical world as interpreted by early man. So this stage world has its structure and landmarks. We observe, for example, that bowler hats are apparently *de rigueur,* and that they are removed for thinking but replaced for speaking. We observe that moonrise and sunset occur in conjunction two nights running, for this is an ideal cosmology, unless we are to suppose the two acts to be separated by an interval of twenty-nine days. The tree by the same token has budded overnight, like an early miracle. All this is arbitrary because theatrical. Our play draws on Greek theater with its limited number of actors, its crises always offstage, and its absent divinity;

on Noh theater with its symbolic tree, its nuances and its ritual dance; on *commedia dell'arte,* improvised before our eyes; on twentieth-century experimental theater; and on vaudeville with its castoff clowns, stumblings, shamblings, delicate bawdry, acrobatics, and astringent pointlessness. The final action partakes of the circus repertoire

> (*They each take an end of the cord and pull. It breaks. They almost fall*) ,

synchronized with a burlesque house misadventure with trousers

> . . . *which, much too big for him, fall about his ankles.*

The student of *Finnegans Wake* will identify this mishap as the play's epiphany[2], the least learned will note that something hitherto invisible has at last been disclosed, and everyone can agree that the final gesture is to a static propriety:

> VLADIMIR: Pull ON your trousers.
> ESTRAGON: (*realizing his trousers are down*) . True.
> *He pulls up his trousers.*
> VLADIMIR: Well? Shall we go?
> ESTRAGON: Yes, let's go.
> *They do not move.*
>
> *Curtain.*

2

This superimposition of dramatic economics was not achieved at once. About 1947, just after writing the *Nouvelles,* Beckett occupied himself with a radically

---

2 Cf. *Finnegans Wake,* p. 508: ". . . I am sorry to have to tell you, hullo and evoe, they were coming down from off him. —How culious an epiphany!"

misconceived dramatic enterprise, a play called *Eleutheria* in three acts, which entailed a large stage, two sets simultaneously on view, a place (Paris) and a time (three consecutive winter afternoons) uncharacteristically specified, and seventeen speaking parts, including a Chinese torturer, an officious member of the audience, and the prompter. "Eleutheria" means "freedom." The theme, clearly related to that of the first *Nouvelle*, "L'Expulsé," concerns a young man's act of secession from his intensely bourgeois family. This theme preoccupied Beckett a good deal at one time; it also underlies the remarkable fragment, "From an Abandoned Work":

> Up bright and early that day, I was young then, feeling awful, and out, mother hanging out of the window in her nightdress weeping and waving. Nice fresh morning, bright too early as so often. Feeling really awful, very violent. . . .

In the play, the family (surnamed Krap) entertains guests (named Piouk and Meck) and the conversation goes like this:

> MR KRAP: Have a cigar.
> DR PIOUK: Thank you.
> MR KRAP: Yes thank you or no thank you?
> DR PIOUK: I don't smoke.
>
> *(Silence)*
>
> MRS MECK ⎫ *(Together)*: I . . .
> MRS PIOUK ⎭
> MRS MECK: Oh, I beg your pardon. You were going to say?
> MRS PIOUK: Oh, nothing. Go on.
>
> *(Silence)*

Or ailments are discussed:

> MRS PIOUK: How is Henry?
> MRS KRAP: Ill.
> MRS PIOUK: What's wrong with him?
> MRS KRAP: I don't know. He's stopped urinating.
> MRS PIOUK: It's the prostate.

Such details, however, lack the fine formal emptiness of *Godot,* partly because they occur in the interstices of an elaborate exposition of familial relationships. Beckett drags the audience, with considerable distaste, up and down all the airshafts of a well-made play. It is from this that Krap *fils,* the young Victor, has absented himself. He scrounges in trash cans, speaks to no one, and is generally found in bed, in a garret flat.

All the rest of the play—two mortal acts—is devoted to punching and poking Victor, in his garret, and beseeching him to explain his conduct. This he will not do, one aspect of his freedom, we may suppose, being freedom from the necessity to devise explanations, even for his own enlightenment. The busybodies include not only Victor's parents, their relatives, and his fiancée (a certain Mlle. Skunk), but also an officious artisan who is on the premises to repair a broken window, and who constitutes himself spokesman of detached practicality. By the third act an exasperated member of the audience has taken up his seat on the stage, determined to see things resolved before midnight; the services of an Oriental torturer have been requisitioned; Victor has made a statement, later retracted as fiction; and alone at last on the bare stage he has lain down "with his back turned to humanity."

Since the figure of interest (and on the stage, not of much interest) has by definition withdrawn from communication, Beckett's problem is, as never before, to fill up the work. To this end he employs, with little conviction, the convention of formal dramatic structure, which is that when someone speaks someone else answers, more or less to the point. And this convention closes round Victor like water round a stone, incapable of assimilating him.

Though it doesn't work in this play, the strategy is not new. All Beckett's writings bring some sustained formal element to the service of some irreducible situation round which the lucid sentences defile in baffled aplomb. If we never understand the world of Watt, that is not because the presentation conceals it; as the presence of irrational terms does not prevent us from following every line of a computation. So in *Molloy* the twin circular journeys, and in *Malone Dies* the parallel narratives, supply the words with something formal to disclose, and circumscribe the implacable mysteries. *Godot* for the same reason is full of small rituals and transparent local rhythms. They are not the mystery, they do not clarify the mystery, or seek to clarify the mystery, they clarify the place where the mystery is, and the fact that, in the presence of the irreducible, people contrive to kill time by rehearsing their grasp of detail.

Let us be clear about this. Victor is not a new moral phenomenon. Beckett has been concerned with the withdrawn man from Belacqua onward. Nor is he structurally a new component. He is this play's version of the familiar surd, the irreducible element which no style, no clarity, no ceremony will dissolve or explain: the thing which makes itself felt, in Beckett's cosmos, as a prevailing and penetrating mystery, seeping through the walls of stage or book. This mystery, this irreducible, is generally of two sorts: (1) in the domain of existence, the implacable *"d'être là"*: as we find ourselves situated on earth ("There's no cure for that") or as Malone finds himself placed in his mysterious room, surrounded by procedures that appear to take no account of his arrival or presence. Or (2) in the domain of will, the arbitrary decision, Molloy's determination to visit his mother, or Victor's to leave home. There is no looking into these sudden precipitations. In large, they make contact with the ambient terror and oppressiveness (what compels us to wait for Godot?). In small, they supply a repertory of comic effects. Part of the trouble with Victor in *Eleutheria* is that his presence confuses these perspectives; his sulkiness verges on being funny at the same time that his intransigence is growing unnerving; he can round on his inquistors by asking them why it is that they find him of such consuming interest, when cripples, fools, nuns, and other outcasts barely detain them.

In the *Nouvelles*, three of which Beckett published though he had the sense not to publish *Eleutheria*, such problems of tact do not arise. "L'Expulsé," a sort of Victor, has generally preferred to keep to his room, and by preference the end of the room where the bed is, so much so that he barely knows the streets of his native town. At the beginning of the story he is recalling how his family finally threw him out.

> Even as I fell I heard the door slam, which brought me a little comfort, in the midst of my fall. For that meant they were not pursuing me down into the street, with a stick, to beat me in full view of the passers-by. For if that had been their intention they would not have closed the door, but left it open, so that the persons assembled in the vestibule might enjoy my chastisement and be edified. So, for once, they had confined themselves to throwing me out, and no more about it. I had time, before coming to rest in the gutter, to conclude this piece of reasoning.
>
> Under these circumstances nothing compelled me to get up immediately. I rested my elbow on the sidewalk, funny the things you remember, settled my ear in the cup of my hand and began to reflect on my situation, notwithstanding its familiarity. But the sound, fainter but unmistakable, of the door slammed again, roused me from my reverie, where already a whole landscape was taking form, charming with hawthorn and wild roses, most dreamlike,

and made me look up in alarm, my hands flat on the sidewalk and my legs braced for flight. But it was merely my hat, sailing towards me through the air, rotating as it came. I caught it and put it on. They were most correct, according to their god. They could have kept this hat, but it was not theirs, it was mine, so they gave it back to me. But the spell was broken.

And the life from which he has been expelled is adequately summed up by the hat:

How describe this hat? And why? When my head had attained I shall not say its definitive but its maximum dimensions, my father said to me, Come, son, we are going to buy your hat, as though it had pre-existed from time immemorial in a pre-established place. He went straight to the hat. I personally had no say in the matter, nor had the hatter. I have often wondered if my father's purpose was not to humiliate me, if he was not jealous of me who was young and handsome, fresh at least, while he was already old and all bloated and purple. It was forbidden me, from that day forth, to go out bareheaded, my pretty brown hair blowing in the wind. Sometimes, in a secluded street, I took it off and held it in my hand, but trembling. I was required to brush it morning and evening. Boys my age with whom, in spite of everything, I was obliged to mix occasionally, mocked me. But I said to myself, it is not really the hat, they simply make merry at the hat because it is a little more glaring than the rest, for they have no finesse. I have always been amazed by my contemporaries' lack of finesse, I whose soul writhed from morning to night, in the mere quest of itself. But perhaps they were simply being kind, like those who make game of the hunchback's big nose. When my father died I could have got rid of this hat, there was nothing more to prevent me, but not I. But how describe it? Some other time, some other time.

This precious youth turns slowly into a bum. In "Premier Amour" (which was never published) he is living in an abandoned stable and devoted to "cerebral supinity, the deadening of the idea of the me and the idea of that small residue of exasperating trifles known as the not-me." Near the canal he comes to be frequented by a certain Lulu.

> Yes, I loved her, that was the name which I gave, and which alas I still give, to what I did, at that period. I possessed no data on the subject, not having previously loved, but I had heard the thing spoken of, naturally, at home, at school, in the brothel, and at church, and I had read romances, in prose and in verse, under the direction of my tutor, in English, French, Italian and German, in which it was spoken highly of. I was therefore well prepared to give a name to what I did, when I discovered myself writing the word Lulu on an old cowpad, or lying in the mud beneath the moon trying to pull up dandelions without breaking the stems.

His idyll, like Molloy's, is of short duration. All he really wants of her is a peaceable shelter, and he finds her clients disturbing. At the beginning of "Le Calmant" he (if it is still he) announces that he no longer knows when he died (whatever that means). He is quite likely in a hospital ("among these assassins, in a bed of terror"), but prefers to imagine himself in his distant refuge, hands clasped, head down, feeble, panting, calm, free, and "older than I could ever have been, if my calculations are correct." He tells himself a story of a nighttime ramble, maybe a real one, in which people came up against him like apparitions and talked no sense that he could follow, and a vision finally came to him of asphalt bursting into infinite flower, while he lay on the pavement immersed in his dream, and people took care not to step on him ("a considerateness which touched me"). In "The End" he is thrown out of the institution which has been harboring him, and after bizarre wanderings takes refuge at last in an abandoned canoe, where he dreams of slowly foundering in the open main, as the water rises slowly through a hole from which with his penknife he has extracted the cork.

All this is capital material for fiction, but not for drama. Since its point is that the protagonist has sundered all relation, so far as he can, with other persons and things, there is simply no way to exhibit him on the stage. The only thing to exhibit is other folks' curiosity about him, which grows tedious. And since Beckett's unwavering concern is with the twilight man, who does not inhabit the rational domain, whom you cannot see with Pythagorean eyes and for whom our moral vocabulary contains only the summary provided in the last sentence of "The End," that he has neither "the courage to stop nor the strength to go on," it would seem clear that for Beckett the drama was a hopeless form. But we know our man by this time; nothing makes him prick up his ears like the word "hopeless." Jettisoning *Eleutheria*, he gave over trying to dramatize the *Nouvelles* and commenced turning them instead into the trilogy. There is no telling whether it was pondering Molloy and Moran that suggested raising the number of idlers to two, for dialogue, and reducing the number of busy folk to two, for concision, and playing a waiting against a journeying, for structure. At any rate, after finishing *Molloy,* perhaps also *Malone Dies*[3], he commenced the impossible play, its two twilight men and much of the quality of their talk transposed from another jettisoned fiction, *Mercier et Camier.*

3

The two men waiting for Godot to come (or for night to fall) are very similar to the two men who were seeking

---

[3] Eleven years later he couldn't be sure. "Round about 1948 in any case."

to retrieve a bicycle and a haversack, on the off chance
that these articles might prove relevant to their needs.
Hear them one rainy morning discoursing of their umbrella:

> For myself, said Camier, I would not open it.
> And might we hear the reason? said Mercier. It is rain-
> ing steadily, it seems to me. You are all wet.
> Your advice would be to open it? said Camier.
> I do not say that, said Mercier. I only ask when we are
> going to open it if we do not open it now.

This futile parasol deserves a moment's attention; there
is nothing like it in *Godot*. Formerly red, tipped by a
betasseled amber ball, it had floated down time's stream
for nearly a half century before getting lodged in the
junkshop where Mercier gave ninepence for it.

> It must have made its debut about 1900, said Camier.
> That was I think the year of Ladysmith, on the Klip. Do
> you remember it? A splendid time. Garden parties every
> day. Life opened before us, radiant. All hopes were
> permissible. We played at sieges. People die like flies.
> Hunger. Thirst. Bang! Bang! The last cartridges. Sur-
> render! Never! We eat corpses. We drink our own urine.
> Bang! Bang! We kept two in reserve. What do we hear? A
> cry of wonder. Dust on the horizon. The column! Tongues
> are black. Hurrah anyhow! Rah! Rah! We sounded like
> ravens. A garrison marshal died of joy. We are saved. The
> century was two months old.
> Look at it now, said Mercier.

Look at the parasol now, or look at the century. Or
look at us:

> How are you feeling? said Camier. I keep forgetting to
> ask.
> I felt well coming downstairs, said Mercier. Now I feel
> less well. Screwed up, if you like, but not to the sticking-
> place. And you?
> A chip, said Camier, in the midst of the limitless
> ocean.

Souvenir from the great dawn of an ampler day, when
garden parties and rescue parties bespoke man's limitless
hope, our parasol (bits of fringe still ornamenting its
perimeter) is irrelevant to a time of rain, middle age, and
doubt. For two pages they debate throwing it away, a
course for which, Mercier concludes, it will perhaps be
time "when it can no longer serve us for shelter, because
of wear, or when we have achieved the certainty that
between it and our present distress there has never existed the least relationship."

Very well, said Camier. But it is not sufficient to know
that we shall not throw it away. It is equally needful to
know whether we are to open it.

Since it is in part with a view to opening it that we are
not throwing it away, said Mercier.

I know, I know, said Camier, but are we to open it immediately or wait until the weather has characterized
itself more fully?

Mercier scrutinized the impenetrable sky.

Go and take a look, he said. Tell me what you think.

Camier went out into the street. He pressed on to the
corner, so that Mercier lost sight of him. On returning,
he said,

There may be clearing patches lower down. Would
you like me to go up on the roof?

Mercier concentrated. Finally he said, impulsively,

Open it, for the love of God.

But Camier could not open it. The bitch, he said, it
is stuck again.

Give it here, said Mercier.

But Mercier was no more fortunate. He brandished
it. But he got himself in hand just in time. Proverb.

What have we done to God? he said.

We have denied him, said Camier.

You will not make me believe that his rancor goes to
these lengths, said Mercier.

Tatter their clothing, divest the surrounding space of
streets and houses, empty their hands of objects boasting

assignable provenance, and they turn easily into Vladimir and Estragon. Between this dialogue and Didi's account of opportunities missed "il y a une éternité, vers 1900" (the less elegiac English text has "a million years ago, in the nineties") —

> Hand in hand from the top of the Eiffel Tower, among the first. We were respectable in those days. Now it's too late. They wouldn't even let us up.

—between Camier's mock Ladysmith and this, what differences of feeling we may discover radiate from the fact that Mercier and Camier have actually in their hands a relic of those times, whereas Didi must make do with memory, and Gogo (who can barely remember the previous day) with Didi's account. Their only possessions are their clothes. Certain of these are involved in the action: two hats (exchanged), one pair of boots (substituted for another), one pair of trousers (falling down), one rope, serving Estragon as a belt (broken). None of them has any history, none bespeaks any past. Indeed all are interchangeable with substitutes in some economy exterior to the action on the stage, as it seems clear that Estragon's trousers served someone of ampler build before they came to him. So much for objects. We may note the presence of food (turnips, carrots, radishes). The universe is also furnished with natural splendors (one tree) and natural phenomena (twilight, darkness, moonlight). Consequently its inhabitants are thrown completely on their own resources:

> VLADIMIR: You must be happy, too, deep down, if you only knew it.
> ESTRAGON: Happy about what?
> VLADIMIR: To be back with me again.
> ESTRAGON: Would you say so?
> VLADIMIR: Say you are, even if it's not true.
> ESTRAGON: What am I to say?
> VLADIMIR: Say, I am happy.

ESTRAGON: I am happy.
VLADIMIR: So am I.
ESTRAGON: So am I.
VLADIMIR: We are happy.
ESTRAGON: We are happy. (*Silence.*) What do we do, now that we are happy?
VLADIMIR: Wait for Godot. (*Estragon groans. Silence.*)

There is one other difference between this world and that of Mercier and Camier. The difference is named Godot: another person, who matters. Whether or not he appears, he supplies tensions no umbrella, bicycle, or haversack can exert. In the play before us these tensions are barely sketched; Beckett was not to concern himself with them until more than a decade later, in *Embers* and *Comment C'est.*

It is more our present business to note why, in transforming the ambiguously aimless journey of the novel into the ambiguously empty waiting of the play, Beckett has emptied the protagonists' world of objects. Objects, in his universe, go with a journey: bicycles, for instance, crutches, a hat secured by a string; in *Comment C'est,* a jute sack, tins of fish, a can opener, used in the journeying, absent in the waiting. The objects Malone inventories in his immobility—a needle stuck into two corks, the bowl of a pipe, equipped with a little tin lid, a scrap of newspaper, a photograph of an ass wearing a boater—these constitute no exception, for Malone's immobility is not a waiting but by definition a terminal phase in a journey, toward nothingness. Thus Malone's objects have histories. Since they joined his entourage they have made a journey through time in his company, undergoing modifications not always at random (he knows under what circumstances the brim came off his hat; he removed it himself, so that he might keep the hat on while he slept). It is even possible to speculate concerning their pre-Malone history; the pipe bowl which he found in the grass must have been thrown away by a man who said, when the stem broke, "Bah, I'll buy myself another." ("But all that is mere supposition.") Thus the static object, like Malone's own immobility, is a momentary cross section of a duration, the present index of a movement in time which may parallel or continue movement in space, as the Beckett journey is apt to become identical with the process of being alive.

But the scanty tale of objects that concern the bums in *Waiting for Godot* contains no item owning a past, a future, or a duration with which our vital sentiments may feel empathy. Like the elements at the beginning of a mathematical problem, the bowler hats, the boots, the pants, the rope, the tree are simply *given*, and the operations that are performed on them do not modify them (as, at the end of the most prolonged computation, x is still x).

There are, it is true, in the play a few things that undergo changes of a different order. These are irreversible changes, the sort prescribed by the Second Law of Thermodynamics, the law with whose gross effects Lucky's great speech is concerned. Reversible events are trivial, like rearrangements of furniture, or of the terms in an equation. By this criterion the status of most of the events in the play is slight, or at most ambiguous. Irreversible things are the ones that *happen*, that declare something more than a system of tautologies, or an economy of displacements. It is the sum of those happenings, however small, whose terms and agents can never again be put back the way they were—the carrot uneaten, the leaves unbudded—that advances by today's quantum the system's articulation, or perhaps its entropy. Of these *Waiting for Godot* contains a real but insignificant number.

Though this is the play in which, as Vivian Mercier

wittily observed, "nothing happens, twice," things at the fall of the final curtain are not precisely as they were. Before our eyes a carrot has come into visibility out of Didi's pocket and vanished again into Gogo's mouth; its subsequent decomposition may be conjectured. Before our eyes, also, the rope has been broken, into two pieces whose combined length will equal the original length, but which can never again be combined. These are both irreversible actions; the world is now poorer by one carrot and one rope. In the interval between the acts there have been three organic changes: the tree has acquired leaves, and Pozzo has lost his sight and Lucky his speech. (We have only Pozzo's word for the latter two). It is not clear whether these count as irreversible events, though certainly the leaves cannot be expected to go back into the tree. In the same interval Gogo's boots have been taken, and a pair of a different color substituted. Didi ventures an explanation of this, inaccurate because based on inadequate data. With the benefit of our later knowledge that the new boots are larger than the old, we can readily amend his hypothesis. The play's other substitution occurs before our eyes: as a result of a sequence of permutations too long to reconstruct, Didi midway through Act II has Lucky's hat on his head, and Didi's hat has replaced Lucky's on the ground. And one further item comes from outside the visible economy of the play, viz. Lucky's second hat, the hat he is wearing on his reappearance in Act II, after having left his first hat on the ground before his exit in Act. I. These substitutions are presumably reversible, though it is not clear how Lucky's second hat would have to be disposed of.

Nor can the tedium of two evenings be said to redeem its own nullity by enhancing the experience of Didi and Gogo, as one may learn by watching bees move about.

They exist in an eternity of stagnation, Gogo's memory defective ("Either I forget immediately or I never forget"), Didi's an eventless assimilation of the same to the remembered same. They are, unlike Murphy, Mercier, Molloy, Moran, and Malone, utterly incapable of the kind of experience you can later tell a story about, and utterly detached from the least affection for objects. They have only their bodies and their clothes: hence the mathematical speed with which their situation can be exhibited. Not having chosen suicide ("sans le courage de finir ni la force de continuer"), they have grown committed, in a kind of fierce negative sanctity, to waiting for the figure with sheep, goats, many affairs, and a white beard (we need not credit any of these details). Their lives correspond exactly to St. John of the Cross's famous minimal prescription, divested of the love of created things, and the divine union is awaited beside the tree, one evening, another evening—every evening, since two terms, in the absence of indications to the contrary, imply a series, perhaps infinite. They are blessed, says Didi, in knowng the answer to the question, what it is they are doing there. They are waiting for Godot to come, or for night to fall. They have kept their appointment, that too they can claim, and it is not by accident that he refers to the saints. "We are not saints, but we have kept our appointment. How many people can boast as much?"

Lest we be tempted to take this rhetorical question for the ridge pole of the play, Gogo replies, "Billions," and Didi concedes that he may be right. The question, climaxing the longest speech either of them is to deliver, retains its torque.

Having reduced the whole of two men's lives to a waiting which epitomizes a moral issue, Beckett causes this situation to be intersected by his other key situation, a journey. Pozzo and Lucky are a little like Moran and his son, seen from the outside instead of through Moran's narrative. They are loaded, as if to emphasize the distinction between waiters and travelers, with every kind of portable property, notably a heavy bag (of sand), a folding stool, a picnic basket (with chicken and wine), a greatcoat, a whip, a watch (genuine half-hunter, with deadbeat escapement,[4] gift of Pozzo's grandfather), a handkerchief, a pocket vaporizer, a rope, glasses, matches, and a briar pipe (by Kapp and Peterson). The watch is often consulted; there is a schedule to observe. If these two, master and servant, steadily on the move, epitomize the busy world from which Didi and Gogo have seceded, there is no record of the act of secession. Rather, the contrasting pairs appear to epitomize not ways of life so much as modes of being. Amid the great void which they contrive to fill up with exercises and conversation, Didi and Gogo circulate about one another with numb but delectable affection, Didi perpetually responsible for Gogo, enraged when Gogo is kicked, and offering to carry him (*Pause*) "if necessary." Gogo for his part rejects a proposed system for hanging themselves on the sole ground, he says, that if it fails his friend will be left alone. Both strike noble if temporary rages on behalf of Lucky, and even, when Lucky is put in the wrong, on behalf of Pozzo; and with infinite delay and ratiocination they do eventually help the blind Pozzo of the second act to his feet. Pozzo, on the other hand, absurd, theatrical, glib, patronizing ("so that I ask myself is there anything I can do in my turn for these honest fellows who are having such a dull, dull time") is capable of nothing but stage turns: the judicious stranger, the picnicker at his

---

[4] See Abbot Payson Usher, *A History of Mechanical Inventions*, chap. xii, p. 313

ease, the eulogist of twilight, the man whose heart goes pit-a-pat—very much, in each of his roles, someone we have seen before. This kaleidoscope of impostors learned all that he knows from Lucky, and we are given at some length a specimen of Lucky's capacity for imparting the things he has in his head. They live with their heads, these two, moving hither and thither, Pozzo talking of buying and selling, and imposing with his campstool and ceremonial a prissy elegance on their halts; Lucky treacherous, miserable, obeying with a precision that does not quite approximate to ritual, and dancing or thinking on command. There is no love here, and the play's waiting seems incontestably preferable to its journeying.

4

For the stage is a place to wait. The place itself waits, when no one is in it. When the curtain rises on *Endgame*, sheets drape all visible objects as in a furniture warehouse. Clov's first act is to uncurtain the two high windows and inspect the universe; his second is to remove the sheets and fold them carefully over his arm, disclosing two ash cans and a figure in an armchair. This is so plainly a metaphor for waking up that we fancy the stage, with its high peepholes, to be the inside of an immense skull. It is also ritual for starting the play; Yeats arranged such a ritual for *At the Hawk's Well,* and specified a black cloth and a symbolic song. It is finally a removal from symbolic storage of the objects that will be needed during the course of the performance. When the theater is empty it is sensible to keep them covered against dust. So we are reminded at the outset that what we are to witness is a dusty dramatic exhibition, repeated and repeatable. The necessary objects include three additional players (two of them in ash cans). Since none of them will move from his station we can think of them after the performance as being kept permanently on stage, and covered with their dust cloths again until to-morrow night.

The rising of the curtain disclosed these sheeted forms; the removal of the sheets disclosed the protagonist and his ash cans; the next stage is for the protagonist to un-cover his own face, which he does with a yawn, culmi-nating this three-phase strip tease with the revelation of a very red face and black glasses. His name, we gather from the program, is Hamm, a name for an actor. He is also Hamlet, bounded in a nutshell, fancying himself king of infinite space, but troubled by bad dreams; he is also "a toppled Prospero,"[5] remarking partway through the play, with judicious pedantry, "our revels now are ended"; he is also the Hammer to which Clov, Nagg and Nell (Fr. clou, Ger. Nagel, Eng. nail) stand in passive relationship; by extension, a chess player ("Me—[he yawns]—to play"); but also (since Clov must wheel him about) himself a chessman, probably the imperiled King.

Nagg and Nell in their dustbins appear to be pawns; Clov, with his arbitrarily restricted movements ("I can't sit.") and his equestrian background ("And your rounds? Always on foot?" "Sometimes on horse.") resembles the Knight, and his perfectly cubical kitchen ("ten feet by ten feet by ten feet, nice dimensions, nice proportions") resembles a square on the chessboard translated into three dimensions. He moves back and forth, into it and out of it, coming to the succor of Hamm and then retreat-ing. At the endgame's end the pawns are forever im-mobile and Clov is poised for a last departure from the

---

[5] This admirable phrase is Mr. Roy Walker's, in the December 1958 Twentieth Century.

board, the status quo forever menaced by an expected piece glimpsed through the window, and King Hamm abandoned in check:

> Old endgame lost of old, play and lose and have done with losing. . . . Since that's the way we're playing it, let's play it that way . . . and speak no more about it . . . speak no more.

Even if we had not the information that the author of this work has been known to spend hours playing chess with himself (a game at which you always lose[6]), we should have been alerted to his long-standing interest in its strategy by the eleventh chapter of *Murphy*, where Murphy's first move against Mr. Endon, the standard P—K$_4$, is described as "the primary cause of all [his] subsequent difficulties." (The same might be said of getting born, an equally conventional opening.) Chess has several peculiarities which lend themselves to the metaphors of this jagged play. It is a game of leverage, in which the significance of a move may be out of all proportion to the local disturbance it effects ("A flea! This is awful! What a day!"). It is a game of silences, in which new situations are appraised: hence Beckett's most frequent stage direction, *"Pause."* It is a game of steady attrition; by the time we reach the endgame the board is nearly bare, as bare as Hamm's world where there are no more bicycle wheels, sugarplums, pain killers, or coffins, let alone people. And it is a game which by the successive removal of screening pieces constantly extends the range of lethal forces, until at the endgame peril from a key piece sweeps down whole ranks and files. The king is hobbled by the rule which allows him to move in any direction but only one square at a time; Hamm's circuit of the stage and re-

---

[6] Or always win. "One of the thieves was saved. It's a reasonable percentage."

turn to center perhaps exhibits him patrolling the inner boundaries of the little nine-square territory he commands. To venture further will evidently expose him to check. ("Outside of here it's death.") His knight shuttles to and fro, his pawns are pinned. No threat is anticipated from the auditorium, which is presumably off the board; and a periodic reconnaissance downfield through the windows discloses nothing but desolation until very near the end. But on his last inspection of the field Clov is dismayed. Here the English text is inexplicably sketchy; in the French one we have,

> CLOV: Aïeaïeaïe!
> HAMM: C'est une feuille? Une fleur? Une toma— (*il bâille*) —te?
> CLOV: (*regardant*) Je t'en foutrai des tomates! Quelqu'un! C'est quelqu'un!
> HAMM: Eh bien, va l'exterminer. (*Clov descend de l'escabeau.*) Quelqu'un! (*Vibrant.*) Fais ton devoir!

In the subsequent interrogatory we learn the distance of this threat (fifteen meters or so), its state of rest or motion (motionless), its sex (presumably a boy), its occupation (sitting on the ground as if leaning on something). Hamm, perhaps thinking of the resurrected Jesus, murmurs "La pierre levée," then on reflection changes the image to constitute himself proprietor of the Promised Land: "Il regarde la maison sans doute, avec les yeux de Moïse mourant." It is doing, however, nothing of the kind; it is gazing at its navel. There is no use, Hamm decides, in running out to exterminate it: "If he exists he'll die there or he'll come here. And if he doesn't . . ." And a few seconds later he has conceded the game:

> It's the end, Clov, we've come to the end. I don't need you any more.

He sacrifices his last mobile piece, discards his staff and whistle, summons for the last time a resourceless Knight and an unanswering Pawn, and covers his face once more with the handkerchief: somehow in check.

Not that all this is likely to be yielded up with clarity by any conceivable performance. It represents however a structure which, however we glimpse it, serves to refrigerate the incidental passions of a play about, it would seem, the end of humanity. It is not for nothing that the place within which the frigid events are transacted is more than once called "the shelter," outside of which is death; nor that the human race is at present reduced to two disabled parents, a macabre blind son, and an acathisiac servant. Around this shelter the universe crumbles away like an immense dry biscuit: no more rugs, no more tide, no more coffins. We hear of particular deaths:

> CLOV (*harshly*) : When old Mother Pegg asked you for oil or her lamp and you told her to get out to hell, you knew what was happening then, no? (*Pause.*) You know what she died of, Mother Pegg? Of darkness.
> HAMM (*feebly*): I hadn't any.
> CLOV (*as before*) : Yes, you had.

We observe particular brutalities: Hamm, of his parents: "Have you bottled her?" "Yes." "Are they both bottled?" "Yes." "Screw down the lids." What has shrunken the formerly ample world is perhaps Hamm's withdrawal of love; the great skull-like setting suggests a solipsist's universe. "I was never there," he says. "Absent, always. It all happened without me. I don't know what's happened." He has been in "the shelter"; he has also been closed within himself. It is barely possible that the desolation is not universal:

> HAMM: Did you ever think of one thing?
> CLOV: Never.
> HAMM: That here we're down in a hole. (*Pause.*) But

beyond the hills? Eh? Perhaps it's still green. Eh?
(*Pause.*) Flora! Pomona! (*Ecstatically.*) Ceres!
(*Pause.*) Perhaps you won't need to go very far.
CLOV: I can't go very far. (*Pause.*) I'll leave you.

As Hamm is both chessman and chess player, so it is conceivable that destruction is not screened off by the shelter but radiates from it for a certain distance. Zero, zero, words we hear so often in the dialogue, these are the Cartesian coordinates of the origin.

Bounded in a nutshell yet king of infinite space, Hamm articulates the racking ambiguity of the play by means of his dominance over its most persuasive metaphor, the play itself. If he is Prospero with staff and revels, if he is Richard III bloodsmeared and crying "My kingdom for a nightman!" if he is also perhaps Richard II, within whose hollow crown

> . . . Keeps Death his court, and there the Antic sits,
> Scoffing his state and grinning at his pomp,
> Allowing him a breath, a little scene
> To monarchize, be feared, and kill with looks—[7]

these roles do not exhaust his repertoire. He is (his name tells us) the generic Actor, a creature all circumference and no center. As master of the revels, he himself attends to the last unveiling of the opening ritual:

> (*Pause. Hamm stirs. He yawns under the handkerchief. He removes the handkerchief from his face. Very red face, black glasses.*)
> HAMM: Me— (*he yawns*) —to play. (*He holds the handkerchief spread out before him.*) Old stancher! (. . . *He clears his throat, joins the tips of his fingers.*) Can there be misery— (*he yawns*)—loftier than mine?

The play ended, he ceremoniously unfolds the handkerchief once more (five separate stage directions govern-

---

[7] I owe this suggestion to Mr. Walker's article.

ing his tempo) and covers his face as it was in the beginning. "Old Stancher! (*Pause*.) You . . . remain." What remains, in the final brief tableau specified by the author, is the immobile figure with a bloodied Veronica's veil in place of a face: the actor having superintended his own Passion and translated himself into an ultimate abstraction of masked agony.

Between these termini he animates everything, ordering the coming and going of Clov and the capping and uncapping of the cans. When Clov asks, "What is there to keep me here?" he answers sharply, "The dialogue." A particularly futile bit of business with the spyglass and the steps elicits from him an aesthetic judgment, "This is deadly." When it is time for the introduction of the stuffed dog, he notes, "We're getting on," and a few minutes later, "Do you not think this has gone on long enough?" These, like comparable details in *Godot*, are sardonic authorizations for a disquiet that is certainly stirring in the auditorium. No one understands better than Beckett, nor exploits more boldly, the kind of fatalistic attention an audience trained on films is accustomed to place at the dramatist's disposal. The cinema has taught us to suppose that a dramatic presentation moves inexorably as the reels unwind or the studio clock creeps, until it has consumed precisely its allotted time which nothing, no restlessness in the pit, no sirens, no mass exodus can hurry. "Something is taking its course," that suffices us. Hence the vast leisure in which the minimal business of *Godot* and *Endgame* is transacted; hence (transposing into dramatic terms the author's characteristic pedantry of means) the occasional lingering over points of technique, secure in the knowledge that the clock-bound patience of a twentieth-century audience will expect no inner urgency, nothing in fact but the actual time events consume, to determine the pace of the exhibition. Clov asks, "Why this farce, day after day?" and it is sufficient for Hamm to reply, "Routine. One never knows." It is the answer of an actor in an age of films and long runs. In *Endgame* (which here differs radically from *Godot*) no one is supposed to be improvising; the script has been well committed to memory and well rehearsed. By this means doom is caused to penetrate the most intimate crevices of the play. "I'm tired of going on," says Clov late in the play, "very tired," and then, "Let's stop playing!" (if there is one thing that modern acting is not it is playing). In the final moments theatrical technique, under Hamm's sponsorship, rises into savage prominence.

> HAMM: . . . And me? Did anyone ever have pity on me?
> CLOV: (*lowering the telescope, turning towards Hamm*): What? (*Pause.*) Is it me you're referring to?
> HAMM: (*angrily*): An aside, ape! Did you never hear an aside before? (*Pause.*) I'm warming up for my last soliloquy.

Ten seconds later he glosses "More complications!" as a technical term: "Not an underplot, I trust." It is Clov who has the last word in this vein:

> HAMM: Clov! (*Clov halts, without turning.*) Nothing. (*Clov moves on.*) Clov! (*Clov halts, without turning.*)
> CLOV: This is what we call making an exit.

By this reiterated stress on the actors as professional men, and so on the play as an occasion within which they operate, Beckett transforms Hamm's last soliloquy into a performance, his desolation into something prepared by the dramatic machine, his abandoning of gaff, dog, and whistle into a necessary discarding of props, and the terminal business with the handkerchief into, quite literally, a curtain speech. *Endgame* ends with an unexpected lightness, a death rather mimed than experienced; if it is "Hamm as stated, and Clov as stated, together as stated," the mode of statement has more salience than a paraphrase of the play's situation would lead one to expect.

The professionalism also saves the play from an essentially sentimental committment to simpliste "destiny." Much of its gloomy power it derives from contact with such notions as T. H. Huxley's view of man as an irrelevance whom day by day an indifferent universe engages in chess. We do not belong here, runs a strain of Western thought which became especially articulate in France after the War; we belong nowhere; we are all surds, ab-surd. There is nothing on which to ground our right to exist, and we need not be especially surprised one day to find ourselves nearly extinct. (On such a despair Cartesian logic converges, as surely as the arithmetic of Pythagoras wedged itself fast in the irrationality of $\sqrt{2}$.) Whatever we do, then, since it can obtain no grip on our radically pointless situation, is *behavior* pure and simple; it is play acting, and may yield us the satisfaction, if satisfaction there be, of playing well, of uttering our *cris du coeur* with style and some sense of timing. We do not trouble deaf heaven, for there is only the sky ("Rien," reports Clov, gazing through his telescope; and again, "Zéro.") We stir and thrill, at best, ourselves. From such a climate, miscalled existentialist, Beckett wrings every available *frisson* without quite delivering the play into its keeping; for its credibility is not a principle the play postulates but an idea the play contains, an idea of which it works out the moral and spiritual consequences. The despair in which he traffics is a conviction, not a philosophy. He will even set it spinning like a catharine wheel about a wild point of logic, as when he has Hamm require that God be prayed to in silence

("Where are your manners?") and then berate him ("The bastard!") for not existing.[8]

The play contains whatever ideas we discern inside it; no idea contains the play. The play contains, moreover, two narrative intervals, performances within the performance. The first, Nagg's story about the trousers, is explicitly a recitation; Nell has heard it often, and so, probably, has the audience; it is a vaudeville standby. Nagg's performance, like a production of *King Lear*, whose story we know, must therefore be judged solely as a performance. Its quality, alas, discourages even him ("I tell this story worse and worse."), and Nell too is not amused, being occupied with thoughts of her own, about the sand at the bottom of Lake Como. The other is Hamm's huffesnuffe narrative, also a recitation, since we are to gather that he has been composing it beforehand, in his head. This time we do not know the substance of the tale, but contemplate in diminishing perspective an actor who has memorized a script which enjoins him to imitate a man who has devised and memorized a script:

> The man came crawling towards me, on his belly. Pale, wonderfully pale and thin, he seemed on the point of— (*Pause. Normal tone.*) No, I've done that bit.

Later on he incorporates a few critical reflections: "Nicely put, that," or "There's English for you." This technician's narcissism somewhat disinfects the dreadful tale. All Hamm's satisfactions come from dramatic self-contemplation, and as he towers before us, devoid of mercy, it is to some ludicrous stage villain that he assimilates himself, there on the stage, striking a stage-Barabbas

---

8 The Lord Chamberlain, a less subtle (or less orthodox) theologian, required that for performances on the English stage "bastard" should be altered to "swine."

pose ("Sometimes I go about and poison wells.") It is to this
that life as play-acting comes.

> In the end he asked me would I consent to take in the
> child as well—if he were still alive. (*Pause.*) It was the
> moment I was waiting for. (*Pause.*) Would I consent to
> take in the child. . . . (*Pause.*) I can see him still, down
> on his knees, his hands flat on the ground, glaring at me
> with his mad eyes, in defiance of my wishes.

"It was the moment I was waiting for": the satisfaction
this exudes is considerably less sadistic than dramatic,
and the anticlimax into which the long performance
immediately topples would try a creator's soul, not a
maniac's:

> I'll soon have finished with this story. (*Pause.*) Unless
> I bring in other characters. (*Pause.*) But where would I
> find them? (*Pause.*) Where would I look for them?
> (*Pause. He whistles. Enter Clov.*) Let us pray to God.

So the hooks go in. There is no denying what Beckett
called in a letter to Alan Schneider "the power of the
text to claw." It strikes, however, its unique precarious
balance between rage and art, immobilizing all characters but one, rotating before us for ninety unbroken minutes the surfaces of Nothing, always designedly faltering
on the brink of utter insignificance into which nevertheless we cannot but project so many awful significances:
theater reduced to its elements in order that theatrical-
ism may explore without mediation its own boundaries:
a bleak unforgettable tour de force and probably its author's single most remarkable work.

Voices In The Dark

il arrive j'aurai une voix plus de voix au monde
que la mienne un murmure eu une vie là-haut ici
verrai de nouveau mes choses un peu de bleu sous
la boue un peu de blanc nos choses petites scènes
ciels surtout et chemins

— Comment C'est

If *Endgame* eviscerates stage drama (as the trilogy did
fiction) the better to inspect its entrails, the plays for radio that succeed *Endgame* abolish the stage and explore
the resources of a world created by voices. "All is a question of voices," reflects The Unnamable more than once.

> I'm in words, made of words, others' words, what others,
> the place too, the air, the walls, the floor, the ceiling, all
> words, the whole world is here with me, I'm the air, the
> walls, the walled-in one, everything yields, opens, ebbs,
> flows, like flakes, I'm all these flakes, meeting, mingling,
> falling asunder.

All this is strictly true of a character in fiction, but he
means more than that. He means too that man is man by
virtue of speech, and that all speech is an echoing of
echoes. This truth radio imitates more intimately than
the printed page. "I'm all these words, all these stran-
gers, this dust of words, with no ground for their settling":
such are the beings created by the loudspeaker, creating themselves instant by instant and vanishing when
they fall silent. "Do not imagine," says Mrs. Rooney after
four other voices have intervened in the twenty seconds
since her last speech, "do not imagine, because I am silent,
that I am not present, and alive, to all that is going on."

This is not simply Mrs. Rooney asserting her grievance, but radio drama asserting its nature, and Beckett turned to radio drama at a crest of preoccupation with the fact that for him to live was to make stories, creating with words beings not himself, but perfecting his own identity in perfecting their words.

In *All That Fall* the illusion of a populous, varied world is so remarkable that the dramatist must more than once remind us that it is illusion merely. He is at pains to remind us, because the play turns less on illusion than on its illusoriness, a purely aural landscape capitalizing eerily on the fact that whatever falls silent disappears. *All That Fall* is full of departures elsewhere, but "elsewhere," not being where our ears are, doesn't exist in the way that "offstage" exists. We can imagine Clov's kitchen ("ten feet by ten feet by ten feet") by a gesture of spatial extension to the right; but where is Mr. Slocum, after we hear the last grinding of his gears? What becomes of Mr. Tyler, Mr. Barrell, and Miss Fitt, after they have spoken for the last time, with half of the play still to be transacted? Where, for that matter, does Mr. Rooney come from, when his voice suddenly joins the consort? The death of the child, on which the structure of incident depends, occurred then in the *néant*; and the question whether Mr. Rooney was guilty is as meaningless as the question whether Pozzo is really Godot, or whether Hamm's savage want of love has really been the principle of dissolution in a universe now patently dissolving. For certainties, Beckett will not cease to tell us, are largely conventions and bounded by a mystery.

Mr. Rooney has come by train from the city, we are meant to understand; and as for the others, we have left them behind at the station; but there is no station, no train, no city, no movement in space; only the convention represented in the printed text by the direction, "Dragging feet, panting, thudding stick," and in the BBC production by an insistent metrical figure on the kettledrums.

The two radio plays, *All That Fall* and *Embers*, focus respectively on the two Beckett conditions, a moving and an immobility. *All That Falls* takes us the long journey to the station and back again, with a waiting between. People move, by cart, by bicycle, by limousine, by train, and on foot, dragging, limping, running. All these movements in space are translated by the aural medium into time, where sounds expend themselves and die. Things that always occur in time, meanwhile: transmogrifications, failings, vanishings; these are presented to us at every instant of the dialogue, so that the play is steeped in transience, a transience the more total because there is nothing whatever that we can see, no tree onstage for two hours, no windows, ash cans, or armchairs. All that fall, says the title; and all are falling. "How is your poor wife?" "No better, Ma'am." "Your daughter then?" "No worse, Ma'am." After a silence, "Nice day for the races, Ma'am." "No doubt it is. (*Pause.*) But will it hold up? (*Pause. With emotion.*) Will it hold up?" Five minutes later, with another interlocutor, "What news of your daughter?" "Fair, fair. They removed everything, you know, the whole . . . er . . . bag of tricks. Now I am grandchildless." A minute later: "It is suicide to be abroad. But what is it to be at home, Mr. Tyler, what is it to be at home? A lingering dissolution. Now we are white with dust from head to foot." As Malone does nothing but die, so in this play human beings have nothing to anticipate but decline. Mrs. Rooney has lost a daughter; were her daughter alive now, "In her forties now she'd be, I don't know, fifty, girding up her lovely little loins, getting ready for the change." Mrs. Rooney is "destroyed with sorrow and pining and gentility and church-going and fat and rheumatism." Mr. Rooney is now blind and anticipates with some relish going deaf and dumb. Mrs. Rooney's dress gets torn; a hen dies beneath Mr. Slocum's car. The car in turn declines to start until violent measures are taken. Most unnerving of all, the very bicycle (*maestro di color che vanno*) has ruptured a tire and bids fair to break its owner's heart: "Now if it were the front I should not so much mind. But the back. The back! The chain! The oil! The grease! The hub! The brakes! The gear! No! It is too much!" It is into a collective process of this kind that children are born.

Thus the mode in which the play itself exists, as a series of auditory effects in time, sustains its theme of transience. The very ditch, we are told, contains rotting leaves ("In June? Rotting leaves in June?" "Yes, dear, from last year, and from the year before last, and from the year before that again.") ; and the ditch itself is no more present to our senses than it is to blind Dan's: "What way am I facing?" "What?" "I have forgotten what way I am facing." "You have turned aside and are bowed down over the ditch." These words create the ditch, for us as for him; when they move on it has gone. We too are blind. Words, similarly, create the ephemerally substantial Mrs. Rooney herself, words and sounds, so vividly that the tour de force of the play consists in the elaborate illusion that her two hundred pounds of bulk are being shouldered by main force into a motor car. This hysterical scene ("Oh . . . Lower! . . . Don't be afraid! . . .We're past the age when . . . There! . . . Now! . . . Get your shoulder under it! . . . Oh! (*Giggles.*) Oh glory! . . . Up! Up! Ah! I'm in!") and its later counterpart the extraction scene ("Crouch down, Mrs. Rooney, crouch down and get your head in the open." "Crouch down! At my time of life! This is lunacy!") make her at the same time vastly substantial to the mind's eye, and vastly decrepit. Yet even Mrs. Rooney is an illusion; all living is an illusion; the very animals whose ways have not changed since Arcady are merely so many baas and bleats, manifestly generated by the sound effects department. (Beckett has said that he would have preferred the approximations of human imitators to the BBC's painstaking illusion.) Pulsating in acoustic space, the soundscape asserts a provisional reality, at every instant richly springing forth and dying.

The background of a play for voices is silence, a silence amidst which the specifically human asserts itself with a special torque. The words do not tumble forth, they are composed, and into sentences, whose Ionic elegance, even as the silence claims it, cries aloud to enter an immobility in which to be savored. "Let us halt a moment," says Mrs. Rooney, "and this vile dust fall back upon the viler worms." The very cries of her heart have a fine rhetorical finesse. ("Oh cursed corset! If I could let it out, without indecent exposure.") This extraordinary combination of vivacity and artifice, which accounts for much of the fascination of the play, does not fail in its turn to become conscious of itself. In the first few minutes we find Mrs. Rooney arrested by her own way of speaking (her word for it, itself a *trouvaille*, is "bizarre") ; and near the end Mr. Rooney restates this theme.

> MRS. ROONEY: No, no, I am agog, tell me all, then we shall press on and never pause, never pause, till we come safe to haven.
> (*Pause.*)
> MR. ROONEY: Never pause . . . safe to haven . . . Do you know, Maddy, sometimes one would think you were struggling with a dead language.

MRS. ROONEY: Yes indeed, Dan, I know full well what you mean, I often have that feeling, it is unspeakably excruciating.

MR. ROONEY: I confess I have it sometimes myself, when I happen to overhear what I am saying.

MRS. ROONEY: Well you know, it will be dead in time, just like our own poor dear Gaelic, there is that to be said.

This is a critical moment in the development of the play's theme. Language itself, it appears, is about to be assimilated into the utter transience the play has now been exploring for sixty minutes: all speech a struggle with dying idioms, and human dignity, which asserts itself in speech, an illusion readily swept away. Then a live language intervenes:

> *Urgent baa.*
> MR. ROONEY: (*startled.*) Good God!
> MRS. ROONEY: Oh, the pretty little woolly lamb, crying to suck its mother! Theirs has not changed, since Arcady.

Arcady, a fictitious past; crying to suck its mother, a tissue of fictions; the pretty little woolly lamb, an anonymous invention, Mrs. Rooney's reality perhaps, but not a shepherd's nor for that matter a zoologist's (theirs too are fictions). Everything, at this moment, reels into unreliability except the sound of the baa (which has known no Grimm's law) and the fact that Mrs. Rooney has constructed another of her impassioned miniatures.

> *Pause.*
> MR. ROONEY: Where was I in my composition?
> MRS. ROONEY: At a standstill.
> MR. ROONEY: Ah yes. (*Clears his throat. Narrative tone.*) I concluded naturally that we had entered a station. . .

His long account of how things were on the train is a "composition" also; "narrative tone" recalls Hamm's unending story, and Nagg's joke. For the work in hand to scrutinize its own mode of being, and having suddenly discerned the conventions upon which it is established to suddenly cancel out all certainties by forcing on our attention a converging series of fictions, as of mirrors facing one another, this is a familiar Beckett technique. It is finally the linchpin of the work that gathers up all these lesser works of the late 1950's, *Comment C'est*. It serves in *All That Fall* to remove into uncertainty forever the question of Mr. Rooney's responsibility, conscious or unconscious, for what happened to the little girl. It is useless to assemble clues. ("Did you ever wish to kill a child?" . . . "I had the compartment to myself as usual. At least I hope so, for I made no attempt to restrain myself." . . . "Say something, Maddy. Say you believe me.") Useless, because all facts are provisional except the fact that sounds are being uttered. Everything is infected with fiction. Mr. Rooney, moreover, is as thoroughly as Murphy divided between a mental life that expresses itself, if at all, in objurgation and narrative, but prefers, presumably, revery ("I dream of other roads in other lands. Of another home, another— (*he hesitates*) —another home. (*Pause.*) What was I trying to say?"), and a bodily existence over which the mind has little control, and in which it has little interest. What the dramatic medium compels us to do is acquiesce in this indifference of expression to fact; a sound or two, a word or two, we find, has the power to make us believe virtually anything. So we can only know what Mr. Rooney tells us, which may in turn be the fiction he chooses to entertain himself with, like so many Beckett characters. In the final moments we know this much, that the train was late because a child fell beneath the wheels (for even in radio plays one is to trust a messenger). It comes as a brutal and shocking fact, rupturing the elegiac tone and the inimitably gentle grotesquerie by which we have been suffused for seventy-five minutes. Until now the indomitable language has absorbed every human shock, and extracted from universal decay a species of melancholy satisfaction. But: "Under the wheels, ma'am." There is no reply. Not even Mrs. Rooney will be able to cope with this for several weeks. It is too terrible for apothegm, epigram, cadence, or plaint. The dead language with which she struggles and from which she wrests the satisfactions of eloquence is suddenly defeated by something intransigently alive: a death. So the play ends, as a dream may terminate in a gunshot, or as "Dante in the Lobster" closed with the dreadful words about a quick death: "It is not." It is open to doubt whether the effect quite coheres: for art has suddenly refused to be art and brought forward living pain.

Embers, on the other hand, Beckett's most difficult work, coheres to perfection, locking us as it does inside the word spinner's prison. There is only one voice for half its duration, Henry's, on the strand. ("That sound you hear is the sea, we are sitting on the strand. I mention it because the sound is so strange, so unlike the sound of the sea, that if you didn't see what it was you wouldn't know what it was.") Taking command of the medium in Hamm's way, he tells us this; so of course we can't be sure; for hooves sound when he calls for them, and the sea, it may be, is another such illusion. He is the director as well as the principal actor; the sound-effects men await his cues. He talks constantly; he talks, he tells us, to drown out the sea (which may not be there). Ada agrees that it may not be there ("You shouldn't be hearing it, there must be something wrong with your brain."), and Ada herself quite likely isn't there, since her voice enters the cosmos at his command, like those hooves. It is through several removes, therefore, that he arrives at the possibility that he may be deluded. He also comes sidewise at the bleakness of his own solipsism. This theme is broached by Ada's voice, which asks, "Who were you with just now? Before you spoke to me," to which he replies, "I was trying to be with my father." (His father he has earlier called "an old man blind and foolish. . . . My father, back from the dead, to be with me. . . . As if he hadn't died.") This is a sort of game he plays, just as Ada's voice, we come to understand, speaks out of a kind of game he plays. Her voice says:

> "I suppose you have worn him out. (*Pause.*) You wore him out living and now you are wearing him out dead. (*Pause.*) The time comes when one cannot speak to you any more. (*Pause.*) The time will come when no one will speak to you at all, not even complete strangers. (*Pause.*) You will be quite alone with your voice, there will be no other voice in the world but yours. (*Pause.*) Do you hear me?"

Though we hear a woman's voice from the loud-speaker, there is in fact no other voice in the world but Henry's. He is telling himself a story, vivid, particular, straining after compassion, the story of Bolton and Holloway, whose setting comes to us with entrancing particularity—

> Standing there in his old red dressinggown might go on fire any minute like when he was a child, no, that was his pyjamas, standing there waiting in the dark, no light, only the sound of the fire, and no sound of any kind, only the fire, an old man in great trouble.

This is more real than that chimerical sea. So is the snow-bound world through which Holloway comes: "Outside all still, not a sound, dog's chain maybe or a bough groaning if you stood there listening long enough." So the fictive world. The present world, on the contrary, is an occasion for delusions and testy imperatives ("Thuds, I want thuds! Like this!"), and the past world one for uncertain probing ("I can't remember if he met you." "You know he met me." "No, Ada, I don't know, I'm sorry, I have forgotten almost everything connected with you.") In his fictions however he moves with easy authority, since here at last everything will compose according to his whim, as Malone knew. But Henry's fiction culminates in an impasse, moving as it does to a situation like one Malone experienced in the flesh: a human encounter.

2

Malone, in bed, near death, records one evening an astonishing fact: "I have had a visit."

> I felt a violent blow on the head. He had perhaps been there for some time. One does not care to be kept waiting for ever, one draws attention to oneself as best one can, it's human. I don't doubt he gave me due warning, before he hit me. I don't know what he wanted. He's gone now. What an idea, all the same, to hit me on the head.

The blow on the head did not preface ampler communication. The visitor registered his presence, no more. "His mouth opened, his lips worked, but I heard nothing." Malone studied him at leisure, however; "He remained some time, seven hours at least." Later Malone draws up a written list of twenty-one questions, to be submitted if the man returns; but he does not. The list begins, "1. Who are you? 2. What do you do for a living? 3. Are you looking for something in particular? What else. 4. Why are you so cross? . . . ." "Strange need," he notes, "to know who people are and what they do for a living and what they want with you."

Strange need, precisely; for how is the question, who are you, to be answered? Perhaps by a name. But let us say we know the name, Godot for instance. Who is Godot, what does he do for a living, and what does he want with Didi and Gogo? These are not really the things we want to know. Sometimes we know them. This man's name is Gaber, he makes his living as a courier of Youdi, and what he wants with Moran is to dispatch him after Molloy. Knowing this, what do we, or what does Moran, know of Gaber? If we idly assimilate his name to Gabriel's, and Youdi's to Yahweh, it is because we can think of nothing better to do, with the data supplied. Or let us have ampler data, a whole autobiography, such as Mercier and Camier were sluiced with in a southbound train:

> An only child I believe, I was born at P—. My parents were originally from Q—. From them it was that I received, along with the spirochete, the majestic nose whose ruins you behold. They were severe with me, but just. At the least deflection from rectitude my father beat me, with his heavy razor strop, until I bled, never failing however to notify my mother, so she could paint me with tincture of iodine or alcohol. Here doubtless is the explanation of my withdrawn and secretive character. . . .

. . . and so on for a thousand mortal words as old Madden rotates himself before our gaze; and from it we learn only this, that old Madden is a bore not *per accidens* but by predilection.

Whether cryptic or copious, talk in the Beckett universe is generally a mode of behavior, like Watt's oscillatory walk or Molloy's extraordinary performance with the sixteen stones. Sometimes, as when Pozzo demands undivided attention and sprays his throat with the vaporizer, it is highly studied behavior. But no more than the facial contortions of Malone's visitor ("his mouth opened, his lips worked, but I heard nothing") does it satisfy the "strange need." This is strangely jarring; we expect spoken words to reach, not merely gesticulate. But it conforms to the decorums of a writer whose sensibility, like Wordsworth's, explores to confines of a universe of objects, in which people are difficult to distinguish from apparitions, or else statistics. Wordsworth, it will be remembered, once on his wanderings encountered a Man whom in his account of the incident he likened successively to (a) a huge stone on a mountain top; (b) a sea beast crawled forth to sun itself; (c) a motionless cloud; and when the Man commenced to speak,

> his voice to me was like a stream
> Scarce heard; nor word from word could I divide;
> And the whole body of the Man did seem
> Like one whom I had met with in a dream.

Not otherwise did Molloy, for whom "to restore silence is the role of objects," observe that when another spoke, the words he heard, "and heard distinctly, having quite a sensitive ear, were heard a first time, then a second, and often even a third, as pure sounds, free of all meaning, and this is probably one of the reasons why conversation was unspeakably painful to me." Over his explanation of this phenomenon presides, we may say, Newton, of the prism and silent face: it was, thinks Molloy, "a defect of the understanding, perhaps, which only began to vibrate on repeated solicitations, or which did vibrate, if you like, but at a lower frequency, or a higher, than that of ratiocination, if such a thing is conceivable, and such a thing is conceivable, since I conceive it."

For Wordsworth is the optimistic poet, as Beckett is

the weeping comedian, of Newton's quiet machine. The statue in the Cambridge antechapel he recognized for what it was, a thing as silent as the face it represented, the marble index of a mind gone elsewhere, and meanwhile the very likeness of the entranced body. We do not fancy it about to speak; Newton is history's first unspeaking sage, his essential posture of operation summed up by a statue. Socrates in the bust is about to say something, or has just finished, but Newton has nothing to say. He engages in no Confucian or Socratic *viva voce* with disciples. His is something more than the normal mathematician's alogia; for we hear of Euclid teaching pupils, and Pythagoras sociably engaged with his brother cultists. He has no talk, he communes with a universe of objects, and makes note of results, each equation formally a tautology, which he is even negligent about publishing. He likened himself to a lone child gathering shells on the shore of the infinite ocean; so Molloy, "sitting on the shore, before the sea, the sixteen stones spread out before my eyes," meditates his problem of groups and cycles. And Wordsworth, having penetrated to the heart of Newton's romance as night after night starlight or moonlight drew his mind back to the statue in the antechapel, became in his turn in emulation of the Newtonian sage the Newtonian poet, the first poet to make a habit of wandering lonely as a cloud, among rocks, and stones and trees, encountering such things as lone thorns, banks of daffodils, mountains, and occasional human apparitions, lost so far as might be in his wise passiveness, indeed perpetually talking to himself "like a river murmuring" so that he was (he says so) grateful for the little dog that barked beside him when persons came near, and reminded him to restrain his mutterings and assume a social demeanor.[1] Through the social world, with which he feels no kinship, as through the world of objects, he moves as anomalously as an octopus in a forest; it is a universe for a clown. And he was the first to make a program of writing years afterward about his own experiences, and about himself in the process of writing about them, as Molloy and Moran and Malone do with such unflagging patience.

All Beckett protagonists enjoy an eerie kinship with earth's diurnal course: "I listen," writes Molloy, "and the voice is of a world collapsing endlessly, a frozen world, under a faint untroubled sky, enough to see by, yes, and frozen too." Again he participates in "the labour of the planet rolling eager into winter," and always he senses "these leaning things forever lapsing and crumbling away, beneath a sky without memory of morning or hope of night." It is in such passages that the sap flows; of encounters with persons Molloy is apt to report only his irritation. "All she asked was to feel me near her, with her," he reports of Mrs. Lousse's affecting entreaty; but "every now and then I interrupted her, to ask what town I was in." Later a charcoal burner exhibited the "strange need," and Molloy can only list it in a calculus of probabilities:

> I asked him to show me the nearest way out of the forest. I grew eloquent. His reply was exceedingly confused. Either I didn't understand a word he said, or he didn't understand a word I said, or he knew nothing, or he wanted to keep me near him. It was towards this fourth hypothesis that in all modesty I leaned, for when I made to go, he held me back by the sleeve. So I smartly freed

---

[1] See Book IV of *The Prelude*. In the next book he discloses his lifelong passion for Geometry, "an independent world, created out of pure intelligence."

a crutch and dealt him a good dint on the skull. That calmed him. The dirty old brute.

Show him a moon through his window, however, and impatience withers; he will move from observation—

> Two bars divided it into three segments, of which the middle remained constant, while little by little the right gained what the left lost—

to hypothesis—

> For the moon was moving from left to right, or the room was moving from right to left, or both together perhaps, or both were moving from left to right, but the room not so fast as the moon, or from right to left, but the moon not so fast as the room—

to poetry—

> And now its tranquil course was written on the walls, a radiance scored with shadow, then a brief quivering of leaves, if they were leaves, then that too went out, leaving me in the dark. . .

a pocket history of romanticism. Malone too feels for *things*, "notably little portable things of wood and stone," "and but for the company of these little objects which I picked up here and there, when out walking, and which sometimes gave me the impression that they too needed me, I might have been reduced to the society of nice people, or to the consolations of some religion or other, but I think not." He fondles them in his pockets, "as a way of talking to them and reassuring them," and when he discards them to make way for new loves, he is at pains to find "a place to lay them where they would be at peace forever, and no one ever find them short of extraordinary hazard, and such places are few and far between."

In this silent world, fount of the silence for which The Unnamable yearns, the silence held off by the go-on of

his own voice yearning for it, in this world the great constants are physical laws: whether bits of natural lore
("Constipation is a sign of good health in pomeranians")
or fanciful bits of efficient causality (Why do trains move
off so smartly late at night? Why, because all along the
line trainsmen are "annelating toward their wives, after
the long hours of continence"); or metaphors for a closed
economy of emotion ("The tears of the world are a constant quantity. For each person who begins to weep
somewhere else another stops. The same is true of the
laugh.") or else a closed economy of effort and result
(" . . . they would contrive things in such a way that I
couldn't suspect the two vessels, the one to be emptied
and the one to be filled, of being in reality one and the
same . . . connected by pipes under the floor."). Murphy's
friend Wylie applies the same analysis to private desire:
"The syndrome known as life is too diffuse to admit of
palliation. For every symptom that is eased, another is
made worse. The horseleech's daughter[2] is a closed
system. Her quantum of wantum cannot vary." It is a
world locally freakish but totally shaped by two laws,
the law of conservation of energy and the second law of
thermodynamics. The former law states that nothing is
added to or subtracted from the system, but simply mu-
tated, and the latter states that the degree of organization
within this closed system grows constantly less and so
constantly less improbable, all actions being irreversible.
The second law of thermodynamics is the real theme of
Lucky's headlong oration, with its litany of labors "left
unfinished for reasons unknown," its stream of elegiac
phrases, "wastes and pines," "fades away," "the great

---

2 "The horseleech hath two daughters, crying, Give, give.": Proverbs
XXX-15. I owe this elucidation to an article by Mr. Samuel Mintz.

cold the great dark," "fading fading fading," and its computation to the nearest decimal of the dead loss per head since the death of Bishop Berkeley.

But this is insanity: several facts cry out against it. One is the extra hat that an unknown source injects into the system of *Waiting for Godot*, in defiance of law No. 1; and later we shall find the protagonists of *Comment C'est* agonizing over the boundless multiplication of sacks and sardine tins that destroys the closed system he has so painfully excogitated. Another affront to system is the dogged human will to keep on. A third is speech, which stubbornly will not remain "behavior."

In such a universe speech has no place; speech constantly threatens it with disruption. Sound, Descartes and Newton can account for, but speech defeats them. A voice reaching out of the interiority of a human person, with the thrust of my utter uniqueness, expressing, pressing out, so much as may be, toward some other person that sense of "I" which I alone have: what has Newton or Clerk Maxwell to say about that? So in Beckett's late dramatic work we find his cosmos dissociating into plays for voices alone, and "actes sans paroles." This dissociation exactly parallels that between thing and man. The second mime summarizes for the eye the physical universe à la *Molloy*: two men, never present to each other because one of them is always in a sack, alternately carrying one another ceaselessly to no end from right to left across a monolinear expanse of space. By contrast, the second radio play, *Embers*, summarizes for the ear the internal world from which reaches the unique voice:

Stories, stories, years and years of stories, till the need came on me, for someone, to be with me, anyone, a stranger, to talk to, imagine he hears me, years of that, and then, now, for someone who . . . knew me, in the old days, anyone, to be with me, imagine he hears me, what I am, now.

Put beside this a paragraph from *Watt*—

> Watt wore no tie, nor any collar. Had he had a collar, he would no doubt have found a tie, to go with it. And had he had a tie, he might perhaps have procured a collar, to carry it. But having neither tie, nor collar, he had neither collar, nor tie.

—and we see at once how this fine exercise in reciprocal negation and the anguish of Henry cannot coexist. Watt's tie and collar belong to the period of "Stories, stories, years and years of stories." That is where the Newtonian universe belongs also: it was a story Europe told itself for many decades. If Beckett's comedy derives from mathematics and system, from the impingement of system, and notably systematic forms of discourse, on experiences to which they seem inappropriate, it is to our quickening sense of persons imprisoned inside all this system that his works owe their grip on our attention. Persons stir because every word is an utterance. Patterns close because all discourse has shape.

The voice brings us to the mystery of the person, owes its very existence to that mystery, a mystery that, sour it and defile it as they will, no Beckett personage ever lays to rest. Krapp, in the most remarkable short dramatic piece in the language, communes with his own voice canned; what was once spoken in intimate urgent re-creation of experience—

> We drifted in among the flags and stuck. The way they went down, sighing, before the stem! (*Pause.*) I lay down across her with my face in her breasts and my hand on her. We lay there without moving. But under us all moved, and moved us, gently, up and down, and from side to side. . . .

—is thirty years later reproduced exactly, and again, and yet again, with precise automatic repetition of nuance, false as three traced signatures: not a voice any more but a hideously exact simulacrum of a voice, on magnetic tape: recollection in tranquillity with an automaton's vengeance: a last bitter parody of those vases celebrated in *Proust*, where the lost past is sealed away. We can see why the author of *Mercier et Camier* and the trilogy expresses a recurrent interest in parrots.

"Bless you Willie . . . ," says Winnie in *Happy Days*,

> . . . just to know that in theory you can hear me even though in fact you don't is all I need, just to feel you there within earshot and conceivably on the qui vive is all I ask. . .

for otherwise,

> . . . what would I do what *could* I do, all day long, I mean between the bell for waking and the bell for sleep? (*Pause.*) Simply gaze before me with compressed lips.

For it is inconceivable that speech should not reach toward another person, and when late in the play it seems at last advisable that she should come to terms with this possibility (". . . it is a long time now, Willie, since I saw you."), it remains inconceivable.

> I used to think . . . (*Pause.*) . . . I say I used to think that I would learn to talk alone. (*Pause.*) By that I mean to myself, the wilderness. (*Smile.*) But no. (*Smile broader.*) No no. (*Smile off.*) Ergo you are there."

Bring, then, persons into juxtaposition, and perhaps by some miracle the locked selves will flower. The whole tension of *Waiting for Godot* depends on this possibility; for Godot being a person and not a physical law, will introduce into the repetitive universe of Didi and Gogo some unpredictable disposition of their affairs: "Let's wait and see what he says." And we see why *Mercier et Camier* fritters into aimlessness, the object of the quest being merely a bicycle. Godot is the perpetual possibility of personal impingement on mechanism; without him, their interrelation, from long habit, has become a shuffling of limited resources, their conversation a game of catch ("Come on, Gogo, return the ball, can't you, once in a way?"), their choice either submitting to protracted existence or terminating it. Godot does not come, but his perpetual possibility animates the weary trickle of potency into history.

Bring, then, persons into juxtaposition, and perhaps . . . *Embers* does so bring them, in Henry's fantasy, and fiction stops dead at a terrible, poignant climax. Bolton, in the story Henry tells to himself, has summoned Dr. Holloway in the dead of night, and when Holloway arrives can only fix his eye and say in anguish, "Please! PLEASE!" The scene is intensely vivid. All Henry's dormant human capacity flows into his evocation of the "old man in great trouble," of Holloway coming to him through a nearly interplanetary silence. ("Outside all still, not a sound, dog's chain maybe or a bough groaning if you stood there listening long enough, white world, Holloway with his little black bag, not a sound, bitter cold, full moon small and white, crooked trail of Holloway's galoshes, Vega in the Lyre very green.") They stand in each other's presence, and all that Henry wanted from the father who despised him and the wife he despised suddenly animates a haunting tableau: Bolton asking mutely for what cannot be specified, for whatever communion looks out of another's eyes.

Then he suddenly strikes a match, Bolton does, lights a candle, catches it up above his head, walks over and looks Holloway full in the eye. (*Pause.*) Not a word, just a

look, the old blue eye, very glassy, lids worn thin, lashes gone, whole thing swimming, and the candle shaking over his head. . . . "We've had this before, Bolton, don't ask me to go through it again." (*Pause.*) Bolton: "Please!" (*Pause.*) "Please!" (*Pause.*) "Please, Holloway!" (*Pause.*) Candle shaking and guttering all over the place, lower now, old arm tired, [with what sympathy Henry's affections invade the old man of his fantasy!] takes it in the other hand and holds it high again, that's it, that was always it, night, and the embers cold, and the glim shaking in your old fist, saying, Please! Please! (*Pause.*) Begging. (*Pause.*) Of the poor.

Holloway covers his face: "Not a sound, white world, bitter cold, ghastly scene, old men, great trouble, no good."

Their great trouble is that they are each of them alone; out of all his intimate sense of his own identity, which no one else can ever share, comes Bolton's "Please!" across the bitter gulf: the distillation of the recurrent Beckett scene in which two men are brought into each other's presence and merely look at each other.

3

Or merely listen to each other—Krapp and the vanished Krapp imprisoned on the tape; or merely badger each other—Victor and the committee of interrogators in *Eleutheria*; or engage in reciprocal tyranny—Hamm and Clov. Or else one, awaited, does not come (Godot); or one, sought, is not there (Murphy, Molloy); or one, there, cannot cease to be (The Unnamable). The Beckett tension is between the person and the mathematical zero; hence his preoccupation with series and permutation, with the unique tenacities of declarative syntax, which so order and encase mute agonies, and with silence. The Beckett plot is simply an encounter between persons: hence the journeyings, the waitings, the confrontations.

And the resolution of the Beckett plot? Either an infinite series, or else an impasse.

His mathematical world is at bottom utterly frustrating, because it cannot assimilate persons and I am a person. His people never cease to court this frustration, because the mind once endowed with an orderly language and with the principles of logic can function in no other way. Yet no system for selecting the sucking stones can fully appease Molloy's fierce appetite for order. ("But I was tired, but I was tired, and I contented myself ingloriously with the first solution that was a solution, to this problem.") No sequence of sentences can approximate the ultimate statement The Unnamable yearns to make, since every sentence must begin somewhere and end somewhere else (*abitus, transitus, aditus,* wrote Geulincx) and no choice of a beginning or an ending can fail to exclude a thousand others. Though his sentences grow longer as tension mounts (the first has two words, the last some 1,700), yet each having chosen its terminus and direction can incorporate no others. And the Lynch family, surely Beckett's most grotesque comic invention, strives in vain to bring its combined ages to 1,000 years; breed though it will, peopling the land with hemophiliacs, idiots, paralytics, and other human variants, it cannot hope that even twins each aged four months can offset the loss of three brothers aged sixty-five, sixty-sixty-four and sixty-three. The great numbers perish while the numerous small ones wax, man's days being limited; and there seems little likelihood of the millenium ever being brought nearer than the eight and a half months that remained just before four deaths rolled back the total by a hopeless seventeen years.

A person cannot be silent, even voyaging through strange seas of thought; there is no interior silence. Nor alone, since we cannot imagine what it is not to be with oneself. Not even by retreating so far as may be within himself can he escape confrontation with the Other, since his very words shape alternate persons, his very musings subdivide himself. Not even by resigning himself, with Molloy, to "senseless, speechless, issueless misery" can he evade the symmetries and permutations that torment the mind.

Oneself, another person, symmetries, tensions: more than a dozen years after the trilogy *Comment C'est*, an unexpected return to fiction, gave these themes their strangest, most abstract and most hauntingly intimate development. Built phrase by phrase into a beautifully and tightly wrought structure, a few dozen expressions permuted with deliberate redundancy accumulate meaning even as they are emptied of it, and offer themselves as points of radiation in a strange web of utter illusion. For this book is founded on nothing recognizable; compared to it even the trilogy is realistic narrative. It is built out of little more than a basic French vocabulary and a stock of phrases, and built before our eyes, employing writing as a metaphor for itself much as *Endgame* employs the stage, calculating the amount of work still ahead, admitting ill-judged phrases with an abstracted "quelque-chose là qui ne va pas," and finishing with relief ("bon bon fin de la troisième partie et dernière"). It evades The Unnamable's difficulties with the sentence by employing none. So thoroughly does syntax give way to rhythm and architecture that we acquiesce without discomfort to the total absence of punctuation. In Molly Bloom's monologue the commas and full stops are merely left out. By contrast it is the mark of Beckett's fierce purity that he makes all thought of them seem irrelevant. The three full stops on these 177 pages are presumably printer's inadvertencies. The book looks like a draft of itself, as *Endgame* feels like a rehearsal of itself; packets of language, set apart by spaces, like notes for paragraphs never to be composed, jotted as some eternal voice dictates ("I say it as I hear it"):

> voice once without quaqua on all sides then in me when I stop panting now in me tell me again finish telling me invocation . . .

> my life last state last version ill said ill heard ill recaptured when the panting stops ill murmured to the mud brief movements of the lower face losses everywhere

From the first words we feel as never before the tension of an alien person:

> how it was I quote before Pim with Pim after Pim how it is part one part two part three I say it as I hear it

Part One is animated throughout by the thought of Pim, whose name occurs in it some fifty times, nearly always as the object of some preposition. Before Pim, with Pim, after Pim; toward Pim, near Pim; the words of Pim, the watch of Pim: these categories sketch a domain of being, of moving, and of knowing in which Pim, Beckett's generic other person, is the stable and ordering principle. Pim confers, it seems, all the meaning that the life before us can aspire to. In the absence of his name, acrid memories circulate without point, small mean words buzz, and we are reduced to such calming expedients as the drawing of the free hand over the face ("that's a help when all fails food for thought"). This, we are given to understand, is "how it was before Pim," and the substance of Part One is the journey toward Pim, a dogged chronicle of slogging through mud: "vast stretch of time when I drag myself and drag myself amazed that I can the cord sawing my neck the sack jolting at my side a hand outstretched

towards the wall the ditch that never come." This journey is over and now being recapitulated; yet as we follow
the narrative, which is generally in the present tense ("I
shall never have any past never had"), Pim lies ahead.
To these facts the reader finds himself paying little attention, so true are they of all fiction. Beckett has paid close
attention, however, and out of the consequent identifica-
tion of Pim past with Pim future he will spin before the
book is finished an infinite series. This possibility the
reader of the first part is unlikely to notice, despite ample
clues; we suppose therefore that our sojourn in this bleak
time will be redeemed by the person so many allusions
promise, and that the minimal assets of this bleak place
(mud, a jute sack, tinned fish, a can opener, a cord) will
assume the proper insignificance of all mere things when
Pim is present at last.

It is legitimate meanwhile to wonder where we are.
Though "la boue" may vaguely recall the place "in the
Marne mud" where Beckett moved his belongings by
wheelbarrow during the hungry winter of 1947, and
where nine years later he wrote *Fin de Partie*, this information is whimsically extraneous to the present book,
the uncertainties of which are not of a geographical
order. Mud, darkness, and an indefinite sense of distance
determine the ambience. Molloy recalled how "the road,
hard and white, seared the tender pastures, rose and fell
at the whim of hills and hollows," but no such order of
experience is in question here. Such precisions belong to
a former life, "up there in the light," where others, it
seems, still move, doubtless like the folk Malone envis-
aged, "their great balls and sockets rattling and clack-
ing like knackers, each on his way." But here there is no
light, nor no speech except soundless "brief movements
of the lower face," nor no walking apparently, since all is

a dragging and crawling ("ten yards fifteen yards half on my left side right foot right hand push pull flat on my belly mute cries half on my right side left foot left hand push pull flat on my belly mute cries not a syllable to be changed in this description"). It is a sort of limbo, one supposes, or a sort of hell. Toward the end of the journey even the sack is lost, with all its contents.

Will Pim brighten the world? No, the sojourn with Pim is distressing beyond expectation. Not a total loss, though:

> happy period in its way part two I speak of part two with Pim how it was good moments good for me I speak of me good for him too I speak of him too happy too in his way I shall know it later I shall know his way of happiness I shall have it I have not yet had everything

Pim's happiness consists chiefly in this, that but for my coming he would be "nothing but a carcass inert and mute forever flat in the mud." His existence as Pim, his very name, depends on my presence. He lies spreadeagled face down throughout our séance, clutching a sack of his own, but from the moment of my arrival commences to emit articulate sounds into the mud, though my efforts to speak are restricted as before to "brief movements of the lower face." Having ascertained by groping which end of him is which ("the cries tell me which end is his head but I could be mistaken"), I take up my position "in the dark the mud my head against his my side pressed against his my right arm around his shoulders he cries no more we rest thus a good while there are good whiles." And what is transacted during our "vie en commun" is first, an incomprehensible song by Pim, in a foreign tongue perhaps, and then a series of startling cruelties.

For a moment the voice of Pim ("a human voice there a

few inches away my dream") seemed to promise more generous intimacies:

> one day we should set forth again together . . . help one another forward fall down in unison and lie there in each other's arms till it be time to go on

—but without explanations the will of this place supervenes; they commence the game of tyrant and victim, that familiar Beckett coupling, like Hamm and Clov, Moran and his son, Pozzo and Lucky, even a little Didi and Gogo. Clov, Lucky, Moran *fils*, are well trained, and pedagogical method is now demonstrated. Clawed beneath the right arm Pim repeatedly utters cries which blows on the skull repeatedly stifle in facefuls of mud; until after aeons of time of being clawed he chances to sing instead of crying, and is encouraged by a blow withheld to interpret the clawed armpit as a command to sing ("question of training"). Next the can opener is jabbed into his rump until he learns ("not stupid merely slow") that this is the signal to speak. These ritual lessons occupy vast tracts of time, and the author does not omit to tabulate the curriculum of stimuli:

> one sing nails in the armpit two speak blade of canopener in the rump three stop thump on the skull four louder handle of canopener in the kidney

> five softer index in the anus six bravo slap athwart the buttocks seven bad same as three eight again same as one or two as needed

All this is executed neither in sorrow nor in anger, but with an analytic fulness of participation on which many pages are expended.

Once trained, Pim can be conversed with. The mute narrator sustains his part with fist, can opener and nails, in a last refinement tracing written questions on Pim's back ("roman capitals from left to right and from top to bottom as in our civilization": two Chinamen would have observed a different convention). And Pim for his part murmurs responses, having to do with his life "up there in the light." His life merges with mine, his voice with my muteness; it is unclear to whom the memories belong.

> that alleged life then he had had invented remembered a little of each no knowing that thing up above he gave it to me I made it mine what I fancied skies especially roads especially . . .

It is the narrator who claims the most vivid and affecting memories, of a lost wife, Pam Prim, whom he can barely bring himself to think about. She terminated, for him, an energetic career ("tried everything building especially was flourishing all branches especially plaster met Pam I believe") . Their intimacy was brief:

> love birth of love increase decrease death efforts to revive through the anus joint vain through the cunt again vain again out of the window threw herself or fell back broken hospital daisies.

Her death in the hospital, forgiving him (for what?), his visits there, sitting on her bed holding before her face the flowers she could not turn her head to see; his walk away from the place, "winter icy road black branches grey with rime she up there at the top dying forgiving all white" —these memories he retraces as Henry in *Embers* does his life with Ada, or causes Pim to recite as Krapp plays again and again the tape which embalms his gone passion. Pim is by turns a Lucky to keep company with and abuse, a Krapp's record of one's own past, shifted out of one's mind into another less painful location, and an intimate self telling stories as Henry tells himself stories. Like the tape he can be switched on and off by the application of stimuli two and three; like oneself, he murmurs with a creative intimacy Krapp's machine cannot approximate; like Lucky, Moran *fils*, or Clov he is a person, inalienably other, filling a need, capable even of evoking present affection ("arm around his poor shoulders rest we've earned it"). He is plied, after these memories, with a fusillade of questions to which he answers yes and no without imparting much enlightenment; and at length is there no more. So much for Pim.

So much, at present, for Pim. That was how the encounter turned out. But, we are given to understand, it always turns out that way, and the narrator neither exults in his own cruelty nor regrets it. For in Part Three he is awaiting in his turn a certain Bom, who will serve him, and has served him before, as he served Pim, after which he will commence the journey to Pim again. Pim, while he waits, is now journeying through the mud to torment another. Now, as he waits himself to play the Pim, having in Part Two played the Bom ("it's our justice"), he reflects on the logistics of the operation: first of the sacks, of which during an infinite number of journeys an infinite number are found, exchanged, permuted, and lost according to a rule as elaborate as the one that governed Molloy's sucking stones: then of the personnel, of whom any number are thinkable, exchanging in sets of four the roles of *bourreau* and *victime*, but each having to do with only two others, the one ahead of him on the route, whom he catches up to and torments, the one behind him who catches up to him and torments him. At intervals half are waiting, half are moving; at alternate intervals, the couples are about their solemn business. For allied reasons, he notes, a three-part book gives an adequate sample, for the invariable rhythm which obtains in this place ("our justice demands it") is journey, torture, wait, be tortured, but phase four repeats phase two so exactly that we can dispense with another torture piece.

Yet it was not wholly a torture piece, despite the can opener: they shared food, memories and the sensation of existing: "more lively there's nothing better." Deprived of Pim we calculate and speculate, alone with the implacable stammering voice, perhaps my own ("I say it as I hear it"). We may guess, indeed, that the risk of this three-part account being incomplete, omitting "a thousand things little visible or not at all in the present version," is negligible, so total was the sharing.

> the small need of a life of a voice on the part of one who has neither
>
> the voice extorted a few words life because of cry that proves it in deep with the blade that's all is needed a little cry all is not dead we drink we give to drink good-bye
>
> they were I quote good moments yes somehow good moments when you think
>
> Pim and I part two and Bom and I part four what that will be when you think
>
> to say after that we knew each other even then
>
> cleaved together two bodies one in the dark the mud
>
> motionless but for the right arm brief flurry now and then all the needful
>
> to say after that that I knew Pim that Pim knew me and Bom and I that we'll know each another even for a moment

But sharing, as he pursues his thoughts, ceases to be one of his terms of reference; he grows preoccupied again with questions of symmetry, of literary tactics (how comes this written account of a place where one lies flat in the mud? Why, one Kram, not one of us, writes down my words in his notebook and then mounts back into the light) ; and questions, once again, of logistics. For the sacks are a puzzle. As he tries explanation after explanation he sounds more and more like a writer trying to salvage a considerable quantity of work in which he has found, too late, a logical flaw. For the whole unimaginable procession moves on a narrow track eastward (as in *Mime II* the two men with sacks are steadily goaded from stage left to stage right), and as each starts a new journey he must find a sack of provisions. But if all the sacks have been in place from eternity then at each place where a sack is to be found there must be an infinite number to provide for the infinite number of travelers each of whom will halt there: whence, total blockage from the outset:

> such a mountain of sacks at the very setting forth that all progress impossible and no sooner imparted to the caravan its unthinkable first impulsion than it at a standstill for ever and frozen in injustice

> then from left to right or west to east the atrocious spectacle on into the black night of future time of a tormentor abandoned who will never be tormented then a little space then his brief journey over prone at the foot of a mountain of victuals the tormented who will never be tormentor then a great space then another abandoned and so on infinitely

In which case, we perceive in this vertigo of ratiocination, every segment of the route would be blocked, and equally, by the same reasoning, our justice. There seems nothing for it but to postulate a superior being who sees to the supply of sacks as they are needed; and he is just putting the finishing touches to the theology and eschatology of this new hypothesis, when the *peripeteia* of the book is suddenly sprung.

For it is simplest to suppose that no component of the problem which has been occupying him for sixty pages has any existence, that he has been telling himself a story, and that the voice whose words he has been repeating ("I say it as I hear it") has been his own. No Pim then, no Bom, no journey, no sack. He tries this out catechetically, and the voice (his own?) agrees:

> all these calculations yes explanations yes the whole story from one end to the other yes completely false yes

Nothing, in this case, is real but the mud and the blackness. Even the higher being, the source of the voice and perhaps of the sacks, disappears; even Samuel Beckett, for that matter, disappears:

> but these stories of voices yes quaqua yes of other worlds yes of someone in another world yes whose dreams so to speak I am yes which he dreams all the time yes tells all the time yes his only dream yes his only story yes . . .

> and these stories of up above yes the light yes the skies yes a little blue yes a little white yes the turning earth yes bright and less bright yes little scenes yes all balls yes the women yes the dog yes the prayers the homes yes all balls yes

But almost the final words are "end of quotation": this solipsism may be a final delusion imparted by the voice, and to imagine that he is merely telling himself a story may be (there is no way to tell, unless he can tell whether the voice is his own) a delusion that comes on schedule while one waits for Bom. At any rate,

> good good end of the third and last part there it is that's how it was end of quotation after Pim how it is

So the work closes, balanced on a knife edge; and so Beckett rounds off in a perfectly insoluble either-or this fullest and most philosophical summary of "the dream yes which he dreams all the time yes tells all the time yes his only dream yes his only story yes."

4

This work contains no ingredient (unless perhaps mud) which we have not encountered before. What is new is the absolute sureness of design. We have had sacks in the second mime, crawling in *Molloy*, a horizontal narrator in *Malone Dies*, pages of broken tentative utterance in *Embers*, tyrant and victim repeatedly, stories told to oneself repeatedly, lost love in *Krapp's Last Tape*, a voice quaqua disturbing limbo in *The Unnamable*, agonies of non-identity in the *Textes Pour Rien*. The blind Hamm and the blind Mr. Rooney were at rest and in motion respectively in an utter darkness, and the latter is also enamored of computations ("Not count! One of the few satisfactions in life?") Even the technique of communicating by a code of blows was adumbrated by Molloy, seeking to impress "one knock yes, two no, three I don't know, four money, five goodbye" on his mother's "ruined and frantic understanding." Everything, moreover, that Beckett has written from *Murphy* onward shows us persons who once were alive in the bright world and have somehow ceased to be so. Murphy never thinks of doubting that he has been fortunate to die into the little chaos within, but no one after him is quite so sure. Paradise in any case, if there ever was one, has been lost, and the subtle argument of *Proust*, that only involuntary memory can briefly restore it, is exactly borne out when Pim helps us recall what without him we cannot reach, the vanished days. It is even true, as we were told it would be in *Proust*, that the attempt to communicate where no communication is possible is "horribly comic," exactly the phrase for the business with fist and can opener.

No, what is novel is simply the scale on which this material is organized, the brilliance no longer local but gone into the bones of a work that tends to stay in the memory as a whole. Not that it hangs there like a static pattern fleshed out: it is a process, a history of effort, the heroic effort to get itself written. The narrator, unlike even The Unnamable, is doing without pencil and paper (how would he even see his notes?), and as he addresses himself to the more intricate calculations of Part Three we watch him assembling and reassembling, by dint of repetition, the data in his memory with the awe we should bring to the spectacle of a Newton born blind. We do not expect sentences, they would be an irrelevant elegance.

And that the master of syntax should have chosen to do without the sentence, even this is not surprising when we recall his thematic distrust of accomplishment. It was almost the last thing left for him to discard from his repertory, and he gained in discarding it a structural wholeness, as of a cantilever bridge, only to be achieved by getting rid of all those little beginnings and endings. Repeatedly similar components intersect at similar angles, like girders, and it is with relief, not annoyance, that we encounter repeatedly like an old friend some tried formulation, "jambe droite bras droit pousse tire dix mètres quinze mètres": a relief we share with the narrator, who for some instants is spared the necessity of invention.

Our author is indomitable, like Pim singing. Wedged in this crack, where the very names are provisional, and without so much as a declarative sentence to call his own, he excogitates a whole grotesque vision of judgment, on the scale of a lesser Dante, with greater authority than when he had all the resources of fiction at his disposal and wrote the tale of Murphy and his friends, "là-haut dans la lumiére." It is at last, to paraphrase the dialogue written eleven years earlier, the situation of him who is helpless, cannot act, in the end cannot write, since he is obliged to write; the act of him who, helpless, unable to act, acts, in the end writes, since he is obliged to write. (Why is he obliged to write? I don't know. Why is he helpless to write? Because there is nothing to write and nothing to write with.) He has always told the same story; the memories of the road outside the hospital where Pam Prim died reach all the way back to a poem in *Echo's Bones*:

> Exeo in a spasm
> tired of my darling's red sputum
> from the Portobello Private Nursing Home . . .

We might even, with all the books and tales before us, arrange the story into a chronolgy. A man (first version) is thrown out of the house by his upright family ("L'Expulsé"), and slowly loses the capacity for human intercourse; or (second version) is so shocked by the gratuitous death of a loved one that he slowly loses the capacity for human intercourse; wanders for some years on the continent and in London (*Murphy*), puzzling over the realities of the Irish world in which he once participated (*Watt*) ; has for a while a companion (*Mercier et Camier*) with whom, having become a twilight man, he is never able to achieve a satisfactory intimacy; rediscovers a need for his mother (*Molloy*) but does not prosecute it; lapses into telling himself endless stories (*Malone Dies*) and so into an inferno of words (*The Unnamable*) in which the last shreds of his identity dissolve; then stirred at last by a hunger he has never admitted (*Godot, Embers*) for the presence and succor of other persons, some other person, excogitates out of his now irremediable darkness (*Comment C'est*) a myth of his hopeless situa-

tion and a fiction of what release into memory another
presence might bring to it. This coheres agreeably and
will very likely some day be the theme of some biographer
or other. We should recall how Moran commenced his
narrative:

> Then I went back into the house and wrote, It is mid-
> night. The rain is beating on the windows. It was not
> midnight. It was not raining.

—and reflect that there is likely not an atom of truth in
these conjectures from start to finish. We have been
cunningly closed up in a huge fantasy; and if anyone is
tempted to see behind blind Hamm the figure, say, of
James Joyce exacting minute services of a disciple, it is
sufficient to note that Malone's tale touches Malone's life
at many points without its eerie abundance of invention
being thereby explained. Fiction is precisely like mathematics in this, that its normal processes handle nonexistent beings (points without magnitude, lines without
breadth, persons without being), and that a knowing
extension of its normal processes will generate beings
that cannot be assimilated by the world of experience.
The surds and the imaginary numbers are irrefutable
productions of a system that finds it has no place for
them.

Beckett's work, in the same way, is far from being a
by-product of hopeless misery. It is the unassimilable
product of a set of operations with words, every word of
which retains its meaning and every operation its validity.
And the work leaps from end to end with comic invention. The population of the world being reduced to four,
concern is expressed about the absence of bicycle wheels.
A man sits on nothing identifiable, in a gray space, while
a figment of his past invention rotates about him, its
two hands propping up its jaw. Twenty-eight people

yearn day and night for the morning when their combined ages will total 1,000 years. The whole world crawls from left to right along an invisible track, subsisting on tinned fish. Or, in a longer perspective, certain general propositons. Item: the universe is a congeries of largely random phenomena, amid which however we can discern certain tokens of stability; these are, bowler hats, bicycles, the letter M. Item: what I am telling you is a story, the substance of which is that it is a story; now since my statement that these facts are fiction is part of the fiction, they may very likely be facts, but if they are facts then you are to believe what they say, namely that they are fictions. (Was it or was it not raining when Moran began to write? For his statement that it was not is contained in the lie which it is the point of the statement to expose as a lie). This last antinomy was known to our fathers as the paradox of the Cretan liar: all Cretans are liars, said the man from Crete. It exercised logic classrooms for centuries.

And indeed Beckett's fictions are at bottom rather like scholarly jokes. It is in the classroom that such mad worlds are postulated, as it is there that a hapless candidate is hauled before examiners and bidden, like Lucky, to take off his hat and think. A, B, and C must fill a water butt. A carries his water twice as far as B and C but walks three times as fast. C's bucket leaks half its contents during an average journey. Express as a ratio their relative frustrations. A textbook prepared about 1835 for the use of the Irish National Schools[3] invites us to "detain the earth a moment at point D" while we perform a small calculation, and directing our attention to a common

---

[3] I owe this analogy to Professor Donald Pearce. Being compiled from miscellaneous sources, the book gives a good cross section of academe's obtuse explicitness.

table, reminds us that were the cohesion "so far destroyed as to convert the wood into a fluid, no support could be afforded by the legs; for the particles no longer cohering together [formulation in its lunacy must pursue the uttermost particles of the obvious], each would press separately and independently, and would be brought to a level with the surface of the earth." This was written a century before Dali. Only pedagogy would convert table legs into water, or solemnly doubt that there is less land in the southern hemisphere than in the northern ("for it is possible that the land may be only rather depressed in the south, and consequently covered by the sea"); or elaborate, with reasons, the truth that vegetables have no stomach; or reflect that whereas a dead body soon begins to putrefy, until nothing remains but dust, "this never happens in life." Even so Malone noted that when you roll over, the head comes to rest x inches from where it was before, x being the width of the shoulders in inches; and Molloy, that a certain inconceivable thing was indeed conceivable since he conceived it.

For Beckett is the first great academic clown since Sterne. If *Comment C'est* (a title for any realistic novel whatever) is from one point of view a grave and mordant image for the lot of man, from another it is like a non-Euclidean geometry, the elaboration of a fantastic premise. All his fictions of the minimal and the deprived, presenting men as less than they are, petty, consistent, stubbornly obsessed, answer rigorously to the conditions of comedy prescribed by Aristotle, the schoolmaster of Europe. His gentle allusive jokes recall those of a schoolmaster who has lived much by himself, a role he knows well how to play. He is never far from the academic *blagueur*, whether indulging his striking talent for exposition (Molloy on the sucking stones becomes in effect a lecture-demonstration), or recalling the conditions under which he learned his French as a single verb in several moods or tenses generates the kind of pointlessly heated vignette with which language textbooks are sprinkled, or casually fondling the problem by which Clov is too tired to be exercised, at what instant, as grains of sand trickle onto a given spot, we may be said to have a heap. And we may remember with what loving care he shaped the story of Louit, who located a man named Tişler who lived in a room on the canal, and passed off this man, did Louit, before a five-man examining committee as an unlettered rustic capable of the mental extraction of cube roots and so of illustrating The Mathematical Intuitions of the Visicelts. Ever and ever evoking the French classes and mathematics classes where his mind was formed, he plays ever bleaker homage to the fact that ours is a classroom civilization, and that schoolmasters are the unacknowledged legislators of the race. Each of his bums has at some far off time been well schooled, "up there in the light," furnished with words and processes, facts and analogies. They have read Geulincx in the Latin, they savor recurring decimals and the laws of permutation, the West has discharged upon them the fulness of its instructional method, and look at them.

Spinning, with a look of foxy innocence, his fantasies of language, mathematics, and logic, fastidious in his low bohemia, evading the nets with which we catch men of letters (no more to tell us than Molloy had to tell the policeman; blank on every pertinent topic), and looking at us out of photographs as though calculating his chances of being given a loaf of bread, this learned vagrant moves through the rigors of today's world like a ghost from the middle ages, as scandalously elusive as the twelfth-century archpoet who "weeping left the country of the laughing" and composed, no one knows when or where, the song beginning

> Estuans intrinsecus
> ira vehementi
> in amaritudine
> loquar meae menti.

And living as we do amid moving toys and vociferous unrealities, shaken by every assault on our beliefs, on our orientation in the world ("I have forgotten which way I am facing." "You have turned aside and are bowed down over the ditch."), on our very identities; acquiescing as abstractions challenge customs, multitudinous data puzzle the will, and an acerb indifference muffles our natures, we quiver as his fantasies of displacement and non-being strike our nerves, half ready to believe (as we draw back) that we indeed wander in a forest, that our intellection permutes stones, that we do no more than tell ourselves tales while we die, or drag our possessions along with us in sacks.

In our fascinated affinity with these twilight men, none of them visible to the eyes with which we pursue our affairs (and what are our affairs?) we barely credit the ritual disavowal—

> never any procession no nor journey no never any Pim
> no nor Bom no never anyone no but me no answer but
> me yes . . .

—and barely notice how cunningly it does not disavow. Yes, yes, I am mistaken, I am mistaken, said B. in the same way, to placate D. These books do not undo the world; it will be here tomorrow. The fascination remains, with the permanence of all ordered things. And the books

are fictions. There is only ourselves, disturbed but ob-
scurely appeased, and the scholar vagrant, comedian of
the impasse, aloof, unassimilable, shy.

Santa Barbara, California
1961

Acknowledgments

My information about the country around Foxrock comes from Vivian Mercier; about Alfred Péron, from Ruby Cohn, who also edited the invaluable Beckett issue of *Perspective*; about the theory of irrational numbers, from Tobias Dantzig's *Number, The Language of Science*. An article by Donald Davie in the Winter, 1958 *Spectrum* prompted the stress I have laid on Beckett's syntax, and conversations with the Rev. Walter J. Ong, S.J. my emphasis on the mysteries of voice and person. I am also indebted to four colleagues at the University of California (Santa Barbara): Donald Pearce, for discussions of *Endgame*, Raymond Federman and John Wilkinson for help with Beckett's French and Geulincx's Latin, Alan Stephens for his critical reading of the finished typescript. Translations from Beckett's French works are his own with the following exceptions: *Molloy* was translated by Patrick Bowles and the *Nouvelles* ("The End" and "L'Expulsé") by Richard Seaver, both in collaboration with the author. All other translations are my own.

Earlier versions of portions of this book have appeared in *Spectrum, Forum, National Review,* and *Perspective,* to the editors of which I am indebted for permission to revise and reprint.